PLANE
TRIGONOMETRY

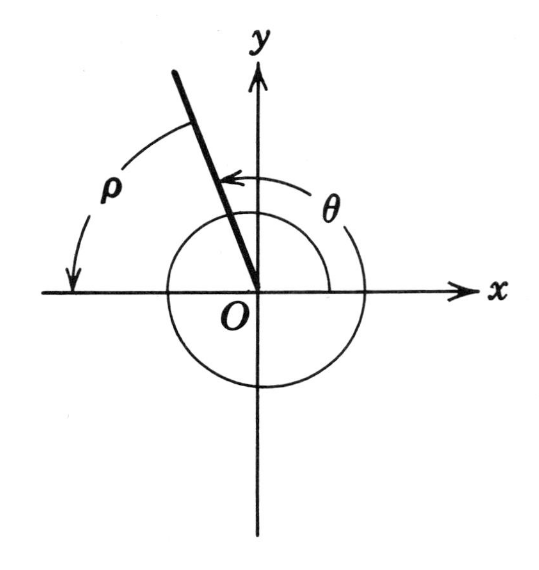

NEW YORK · JOHN WILEY & SONS, INC.

LONDON

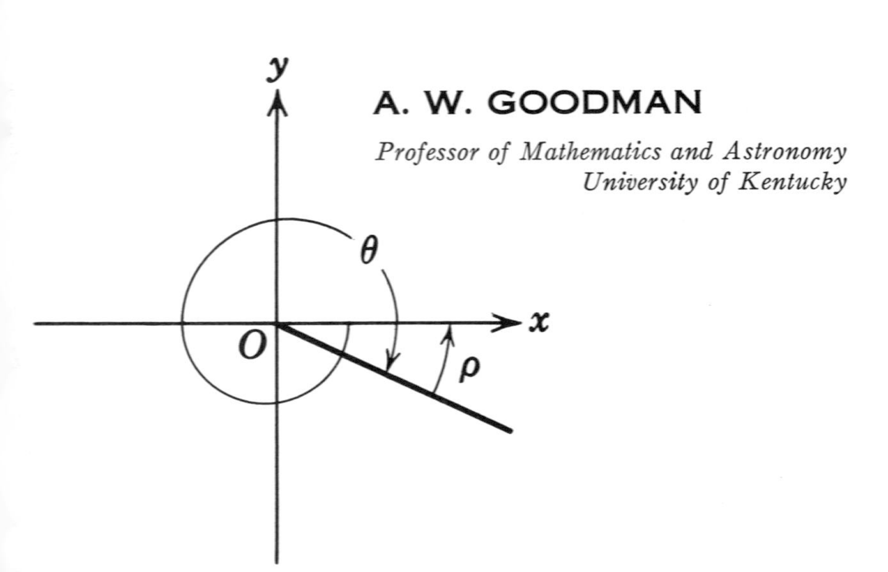

A. W. GOODMAN

Professor of Mathematics and Astronomy
University of Kentucky

PLANE TRIGONOMETRY

SECOND PRINTING, SEPTEMBER, 1961

Library of Congress Catalog Card Number: 59-9344

Printed in the United States of America

PREFACE FOR THE STUDENT

★ Don't be frightened. Trigonometry is an easy subject, and you too can learn it. All that is required is a little effort on your part.

If you have had trouble with your mathematics courses in the past, there are several possible causes. It is easy for you to claim that you had poor teachers who were either boring, incompetent, overbearing, or repulsive, or a combination of these. You might even be right. But if you had a good textbook as you probably did, you really have no excuse. By studying a good textbook, you could and should learn any subject, despite a poor teacher. This brings us to the central point, "studying."

You probably just don't know how to study. No one has ever told you. Do you sit with the book open in front of you for an hour, and then claim you have been studying for an hour? Rubbish! I may as well sit with my feet dangling in the pool, and then claim I have been swimming for an hour. Or I may as well listen to Rubinstein piano recordings on the phonograph for an hour, and then claim I have been practicing piano for sixty minutes. Obviously, whether it is playing piano, swimming, or studying mathematics, you must actively participate in order to really learn a subject.

Here is a list of hints that may help you do this when you study mathematics. Since we are all individuals, some of the items in this list may not apply to you, but you may be able to add to this list some that do seem to help you.

1. After each sentence that you read, ask yourself: Does it make sense? Is it correct?

2. If the sentence or equation doesn't make sense, is there a misprint you can spot and correct for yourself?

3. If the sentence or equation still doesn't make sense, after a reasonable effort on your part, go on to the next item, and keep coming back to the difficult part. It may be that later parts of the exposition will clarify the earlier muddy sentence or equation.

4. After reading a section or paragraph, close your eyes and see how much you can remember. If you have just read a proof of a theorem, you should be able to reproduce it. Close the book, take a blank sheet of paper, and see if you can write down the proof. Open the book and see how far off you are.

5. After you have read several pages covering a number of related ideas, close the book and see if you can make an outline of the material. Make a diagram using arrows to show how the various ideas are connected.

6. Memorize word for word the statements of the theorems. Definitions of new words should receive similar respectful treatment. Although memorization without understanding is worthless, you should memorize any item that appears to be essential at the same time that you are trying to understand it, because memorization and understanding reinforce one another.

7. In working problems do not work toward the answer in the back of the book. Postpone looking at the answer until you have finished all the numerical work.

8. Must you study with the radio or the television set turned on? Most professional scholars prefer quiet when they are studying, although some of the truly great intellects seem to be able to work well even when it is noisy. If you are doing poor work, why not try for one semester to have absolute quiet when studying? See if you don't do better. If not, then at the end of the semester turn your radio or your roommate back on again.

9. Not all studying is done at a desk with a book. There are many times during the day when the mind is free to think: while brushing your teeth, while waiting for a bus, or riding the bus, while walking from one classroom to the next one, while delivering a paper route, etc. During such periods you should try to recall the important formulas, theorems, and proofs. Are there blank spots and fuzzy places? When you have a chance to look in the book, fill in the blank spaces and clear up the fuzzy ones.

The brain is very much like a muscle, and like a muscle you must use it in order to develop it. If you don't use it, it can atrophy. The man who waits until he gets to college to start studying has already done damage to his brain that he can never completely repair, although he can partly recover the lost ground by very hard work. Those who advise students in grade school and high school to avoid mathematics either because it is hard or useless are sabotaging the educational program of their country.

Now a word about this particular book. If you are working through this book without the guidance of a teacher, then you might very well omit the starred (★) sections without too much loss. The starred material is either very difficult material, which you might well skip completely or postpone for a time; or it is material that is not absolutely essential to the study of trigonometry.

The starred problems are somewhat difficult, and the double starred (★★) problems are still more difficult. If you find that trigonometry is hard for you, skip all the starred problems, and concentrate on the others. If, on the other hand, most of the problems seem to be too easy, the starred problems will probably keep you busy. One would expect an A student to try all of the starred problems, and to solve most of them.

When a new word or phrase is introduced, it is set in italics and the sentence in which it is used defines it. For example, in Chapter 4 the sentence,

"An angle is said to be in *standard position* if the vertex of the angle coincides with the origin and the initial side falls on the positive x-axis,"

defines the phrase *standard position* for an angle. You should realize that this is a definition giving the meaning of this phrase, and the italics are an automatic warning device telling you that you should learn this new word or phrase and its meaning. Later, if you have forgotten the meaning of some word or phrase you can look it up in the index. Here you will find a reference to the page on which the concept is defined, and in addition a list of other pages of the book where this concept is used. The index is there to help you, and it can help you only if you use it.

I have set in boxes those formulas you should memorize because of their importance. Of course, your teacher may have a different opinion on the amount of memory work that should be required of his students. In case you are in doubt as to which formulas to memorize, you should consult him.

Students frequently ask me why they should learn this topic or that proof, etc. They want to know where the item in question will be used, and although they don't say so, what they frequently want to know is, can it be used to make money. Instead of trying to answer the specific question, it is better to shift the subject matter and then ask the question again. Why should you do anything at all in life? Why should you learn to swim? Why should you learn to play a musical instrument? Why learn to appreciate classical music by listening to it? Basically, the answer is the same in all cases. You do these things because they are fun. Or if they aren't fun at first, you hope that as you acquire proficiency, they will become fun. Only a few professionals make money from playing basketball, or swimming, or listening to classical music, but nearly everyone enjoys at least one of these activities, and some fortunate individuals enjoy all three. If exercising your muscles by swimming or pole vaulting can give pleasure, there is no reason why you can't also enjoy exercising your brain by doing mathematics.

Mathematics is the greatest game ever invented by man.

Why don't you learn to play the game a little bit, and see if you don't enjoy it?

A. W. GOODMAN

Lexington, Kentucky
March, 1959

PREFACE FOR THE TEACHER

★ This book is neither ultramodern nor purely conventional. Most of trigonometry is reasonably well standardized, so I will mention only those few items in which this book differs from the majority of the textbooks currently on the market.

In Chapter 1 the trigonometric functions are defined for an acute angle as ratios of sides in a right triangle. Please don't jump. I am well aware that most textbooks now begin immediately with the general angle. This modern treatment is superior, so its advocates claim, because it disposes of the definitions once and for all, and saves the trouble of later changing the definitions. But how does the student regard this sophisticated approach? The answer is obvious: he doesn't even know it is sophisticated and he cares less. All that he sees is a confusing array of ratios which are unmotivated and therefore uninteresting to him. Very likely this sets up in him a subconscious resistance to learning the ratios. On the other hand, with the classical presentation, the importance of the ratios is first illustrated with suitable practical problems, and then after the student is convinced of their usefulness, names are given to the ratios, and he begins the study of their properties.

A really clever teacher will hint to his class that these definitions, given only for acute angles will later be enlarged to include all angles, and he will stimulate the more active students to wonder how this can be done. Only another Descartes in the class will actually anticipate the answer, but some of the more curious might look ahead in the book, and even those who merely wait patiently to be shown must admire the skillful way in which the definitions of the trigonometric functions for acute angles are extended to the general case.

Actually the modern treatment defines the trigonometric functions only for real θ, and not for complex θ. The teacher who is really sincere about his desire to give a definition of $\sin \theta$ valid for all θ should start his trigonometry course with some material on infinite series and then define $\sin \theta$ by its Maclaurin series

$$\sin \theta = \theta - \frac{\theta^3}{3!} + \frac{\theta^5}{5!} - \cdots$$

Of course this is obviously impractical. It is far better to give the student a narrow definition valid only in a limited range, and then as his knowledge of mathematics expands, modify the definition to fit the enlarged picture. Indeed this process of modifying a definition is one of the central features of modern mathematics, and it seems a shame to deny a student the opportunity to observe this process in trigonometry where it occurs in a very simple and clear form.

In Chapter 7, the addition formulas for the trigonometric functions are proved. The proofs are based ultimately on the invariance of the distance between two points under a rotation of the plane. The advantage of this type of proof is that it is valid for all real angles. The traditional proof given by stacking one triangle on top of another is valid only for angles in a certain restricted range, and the extension of this range is always a nuisance. In most cases the student is expected to accept on faith the general validity of the addition formulas.

In Chapter 5, I present a duality principle for trigonometric identities. Although this material is extremely simple and is perhaps known to many mathematicians, I have never seen it in print before. There is a possibility that this duality principle represents a small but new contribution to trigonometry.

This book can be used in a variety of ways as indicated.

Course of 45 Lessons

Chapter	1	2	3	4	5	6	7	8	9	10	11	13	14	Exams
Number of lessons	5	5	2	2	4	4	5	2	2	2	2	1	3	6

A short course in which the emphasis is on the applications of trigonometry could use the following plan:

Course of 30 Lessons

Chapter	1	2	3	4	5	6	8	13	Exams
Number of lessons	5	5	2	2	4	4	2	2	4

If the students have had trigonometry in high school, so that the practical applications can be safely ignored, the course could begin with Chapter 4:

Course of 30 Lessons—Analytical Trigonometry

Chapter	4	5	6	7	8	9	10	11	13	14	Exams
Number of lessons	2	4	2	5	2	2	2	2	1	3	5

A. W. GOODMAN

Lexington, Kentucky
March, 1959

CONTENTS

PLANE TRIGONOMETRY

SOME PRELIMINARY NOTIONS

★ 1. A Five-Minute History of Mathematical Symbols. In the early days of mathematical study, ideas were expressed by long complicated sentences in the language then in vogue (Greek, Arabic, Latin, etc.). Little by little the early geniuses realized that the sentences could be shortened if some symbols were used for words, and often they merely chose the first letter of the key word. If such a system were in use today, "solve the equation $x^4 - 3x^2 + 2 = 0$ for x" might read:

Find *u* so that: *ututututmthtutuptweqz.*

Here *u* represents the unknown, *t* stands for times, and *p* and *m* stand for plus and minus, respectively. The letter pairs, *th* for three and *tw* for two, would be used to avoid confusion with *t* for times. Clearly *z* would mean zero, and *eq* would mean equals.

Although such a system is bad, it is not completely impossible. Indeed, despite the handicaps imposed by poor notation, the early mathematicians made remarkable discoveries. What made matters worse was the fact that communication was slow, and libraries rare, so that for the most part each society developed its own system of symbols. Thus today when an archeologist unearths a manuscript, a mere knowledge of mathematics and the language of the manuscript may not be sufficient for reading the treasure. He would also need to know the symbols used by the writer before he could distinguish a valuable mathematical document from an account of a military expedition or the records of some collector of taxes.

The symbols we now use were introduced little by little and all of them within the past five hundred years. Table 1 gives more detailed information. Once introduced the symbols did not become popular overnight. On the contrary, often fifty years or more elapsed before anything resembling a unanimous adoption of the symbol was achieved.

TABLE 1

Symbol	Meaning or Name	Date Introduced	Inventor
$+$	Plus	1486	Unknown
$-$	Minus	1486	Unknown
$\sqrt{\ }$	Square root	1526	Christoff Rudolff
( )	Parentheses	1556	Nicolo Fontana Tartaglia
$=$	Equals	1557	Robert Recorde
.	Decimal point	1617	John Napier
$>$	Greater than	1631	Thomas Harriot
$<$	Less than	1631	Thomas Harriot
$\times$	Multiplication	1631	William Oughtred
$\cdot$	Multiplication	1631	Thomas Harriot
AB	Multiplication by juxtaposition	1637	René Descartes
x, y, z	Letters near the end of the alphabet for unknown quantities	1637	René Descartes
$a, b, c, \cdots$	Letters near the beginning of the alphabet for known quantities	1637	René Descartes
$\div$	Division	1659	Johann Rahn
$\leqq$	Less than or equal to	1734	Pierre Bouguer
$\geqq$	Greater than or equal to	1734	Pierre Bouguer
a^n	The exponent notation		See below
$a^1, a^2, a^3, \cdots$	n a positive integer	1637	René Descartes
$a^{-1}, a^{1/2}, \cdots$	n a negative integer or a fraction	1659	John Wallis
a^n	n any real number	1676	Isaac Newton
π	The ratio of circumference to diameter in a circle	1706	William Jones

Today mathematicians are in a much more fortunate position. All of the symbols[1] in the table and a great many other symbols used in higher mathematics are used throughout the civilized world, always with the same meaning. As a result, new mathematical discoveries made and published in one part of the world can be immediately read and understood by mathematicians everywhere.

[1] There is one exception to this statement. In many countries the comma is used for the decimal point instead of the period.

The reader who wants more details on the history and the early development of mathematics would do well to consult one or more of the following books:

Howard Eves, *An introduction to the history of mathematics*, Rinehart and Co., New York, 1953.
Vera Sanford, *A short history of mathematics*, Houghton Mifflin Co., New York, 1930.
Florian Cajori, *A history of mathematics*, 2nd ed., The Macmillan Co., New York, 1919.
W. W. Ball, *History of mathematics*, The Macmillan Co., New York, 1908.

★ **2. Mathematical Symbols as an International Language.** The collection of marks shown here represents the first ten notes of *La Marseillaise* to every musician no matter what country he is in. When we say

that musical notations are international we mean just this: the printer may distribute copies of a piece of music all over the world, and trained musicians everywhere will read and play this piece the same way.

To some extent mathematics is also international and the collection of symbols

$$A + B = C$$

has the same meaning to mathematicians everywhere. The reader will no doubt notice that mathematics is not completely symbolized. Consider the slogan:

(S) Equals added to equals gives equals.

Of course A. F. (the Average Frenchman) would find this statement meaningless. If we try to use symbols, and change from a slogan to a precise statement, then (S) might be written:

(SE) If $A = B$ and $C = D$, then $A + C = B + D$.

Observe that (SE) is now mostly symbols, and only three words are left. Mr. A. F. might still be puzzled by the appearance of the statement.

He would expect to see

(SF) Si $A = B$ et $C = D$, alors $A + C = B + D$.

But he would not be puzzled long, for he would guess rather quickly the meaning of the three English words in (SE). Conversely, any American familiar with the slogan (S) could look at (SF) and deduce quite rapidly that "*Si*" means "if," "*et*" means "and," and "*alors*" means "then." The reader might amuse himself by translating one sentence from each of the following foreign languages into English.

German:	Wenn	$A = B$ und	$C = D$, dann ist	$A + C = B + D$.
Dutch:	Als	$A = B$ en	$C = D$, dan geldt	$A + C = B + D$.
Spanish:	Si	$A = B$ y	$C = D$, entonces	$A + C = B + D$.
Italian:	Se	$A = B$ e	$C = D$, allora	$A + C = B + D$.
Russian:	Если	$A = B$ и	$C = D$, то	$A + C = B + D$.

Why do we mention this? Because we want to emphasize that a knowledge of mathematics and mathematical symbols makes it easier for one to learn a foreign language. If the student wants to learn a foreign language, French for example, he will find it quite helpful to buy an elementary algebra book in French, and to read through it. He will find that his knowledge of algebra will enable him to guess at a large majority of the French words and will save him many useless and tedious hours of looking up words in a French-English dictionary.

3. The Greek Alphabet. As the use of symbols grew, certain symbols were reserved for certain ideas, thus: r meant radius, h meant height, t meant time, d meant distance, r meant rate—but already the alphabet is being crowded, for here we have r with two different meanings, (1) radius (2) rate. As mathematics expanded and more and more new concepts were added, it became obvious that no one symbol could be permitted to represent one concept only. Either some symbols must do double duty, or new symbols must be introduced to relieve congestion. The early scholars all knew Greek, so it was quite natural for them to introduce Greek letters, and these letters are still with us today in mathematics, though the study of the Greek language has dwindled almost to zero.

For ready reference we give the complete Greek alphabet, but the student is advised *not* to learn it. Instead he can learn a few letters at a time, referring to this alphabet as the need arises. He already knows π, which has been reserved the world over for the ratio circumference/diameter in a circle, and is almost never used for anything else. In this book we shall use only those letters that are marked with an asterisk (*). As one goes on in mathematics into calculus, advanced calculus, number theory, etc. more and more of these Greek letters will be used, but they will be introduced gradually and should never cause the student any trouble.

*Alpha	A, α	Iota	I, ι	*Rho	P, ρ
*Beta	B, β	Kappa	K, κ	Sigma	Σ, σ, ς
*Gamma	Γ, γ	Lambda	Λ, λ	Tau	T, τ
Delta	Δ, δ	Mu	M, μ	Upsilon	Υ, υ
Epsilon	E, ε	Nu	N, ν	*Phi	Φ, φ
Zeta	Z, ζ	Xi	Ξ, ξ	Chi	X, χ
Eta	H, η	Omicron	O, o	Psi	Ψ, ψ
*Theta	Θ, θ	*Pi	Π, π	*Omega	Ω, ω

4. Subscripts. Suppose that we have a problem involving the radii of four circles (the exact nature of the problem is unimportant). It is natural to use the letter r for the radius of one of the circles, and R for the radius of the second circle, since both r and R tend to remind us of the word radius. For the radius of the third circle, we might choose the Greek letter ρ (rho) which corresponds to the English r. But now we are stuck for a suitable choice of symbol for the radius of the fourth circle. The way out is quite simple. We return to the letter r and put little numbers (called subscripts) just below the letter, thus: r_1, r_2, r_3, r_4, and use these to represent the radii of the four circles. These symbols are read: r sub-one, r sub-two, etc. If we are in a hurry we may just say: r-one, r-two, etc. In the symbol r_2, the number 2 is written below the line (subscript) in order to distinguish it from $r2$, which would be interpreted as the product of r and 2.

5. One Symbol with Several Meanings. Mathematics is sometimes called "the language of science." In any complicated language it frequently happens that one word may have a variety of meanings. For example in English the word "bridge" may mean: (1) a structure carrying a roadway for autos, erected over a river, (2) the upper bony part of the nose, (3) the part of a pair of glasses that rests on the nose, (4) a device for securing artificial teeth, (5) a support for the cue stick in the game of billiards, (6) a portion of an electric circuit, or (7) a card game. The rich variety of meanings for the word "bridge" does not cause any difficulty and no one complains about the English language because it has a large number of words each with a multitude of meanings. In any given sentence the meaning of the word "bridge" is clear from the way in which it is used in the sentence.

Similarly, in mathematics a symbol can be used with several different meanings. For example, what does the letter A represent in Fig. 1? Actually, it can denote the point which is the intersection of the two lines, or it can represent the angle formed by the two lines, or it can denote the measure of the angle, in this case 40°. Each of these three items (the point, the angle, and the measure of the angle) is logically distinct and it may seem to be improper to use one letter A for all three. But how much more confusing it would be to use three different letters at each corner of the triangle. It is better to use just one letter A. An alert student will have no trouble in discerning from the context just which of the items the letter represents at a given time, just as he can determine the meaning of the word "bridge" from the way it is used.

FIGURE 1

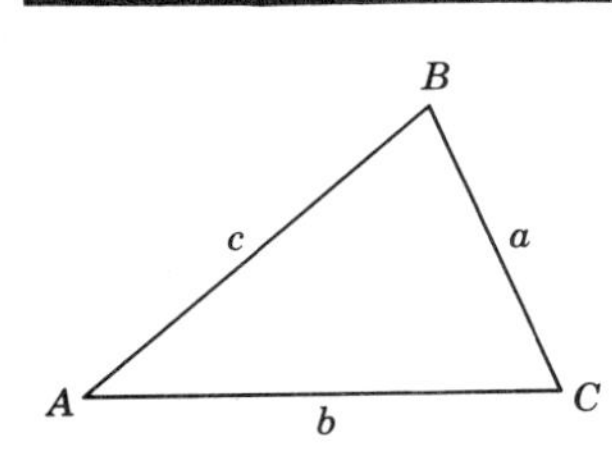

6. What Is a Theorem? A rough definition is this: a theorem is a statement or assertion that can be proved. We will not try to polish this definition, but we want to indicate what the rough spots are. The statement "George Washington was the first president of the United States" can be "proved" by consulting several history books. However we do not call this statement a theorem, (1) because it does not deal with a mathematical object and (2) because the proof is not given by a logical argument. In this case the proof given is "proof by appeal to higher authority" and such proofs by appeal are never allowed in mathematics.

The assertion "$2 + 2 = 4$" is a valid statement, and it can be proved by a logical argument, beginning with the three definitions $1 + 1 = 2$, $1 + 2 = 3$, and $1 + 3 = 4$ and using the associative law of addition. Still we do not wish to call $2 + 2 = 4$ a theorem, because it is not very interesting, and also it is not very important for the development of mathematics.

Mathematics is populated with millions of facts, formulas, laws, and propositions, each one provable by a logical argument. To call every such item a theorem would be ridiculous. The fascinating and important facts would be swallowed up and lost in the sea of dull and trivial items. The honorable title of "Theorem" is reserved for those facts, formulas, laws, or propositions that are either very interesting, or very important, or both.

Although one man's theorem may be another man's proposition, this should not confuse the student. The important thing to remember is this: whether it is a mathematical fact, formula, law, proposition, or theorem, it can be proved by logical arguments.

One should not demand a proof of every assertion, because this is logically impossible. Certain of the simplest assertions are needed as "building blocks" with which to give the proofs of the more complicated ones. Since every proof needs some building blocks it is clear that in order to begin somewhere, some of the assertions must be assumed valid without proof. Such assertions are called *axioms* or *postulates*. For example, in plane geometry the assertion "Through any pair of points one and only one line can be drawn" is an axiom. Any attempt to prove it would only result in introducing other and more complicated axioms.

7. The Notation Q.E.D. We put the symbols Q.E.D. at the end of a proof. These letters abbreviate the Latin phrase *Quod erat demonstrandum* which means "which was to be demonstrated." These letters serve to notify the student that the proof of the theorem has been completed. He may not understand the proof, but at least he can locate the point at which the proof stops, and then reread the proof until it does become clear.

8. The Pythagorean Theorem. This is the most famous and probably the most useful theorem in plane geometry.

Theorem 1. *In a right triangle the square of the hypotenuse equals the sum of the squares of the sides.*

In symbols

$$c^2 = a^2 + b^2.$$

The proof we give below is at least a thousand years old. It is a little different from the ones found in the standard textbooks, and we believe it is shorter, simpler, and prettier.

In a square each of whose sides has length $a + b$ mark off points R, S, V, P, as shown in Fig. 2, and draw the lines RS, SV, VP, and PR. The result will be four corner triangles each congruent to the given right triangle, and hence each having an area $ab/2$. But for the angles, $A + B + C = 180°$, and $C = 90°$, hence $A + B = 90°$. It follows that each of the inner angles at R, S, V, and P is a right angle, so the figure $RSVP$ is a square. Let us examine the areas.

Area of outer square = area of inner square + area of four triangles:

$$(a + b)^2 = c^2 + 4 \times \left(\frac{ab}{2}\right),$$

$$a^2 + 2ab + b^2 = c^2 + 2ab,$$

$$a^2 + b^2 = c^2.$$

Q.E.D.

FIGURE 2

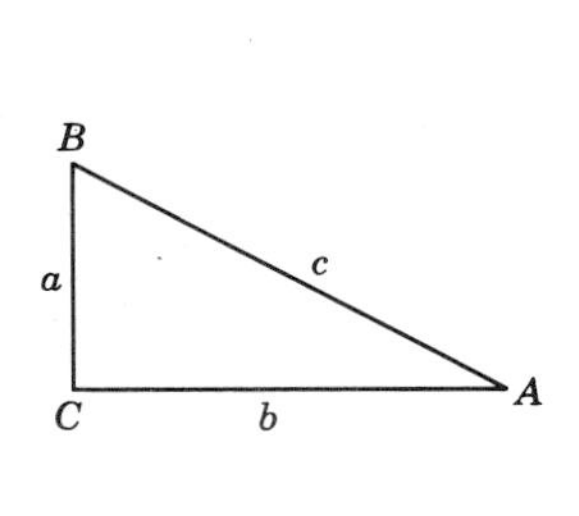

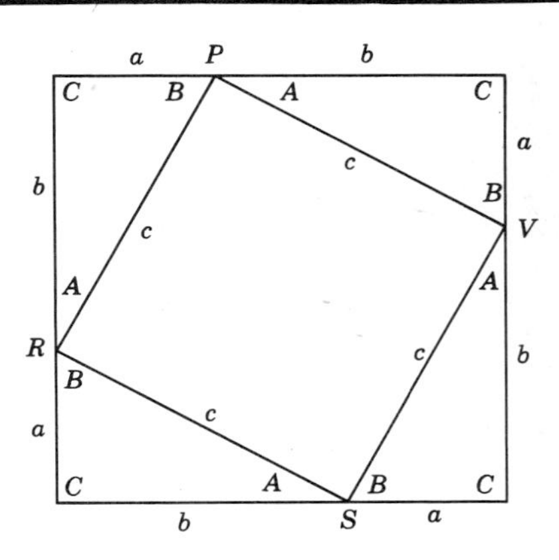

★9. **Function Notation.** Just as we use x to represent a number in mathematics, we need some notation for a function. A *function* is a correspondence between two sets of numbers, such that when one number from the first set is given, its mate in the second set can be determined. Thus y is called a function of x if whenever x is known y can be found. As examples of functions we cite:

$$y = 5x + 3, \tag{1}$$

$$y = x^3 - 2x^2 + 3x - 4, \tag{2}$$

$$y = 2^x, \tag{3}$$

$$y = \frac{x^5 + 3x^3 - 22}{x^2 + \pi}. \tag{4}$$

In each of these examples, whenever x is a number we can compute y. We call x the *independent variable*, because it can run freely, and y is called the *dependent variable*, because it must tag along.

In these examples, the functions are explicitly known. When we wish to talk about an unknown function, or just to talk about functions in general, we use the symbol

$$y = f(x)$$

(read, y equals f of x).

Here the f does not multiply x, but it is a machine or an operator that produces from each x its mate y. For example, if $x = 2$ and if $f(x)$ is the particular function given by equation (1), then

$$f(2) = 5 \times 2 + 3 = 13.$$

Briefly: to find $f(2)$, knowing $f(x)$, just replace x by 2 wherever x occurs. For this same function we have

$$f(1) = 5 \times 1 + 3 = 8,$$

and

$$f(3) = 5 \times 3 + 3 = 18.$$

Notice that

$$f(1) + f(2) = 8 + 13 = 21,$$

but

$$f(1 + 2) = f(3) = 18.$$

Therefore,

$$f(1 + 2) \neq f(1) + f(2).$$

EXERCISE 1

In Problems 1 through 18 find the third side of the right triangle with sides a, b, and c, where c is the hypotenuse.

1. $a = 3,\quad b = 4.$	**2.** $a = 6,\quad b = 8.$	**3.** $a = 5,\quad b = 12.$
4. $a = 9,\quad b = 40.$	**5.** $a = 4,\quad c = 5.$	**6.** $b = 9,\quad c = 41.$
7. $b = 12,\quad c = 20.$	**8.** $a = 2,\quad b = 3.$	**9.** $b = 5,\quad c = 6.$
10. $a = 7,\quad b = 11.$	**11.** $a = 7,\quad c = 11.$	**12.** $b = 7,\quad c = 11.$
13. $a = 5,\quad b = 4.$	**14.** $a = 2,\quad b = 4.$	**15.** $a = 3,\quad b = 6.$
16. $a = 4,\quad b = 8.$	**17.** $a = 8,\quad b = 16.$	**18.** $a = 40,\quad b = 80.$

★ **19.** The number set (a, b, c) is called a Pythagorean triple if a, b, and c are all positive integers (whole numbers) and $a^2 + b^2 = c^2$. Prove that if (a, b, c) is a Pythagorean triple and k is a positive integer then (ka, kb, kc) is a Pythagorean triple.

★ **20.** Prove that if s and t are any positive integers with $s > t$, and if

$$a = s^2 - t^2, \qquad b = 2st, \qquad c = s^2 + t^2,$$

then (a, b, c) is a Pythagorean triple.

★ **21.** In the formulas of Problem 20 find s and t so that these formulas generate the Pythagorean triples (3, 4, 5), (5, 12, 13), and (9, 40, 41).

★★★ **22.** Try to find three positive integers such that $a^3 + b^3 = c^3$.

★ **23.** Give all possible interpretations of the expression

$$\frac{\frac{\frac{A}{B}}{C}}{D}$$

and simplify this expression for each interpretation. There are five interpretations, but only four different answers.

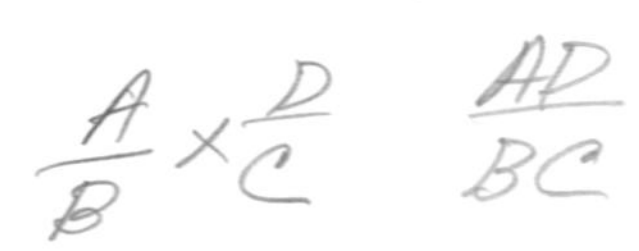

★**24.** If A, B, and C are all different from zero, when is

$$\frac{\frac{A}{B}}{C} = \frac{A}{\frac{B}{C}}$$

25. If $f(x)$ is given by equation (2) in §9 show that $f(1) = -2$, $f(2) = 2$, $f(3) = 14$, $f(0) = -4$, and $f(-2) = -26$.

26. If $f(x)$ is given by equation (3) in §9 show that $f(1) = 2$, $f(5) = 32$, $f(0) = 1$, and $f(-1) = \frac{1}{2}$

★**27.** For the function $f(x) = x^2$ prove that $f(x) = f(-x)$, and that $f(x+5) = x^2 + 10x + 25$.

★**28.** For the function $f(x) = x^7$ prove that $f(-x) = -f(x)$, and that $f(xy) = x^7y^7$.

★**29.** For the function $f(x) = 11x$ prove that $f(x + y) = f(x) + f(y)$.

★**30.** For the function $f(x) = 3^x$ prove that $f(x + y) = f(x)f(y)$.

CHAPTER 1

TRIGONOMETRIC FUNCTIONS OF AN ACUTE ANGLE, AND APPLICATIONS

1. Objective. We begin by learning how to measure the heights of trees and tall buildings without climbing them. The same method can be used to measure the widths of rivers without crossing them. A systematic study of the methods used reveals many other interesting applications.

2. Measuring the Height of a Tree. The direct way to measure the height of a tree is to climb up the tree carrying a sufficiently long rope with a weight tied to the end of the rope. The rest of the operation is obvious, and no elaborate description is needed. This method has several disadvantages: (1) The top branches of a tree will not support the weight of a man, (2) the rope will not be straight because usually the branches of the tree will interfere, (3) considerable effort is required to climb a tree.

A smart man (S. M.) will proceed as follows. On a sunny day S. M. will select a time when the tree casts a shadow of reasonable length and he will measure this length. At the same time S. M. will drive a stake vertically into the ground, and he will measure both the height of the stake above ground and the length of its shadow (see Fig. 1).

Suppose that the measurements are as indicated in the figure. The triangles ABC and $A'B'C'$ are similar because: (1) the sun is so far away that the lines AB and $A'B'$ are parallel; (2) the tree and the stake are supposed to be vertical, so lines BC and $B'C'$ are parallel; and (3) the ground is level, at least near the tree and the stake, so that the lines AC and $A'C'$ are parallel. For similar triangles the ratios of corresponding sides are equal. If we let x denote the unknown height BC, then

$$\frac{BC}{AC} = \frac{B'C'}{A'C'} \quad \text{or} \quad \frac{x}{40} = \frac{3}{2}. \tag{1}$$

If we multiply both sides of (1) by 40 we find the height of the tree, $x = 40(3/2) = 60$ ft. It is obvious that a little thinking is far superior to direct assault by brute force, i.e., climbing the tree.

FIGURE 1

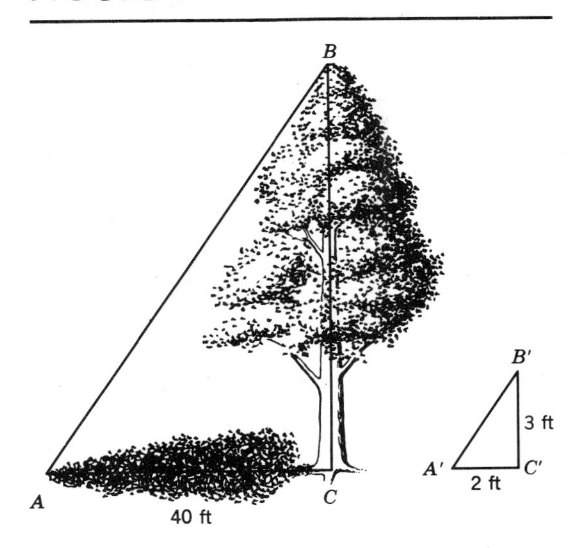

Questions: What would S. M. do if the sun were not shining, and if he were too much in a hurry to wait for a sunny day? What would S. M. do if the tree were not vertical, or if the ground were not level?

3. Measuring the Width of a River. The direct way is to tie one end of a rope or measuring tape to a rock or tree close to one bank of the river, and holding firmly onto the other end wade or swim across the river. The reader may amuse himself by listing the disadvantages of this method.

Our friend S. M. might proceed as follows. First, standing at a point C (see Fig. 2*a*) S. M. sights a convenient object B, a large rock or tree, close to the bank on the other side of the river. Then turning at right angles to his line of sight, he paces off a convenient distance, say 100 ft, to a point A and then again sights on the same object. The angle at A can be measured. If elaborate instruments are not available, crude ones can be built. But it is not necessary that S. M. be able to measure the angle at A. It is required only that he draw an angle A' equal to A on an auxiliary piece of paper (Fig. 2*b*). Then he draws $A'C'$ some convenient length such as 10 in. At C' he draws a right angle, and then completes the triangle by finding B', the point of intersection of the perpendicular and the second side of the angle A'. Finally he measures the side $B'C'$ and finds that it is 4 in. The two triangles ABC and $A'B'C'$ are similar, and so, just as in the preceding example

$$\frac{BC}{AC} = \frac{B'C'}{A'C'} \tag{2}$$

or

$$\frac{x}{100} = \frac{4}{10},$$

hence, the width of the river is $x = 100(4/10) = 40$ ft.

If the 60-ft tree of §2 happened to be near the edge of this 40-ft river, then S. M. could chop it down, and cross the river quite safely and without getting wet.

FIGURE 2

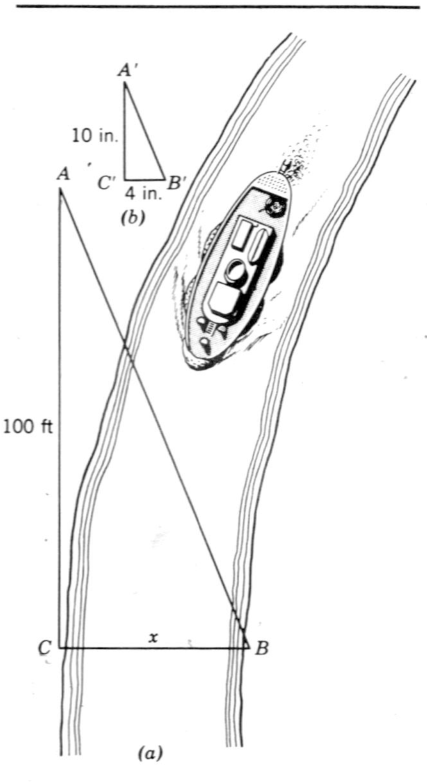

4. The Trigonometric Functions of an Acute Angle. In the two problems that we have just worked there is a common element. Indeed the ratio

$$\frac{BC}{AC} \tag{3}$$

is the same for any two right triangles ABC with right angle at C, and with the same angle A. Stated differently, this ratio does not depend on the size of the triangle, but only on the size of the angle A.

If now we had a table of such ratios for a large number of different angles, then the solution of these two problems (and many others) would be greatly simplified. In measuring the height of the tree, S. M. would not need the auxiliary stake, nor the sunlight. He would merely measure the angle A and the distance of the point A from the base of the tree. He would find the ratio BC/AC from a table. The computation would then be $x/40 = 1.5$ (from the table) and hence $x = 60$ ft just as before.

In measuring the width of the river, S. M. would not need to make the auxiliary drawing of Fig. 2*b*. He would merely measure the angle A, and the distance AC, and find the ratio BC/AC from a table. The computation would be $x/100 = .4$ (from the table), and so $x = 40$ ft for the width of the river.

There are six possible ratios associated with the three sides of a triangle. Each ratio has been given a name, and the student is advised to memorize these names with their abbreviations and meanings as quickly as possible.

FIGURE 3

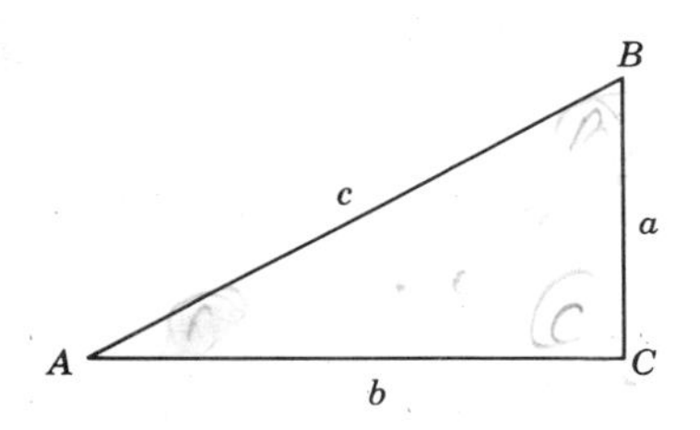

Definition 1. *In a right triangle ABC with the right angle at C (Fig. 3):*

$$\text{sine of } A = \sin A = \frac{\text{side opposite the angle } A}{\text{hypotenuse}} = \frac{a}{c},$$

$$\text{cosine of } A = \cos A = \frac{\text{side adjacent to the angle } A}{\text{hypotenuse}} = \frac{b}{c},$$

$$\text{tangent of } A = \tan A = \frac{\text{side opposite the angle } A}{\text{side adjacent to the angle } A} = \frac{a}{b},$$

$$\text{cotangent of } A = \cot A = \frac{\text{side adjacent to the angle } A}{\text{side opposite the angle } A} = \frac{b}{a},$$

$$\text{secant of } A = \sec A = \frac{\text{hypotenuse}}{\text{side adjacent to the angle } A} = \frac{c}{b},$$

$$\text{cosecant of } A = \csc A = \frac{\text{hypotenuse}}{\text{side opposite the angle } A} = \frac{c}{a}.$$

Trigonometry is a very easy subject because all of the hard work connected with it was done years ago and carefully preserved for our use. The hard work is just the computation of sin, cos, etc. for various angles, and making a table of the results. Such a table is given as Table B in the Appendix of this book, and a portion of this table is reproduced here for ready reference.

Radians	Degrees	Sin	Tan	Cot	Cos		
.3142	**18° 00′**	.3090	.3249	3.078	.9511	**72° 00′**	1.2566
171	10	118	281	047	502	71° 50′	537
200	20	145	314	018	492	40	508
.3229	30	.3173	.3346	2.989	.9483	30	1.2479
258	40	201	378	960	474	20	450
287	50	228	411	932	465	10	421
.3316	**19° 00′**	.3256	.3443	2.904	.9455	**71° 00′**	1.2392
345	10	283	476	877	446	70° 50′	363
374	20	311	508	850	436	40	334
.3403	30	.3338	.3541	2.824	.9426	30	1.2305
432	40	365	574	798	417	20	275
462	50	393	607	773	407	10	246
.3491	**20° 00′**	.3420	.3640	2.747	.9397	**70° 00′**	1.2217

Suppose that we want sin 18°. We look in the column headed Degrees and find 18° 00′ in the first row below the heading. Then just opposite in the same row but in the next column we find .3090. Since this column is headed Sin we infer that

$$\sin 18^\circ\ 0' = .3090,$$

which is the case. In the same manner, looking under the headings Tan, Cot, and Cos, and in the proper rows we find that:

$$\tan 18^\circ\ 30' = .3346,$$
$$\cot 19^\circ\ 10' = 2.877,$$
$$\cos 19^\circ\ 50' = .9407.$$

The values of sec and csc are not tabulated here because they are not needed.

This table can be used for the inverse process. Suppose that we want to find the angle α such that $\tan \alpha = .3378$. We look in the column headed Tan until we find this number and then observe that it is in the same row with 18° 40′, so we infer that $.3378 = \tan 18^\circ\ 40'$, or $\alpha = 18^\circ\ 40'$.

As an aid in memorizing the definitions, the student should observe that the trigonometric functions can be arranged in pairs of reciprocals:

$$\sin A = \frac{a}{c} = \frac{1}{\csc A}, \qquad \sin A \text{ and } \csc A \text{ are reciprocals,}$$

$$\cos A = \frac{b}{c} = \frac{1}{\sec A}, \qquad \cos A \text{ and } \sec A \text{ are reciprocals,}$$

$$\tan A = \frac{a}{b} = \frac{1}{\cot A}, \qquad \tan A \text{ and } \cot A \text{ are reciprocals.}$$

EXERCISE 2

In each of the four right triangles of Problems 1 to 4 give all six of the trigonometric functions of each of the acute angles pictured. Notice, there are $2 \times 6 \times 4 = 48$ items for the complete answer.

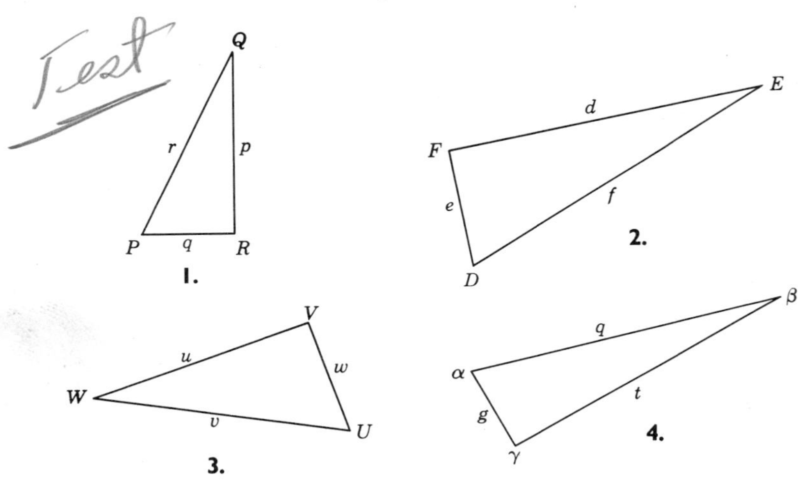

Find from Table B the trigonometric functions of the angles listed below:

5. sin 13° 10′. **6.** tan 22° 30′. **7.** cot 15° 50′. **8.** cos 9° 40′.
9. sin 24° 10′. **10.** tan 28° 40′. **11.** cot 29° 30′. **12.** cos 26° 00′.
13. sin 44° 20′. **14.** tan 40° 10′. **15.** cot 35° 00′. **16.** cos 36° 50′.

In Problems 17 through 28, use Table B to find the angle.

17. $\sin A = .0029$. **18.** $\cos B = .9995$. **19.** $\tan C = .1405$.
20. $\cot D = 343.8$. **21.** $\sin E = .2334$. **22.** $\cos F = .9520$.

23. $\cot G = 2.300.$ **24.** $\tan \alpha = .9490.$ **25.** $\cos \beta = .9171.$

26. $\sin \gamma = .6884.$ **27.** $\tan \theta = .7400.$ **28.** $\cot \varphi = 1.054.$

★**29.** Using elementary geometry find the sin, cos, tan, and cot of 45° by considering an isosceles right triangle. Check your answers in Table B.

★**30.** Repeat Problem 29 for the angles 30° and 60° by considering a 30°-60°-90° triangle, obtained by bisecting an equilateral triangle.

31. Prove that for any angle A, $\sin A \csc A = 1$, $\cos A \sec A = 1$, and $\tan A \cot A = 1$.

5. The Cofunctions. The reader has probably noticed that in Table B the angles listed in the left-hand column do not exceed 45°. There is no need to extend the table, because the trigonometric functions for angles between 45° and 90° can be obtained from Table B in a simple way, which we will now show.

First observe that in the right triangle of Fig. 3, the angles A and B are complementary, i.e.,

$$A + B = 90^\circ \quad \text{or} \quad B = 90^\circ - A. \tag{4}$$

Then from the definition of sin and cos it is easy to see that,

$$\sin A = \frac{a}{c} = \cos B = \cos (90^\circ - A). \tag{5}$$

Now suppose that $A = 70^\circ$ and we wish to find sin 70°. Then $B = 90^\circ - A = 20^\circ$ and equation (5) tells us that $\sin 70^\circ = \cos 20^\circ$. But from Table B, $\cos 20^\circ = .9397$, hence $\sin 70^\circ = .9397$.

This process will work for any one of the trigonometric functions. We will need equations similar to (5) for the other trigonometric functions. It is easy to see, using the definitions of the trigonometric functions, and referring to Fig. 3, that :

$$\cos A = \frac{b}{c} = \sin B = \sin (90^\circ - A), \tag{6}$$

$$\tan A = \frac{a}{b} = \cot B = \cot (90^\circ - A), \tag{7}$$

$$\cot A = \frac{b}{a} = \tan B = \tan (90^\circ - A), \tag{8}$$

$$\sec A = \frac{c}{b} = \csc B = \csc (90^\circ - A), \tag{9}$$

$$\csc A = \frac{c}{a} = \sec B = \sec (90^\circ - A). \tag{10}$$

It would be too much to memorize all six of these equations, but fortunately it is not necessary. All of the material can be wrapped up in a neat little package (see Theorem 1).

Definition 2. *Cosine is called the cofunction of sine. Cotangent is called the cofunction of tangent. Cosecant is called the cofunction of secant. Conversely in each case the second-named function is also called the cofunction of the first one.*

Theorem 1. *For any acute angle A, the trigonometric function of A is equal to the cofunction of the complement of A.*

Since this is a condensed statement of equations (5), (6), (7), (8), (9), and (10), this theorem is proved as soon as the student checks that these equations are correct.

Let us now take another look at Table B. At the bottom of each column headed by a trigonometric function, is the appropriate cofunction. Thus Cos is at the bottom of the column headed Sin, and Sin is at the bottom of the column headed Cos. In the right-hand column each angle is the complement of its mate standing in the same row in the left-hand column. For example, 20° and 70° stand in the same row; 38° 50′ and 51° 10′ stand in the same row, etc. The table is thus arranged so that Theorem 1 and Definition 2 can be completely forgotten if the following very simple working rule is used.

Rule 1. *If* $0° \leqq A \leqq 45°$, *use the left-hand column for the angle and the headings at the top. If* $45° \leqq A \leqq 90°$, *use the right-hand column for the angle and the headings (footings?) at the bottom.*

EXERCISE 3

1. Prove equations (5), (6), (7), (8), (9), and (10) using Definition 1.

Find from Table B the trigonometric functions of the angles listed below:

2. sin 63° 10′. **3.** tan 52° 30′. **4.** cot 45° 50′. **5.** cos 49° 40′.
6. sin 74° 10′. **7.** tan 78° 40′. **8.** cot 79° 30′. **9.** cos 66° 00′.
10. sin 84° 20′. **11.** tan 80° 10′. **12.** cot 85° 00′. **13.** cos 76° 50′.

Given the trigonometric functions, use Table B to find the angles listed below:

14. $\sin A = .9511$. **15.** $\cos B = .1822$. **16.** $\tan C = 3.450$.
17. $\cot D = .3249$. **18.** $\cos E = .3256$. **19.** $\tan F = 1.492$.
20. $\cot G = .8002$. **21.** $\sin \alpha = .9799$. **22.** $\cos \beta = .7009$.
23. $\sin \gamma = .7771$. **24.** $\tan \theta = 1.949$. **25.** $\cot \varphi = .3443$.

6. The Variations of the Trigonometric Functions. Let us examine how sin A behaves as the angle A takes on increasing values. In Fig. 4, we have drawn a set of four triangles, and in each the hypotenuse $c = 1$.

FIGURE 4

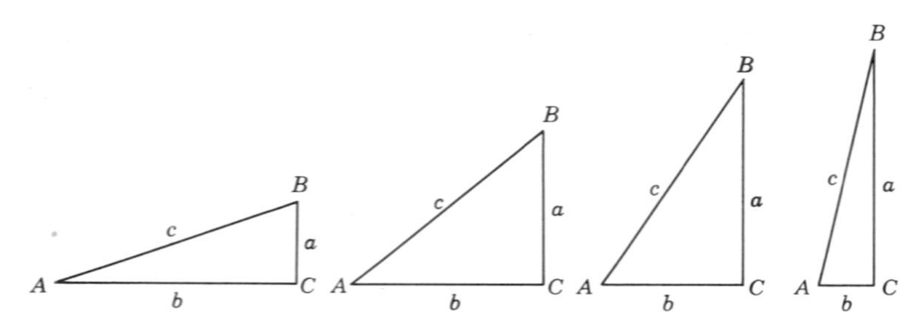

Since $\sin A = a/c$, and since $c = 1$ for all four triangles, it follows that $\sin A = a$. From the picture it is clear that as the angle A increases so does the side opposite it, and hence so does sin A. Therefore: *sin A increases as A increases.*

Similarly $\cos A = b/c = b$ (since $c = 1$), and from the picture, side b grows shorter as the angle A increases. Therefore: *cos A decreases as A increases.*

Tan $A = a/b$, and in Fig. 4 it is obvious that a (the numerator) increases and b (the denominator) decreases as A increases. This means that the fraction increases and therefore: *tan A increases as A increases.*

A similar argument will show that: *cot A decreases as A increases, sec A increases as A increases, and csc A decreases as A increases.*

We can say more about these functions. Notice that in a right triangle the side a is always less than the hypotenuse, but that as the angle A approaches 90°, the side a becomes closer and closer in length to the hypotenuse. On the other hand, when the angle A is near zero, the side a is also near zero. Thus, $0 \leqq a \leqq c = 1$, and since in this case $\sin A = a$, we have

$$0 \leqq \sin A \leqq 1.$$

Since the side $b \leqq c = 1$, we have similarly that $0 \leqq \cos A \leqq 1$.

On the other hand $\tan A = a/b$ may become as large as we please, if b is close enough to zero. We say that tan A is unbounded (or that tan A tends to infinity as A tends to 90°). We leave the discussion of the three remaining trigonometric functions to the student. The material is summarized in Table 1.

Here the symbol ∞ is not used as a number, but merely to indicate that when the angle is near 0° (or 90°) the function in question is very large.

As an aid to memorizing these results, the student should note that the functions sin, tan, and sec are increasing, while it is their *cofunctions* cos, cot, and csc that are decreasing.

TABLE 1

As A increases from 0° to 90°

		From	To			From	To
$\sin A$	increases	0	1	$\csc A$	decreases	∞	1
$\cos A$	decreases	1	0	$\sec A$	increases	1	∞
$\tan A$	increases	0	∞	$\cot A$	decreases	∞	0

7. Solving a Triangle. To solve a triangle means to find the lengths of all the sides, and the sizes (magnitudes) of all the angles. Of course, some information must be given first. In a right triangle we would need either one side and one acute angle, or two sides.

Example 1. Solve the right triangle ABC given $c = 3000$ and $A = 25° 0'$, where the right angle is at C.

Solution. The angle B is easily found because in a right triangle $A + B = 90°$. Hence $B = 65° 0'$.

To find the other two sides it will be helpful to make a drawing, see Fig. 5. It is good practice to make an accurate drawing to scale, because the drawing then will aid in checking the answers for large errors. Suppose now that we wish to find a. The side a occurs in four of the trigonometric functions of the angle A,

FIGURE 5

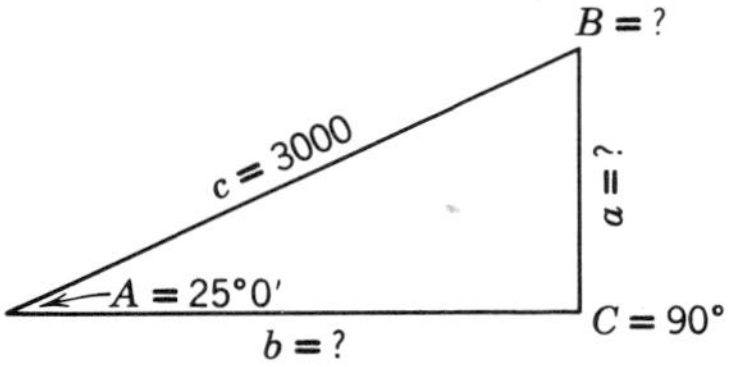

$$\tan A = \frac{a}{b}, \qquad \csc A = \frac{c}{a},$$

$$\cot A = \frac{b}{a}, \qquad \sin A = \frac{a}{c},$$

so which one shall we use? Clearly a and b are both unknown at this stage, so neither $\tan A$ nor $\cot A$ will help us much, since each one contains both unknowns. Also $\csc A$, can be rejected because Table B does not list it. We have left only $\sin A$, but this will give us what we need, because in the equation

$$\sin A = \frac{a}{c}, \qquad \text{or} \qquad \sin 25° 0' = \frac{a}{3000},$$

there is only one unknown. We multiply both sides of this equation by 3000, and use Table B for sin 25° 0′. We find

$$a = 3000 \sin 25^\circ\, 0' = 3000 \times .4226 = 1267.8.$$

Since the side c was given only to the nearest unit, we state the answer also to the nearest unit, thus $a = 1268$. A more detailed discussion of approximations will be given in the next section.

To find b we have,

$$\cos A = \frac{b}{c} \qquad \text{or} \qquad \cos 25^\circ\, 0' = \frac{b}{3000}.$$

Therefore,

$$b = 3000 \cos 25^\circ\, 0' = 3000 \times .9063 \qquad \text{(Table B)}$$
$$= 2718.9 = 2719 \qquad \text{(to the nearest unit).}$$

Notice that we could have found b from a using

$$\tan A = \frac{a}{b} \qquad \text{or} \qquad \tan 25^\circ\, 0' = \frac{1267.8}{b}.$$

Thus,

$$b = \frac{1267.8}{\tan 25^\circ\, 0'} = \frac{1267.8}{.4663} = 2718.9 \qquad \text{(to the nearest tenth).}$$

However, this is not good practice, because an error in computing a in the first part would automatically give an error in b also. It is much better to use $\tan A = a/b$ as a check, thus:

$$\tan A = \frac{a}{b} = \frac{1267.8}{2718.9} = .46629 \cdots = .4663.$$

(to four significant figures).

But the table gives tan 25° 0′ as .4663 so the answers for a and b are checked simultaneously.

FIGURE 6

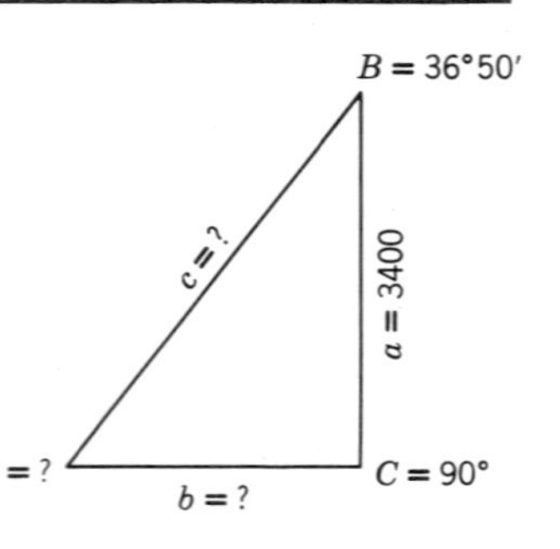

Example 2. Solve the right triangle ABC, given $a = 3400$, and $B = 36^\circ\, 50'$ (Fig. 6).

Solution. Since $A + B = 90^\circ$ we find $A = 53^\circ\, 10'$. To find c we have

$$\cos B = \frac{a}{c}.$$

Therefore,

$$c = \frac{a}{\cos B} = \frac{3400}{\cos 36^\circ\, 50'} = \frac{3400}{.8004} = 4247.8 \cdots = 4248$$

(to the nearest unit).

To find b, we could write $\cot B = a/b$, but it is easier to compute b if we use $\tan B = b/a$. Then:

$$b = a \tan B = 3400 \tan 36^\circ 50' = 3400 \times .7490 = 2546.6 = 2547$$

(to the nearest unit).

As a check,

$$\sin B = \frac{b}{c} = \frac{2546.6}{4247.8} = .59951 \cdots.$$

But from Table B, $\sin 36^\circ 50' = .5995$, and so the answers for a and b check.

FIGURE 7

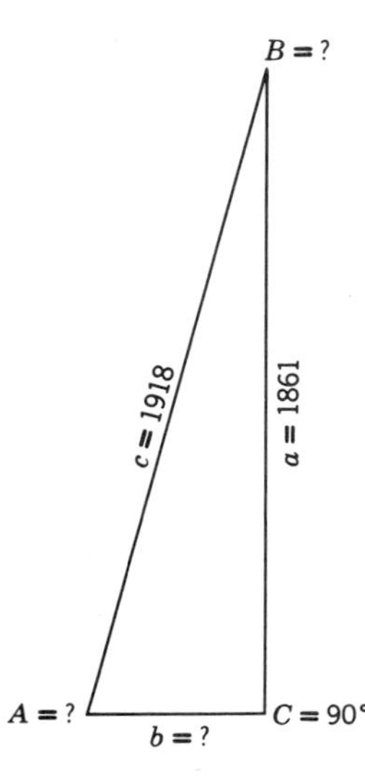

Example 3. Solve the right triangle ABC, given $a = 1861$ and $c = 1918$ (Fig. 7).

Solution.

$$\cos B = \frac{1861}{1918} = .97028 \cdots,$$

and since (from Table B) $\cos 14^\circ 0' = .9703$, we have $B = 14^\circ 0'$ to the nearest minute and $A = 90^\circ - 14^\circ 0' = 76^\circ 0'$ with the same accuracy.

We could compute b using the Pythagorean Theorem, but this is not properly trigonometry. Instead we use $b/c = \sin B$. This gives (to the nearest unit):

$$b = c \sin B = 1918 \sin 14^\circ 0' = 1918 \times .2419 = 463.9642 = 464$$

The Pythagorean Theorem could be used as a check, but it is quicker to use $b/a = \tan B$. Thus

$$b = a \tan B = 1861 \tan 14^\circ 0' = 1861 \times .2493 = 463.9473.$$

Since this agrees in the first four figures with the b obtained previously, and since Table B gives only 4-figure accuracy, this check is acceptable.

EXERCISE 4

Solve the following triangles. In each case assume the right angle is at C. Give sides to the nearest integer (unit) and angles to the nearest 10 minutes.

1. $c = 1776$, $A = 30^\circ 40'$. **2.** $c = 1914$, $A = 36^\circ 50'$.
3. $c = 1984$, $B = 12^\circ 50'$. **4.** $c = 2000$, $B = 10^\circ 10'$.
5. $a = 2001$, $c = 3000$. **6.** $a = 1776$, $c = 4004$.
7. $a = 1915$, $A = 39^\circ 40'$. **8.** $a = 1861$, $A = 68^\circ 30'$.
9. $a = 1898$, $b = 2000$. **10.** $a = 1776$, $b = 1984$.

8. Approximations and Significant Figures. The number π is frequently given as 3.14, sometimes given as 3.1416, and occasionally as 3.14159265. Of course, not all of these values for π can be correct, and the truth is that none of them is. It can be proved that π cannot be written using only a finite number of integers, but the proof is difficult and the student must postpone studying it until he has progressed much further in mathematics. However, there is nothing to prevent us from using a symbol for the ratio of the circumference of a circle to its diameter, and as the reader is aware, the Greek letter π has been universally adopted.

It can be proved that:

(11) $$3.135 \leqq \pi \leqq 3.145,$$

or still better

(12) $$3.14155 \leqq \pi \leqq 3.14165,$$

or even better yet

(13) $$3.141592645 \leqq \pi \leqq 3.141592655.$$

When we write $\pi = 3.14$, what we really mean is that π satisfies the inequality (11). In this case we say that $\pi = 3.14$ to two decimal places. We also say $\pi = 3.14$ to three significant figures, or with 3-figure accuracy. Similarly,

Statement	Means	Degree of accuracy
$\pi = 3.1416$	Inequality (12)	5 significant figures,
$\pi = 3.14159265$	Inequality (13)	9 significant figures.

Approximate numbers also arise in measuring or weighing. The statement that my yard is 52 ft wide means that the true width d lies between 51.5 and 52.5 ft, and the statement is correct to two significant figures. If I assert that $d = 52.0$ ft, then I mean that $51.95 \text{ ft} \leqq d \leqq 52.05$ ft and I am now claiming that my measurement is correct to three significant figures.

On the other hand, not all numbers are approximations. When we write that $x = 3$ is a solution of the equation $x^3 - 3x^2 + 2x - 6 = 0$, we do not mean that the solution is a number somewhere between 2.5 and 3.5. True enough 3 does lie in this interval, but 3 is the *exact* solution, and no amount of refinement in our computations will yield any closer estimation of the solution. Similarly, $\sqrt{16} = 4$ is an exact assertion, and not an approximate one.

Logically we should have a special symbol to distinguish approximations from exact assertions. Perhaps the student would enjoy writing,

$$\sqrt{3} \stackrel{a}{=} 1.732,$$
$$\sqrt{4} = 2,$$

putting "a" over the equal sign when an approximation is intended. Such a distinction is not made in most textbooks, nor will it be made in this one. The reason is quite simple: it is assumed that the reader is sufficiently mature and sufficiently intelligent to know which numbers are approximations and which numbers are exact, so that there is no need to clutter up the equations with unnecessary adornments.

The mean distance from the earth to the sun is usually given as 92,900,000 miles. How many significant figures are there in this measurement? One cannot answer this question without further information, because we cannot tell which of the zeros are there merely to place the decimal point. Surely we suspect that the distance is not known with an error of only half a mile. The difficulty can be removed by introducing scientific notation.

Definition 3. *A number N is written in scientific notation if it has the form*

$$N = A \times 10^m$$

where $1 \leqq A < 10$, *and m is an integer.*

For example, the mean distance from the earth to the sun, written in scientific notation, is 9.29×10^7 miles. This suggests the following convenient

Convention I. *When scientific notation is used, the number of digits in A is the number of significant figures in N.*

With this mode of writing the number it is easy to see that the distance 9.29×10^7 miles is accurate to three significant figures, and that all of the zeros in 92,900,000 are "dummies" used merely to locate the decimal point.

As an example of a very small number, consider the statement that the average diameter of a red blood cell is .00074 cm. Here it is obvious that we have 2-figure accuracy although five digits were needed to write the number. The first three zeros are "dummies" used only to locate the decimal point, and they disappear when we write the number in scientific notation as 7.4×10^{-4} cm.

To change a given number N to scientific notation, move the decimal point in N until it stands just after the first nonzero digit. If q is the number of places the decimal is moved, then

$m = q > 0$	if N is large:	$10 \leqq N$,
$m = 0$	if N is intermediate:	$1 \leqq N < 10$,
$m = -q < 0$	if N is small:	$N < 1$.

Example 4.

Usual Notation	Work	q	Scientific Notation
$a = 3450.2$	3.4 5 0. 2	3	$a = 3.4502 \times 10^3$,
$b = .000543$	.0 0 0 5. 4 3	4	$b = 5.43 \times 10^{-4}$,
$c = 2.34$	2.34	0	$c = 2.34 \times 10^0$.

To change from scientific notation to the usual notation reverse the procedure.

The student is already familiar with the process of rounding off a number. For example, if we know that $\pi = 3.14159265$ with 9-figure accuracy, then rounding off to a lesser degree of accuracy would give:

$\pi = 3.1415926$	8-figure accuracy,	$\pi = 3.1416$	5-figure accuracy,
$\pi = 3.141593$	7-figure accuracy,	$\pi = 3.142$	4-figure accuracy,
$\pi = 3.14159$	6-figure accuracy,	$\pi = 3.14$	3-figure accuracy.

Only the first of these entries needs explanation. When the digit to be dropped is less than 5, no change is made in the preceding digit. If the dropped digit exceeds 5 then 1 is added to the preceding digit. We are in a quandary if the dropped digit is a 5. There is no scientific way of deciding whether to increase the preceding digit. Merely for the sake of uniformity we agree to the rule: When the dropped digit is 5 make the preceding digit even (0, 2, 4, 6, or 8).

In trigonometric computations we agree to set up the following correspondance between accuracy in the measurement of lengths and angles:

Lengths	Angles
2-figure accuracy	Nearest degree,
3-figure accuracy	Nearest multiple of 10 minutes,
4-figure accuracy	Nearest minute,
5-figure accuracy	Nearest tenth of a minute.

For example, if the sides of a right triangle were given as $a = 4.000$ in. and $b = 7.500$ in. (4-figure accuracy) we would compute angle A to the nearest minute.

★ It is not easy to give a general rule describing the number of significant digits in an answer resulting from a series of computations. We do not attempt to discuss this difficult problem, but we will give two examples to show that there is a difficulty.

Example 5. *Multiplication.* Let $a = 111$ and $b = 123$ (each with 3-figure accuracy). Then, using the numbers as they are given

$$ab = 111 \times 123 = 13{,}653.$$

However the extreme possibilities are

$$\begin{aligned} \text{Smallest: } & 110.5 \times 122.5 = 13{,}536.25 \\ \text{Largest: } & 111.5 \times 123.5 = 13{,}770.25 \end{aligned}$$

Hence the third digit in the answer could be 5, 6, 7, or 8 (after rounding off). Thus, the product ab is accurate only to *two* significant figures, although a and b were both given with 3-figure accuracy.

Example 6. *Subtraction.* Let $a = 12{,}359$ and $b = 12{,}342$ (each with 5-figure accuracy). Then

$$a - b = 12{,}359 - 12{,}342 = 17.$$

However the extreme possibilities are

$$\begin{aligned} \text{Smallest: } & 12{,}358.5 - 12{,}342.5 = 16 \\ \text{Largest: } & 12{,}359.5 - 12{,}341.5 = 18. \end{aligned}$$

Thus the difference $a - b$ is accurate to only *one* significant figure, although a and b were given to *five* significant figures.

EXERCISE 5

1. Given that the base of the natural logarithms is $e = 2.718281828459 \cdots$, write e with: (*a*) 11-figure accuracy, (*b*) 9-figure accuracy, (*c*) 6-figure accuracy, (*d*) 4-figure accuracy.

2. Change each of the following numbers to scientific notation (assume 3-figure accuracy): (*a*) 34.5, (*b*) 34,500, (*c*) 345,000,000,000, (*d*) .345, (*e*) .00345, (*f*) .000000000345.

3. The following numbers are in scientific notation; change them to the usual notation. (*a*) 7.11×10^2, (*b*) 7.11×10^5, (*c*) 7×10^8, (*d*) 7.711×10^{-2}, (*e*) 7.77111×10^{-3}, (*f*) 7.71×10^{-5}.

4. Round off to four significant figures (*a*) 2.9999, (*b*) 2.9995, (*c*) 2.9985, (*d*) 9.9999.

9. Interpolation. Suppose that in a certain right triangle $a = 5.000$ in. and $b = 9.000$ in., and we are asked to find the angle A. Clearly

$$\tan A = \frac{5.000}{9.000} = .5556$$

to four significant figures. If we look in Table B we do not find any angle with this tangent. The best we can do is $\tan 29° \, 00' = .5543$ which is too small, and $\tan 29° \, 10' = .5581$ which is too large. We infer that A lies somewhere between these two angles, and to estimate A we proceed with the scheme shown below:

$$10' \left[\begin{array}{l} \tan 29^\circ\, 10' = .5581 \\ x \left[\begin{array}{ll} \tan A & = .5556 \\ \tan 29^\circ\, 00' & = .5543 \end{array} \right] 13 \end{array} \right] 38$$

Observe that in this scheme, the values of the trigonometric functions are arranged in decreasing order so that the subtractions, as indicated by the tie-lines are easy to perform. The difference between .5581 and .5543 is .0038, but we record merely 38 (economy of time and energy). Similarly, 13 represents the difference between .5543 and .5556. On the other side $10'$ is the difference between the two angles located in the table, and x is the unknown difference between angle A and $29^\circ\, 0'$. To find x we set up the proportion

$$\frac{x}{10'} = \frac{13}{38}$$

and solve for x. Thus $x = 10' \times 13/38 = 3.4'$. Table B is a four-figure table so we are justified in computing only to the nearest minute, and therefore we round off using $x = 3'$. Finally, x is the difference $A - 29^\circ\, 0'$, hence $A = 29^\circ\, 3'$.

If some purist insists on using the true differences .0013 and .0038 in place of 13 and 38, his proportion will yield

$$x = 10' \times \frac{.0013}{.0038} = 10' \times \frac{.0013 \times 10{,}000}{.0038 \times 10{,}000} = 10' \times \frac{13}{38} = 3.4',$$

and $A = 29^\circ\, 3'$, just as before.

Example 7. Find C if $\cos C = .8998$.

Solution. From Table B

$$10' \left[\begin{array}{l} \cos 25^\circ\, 50' = .9001 \\ x \left[\begin{array}{ll} \cos C & = .8998 \\ \cos 26^\circ\, 00' & = .8988 \end{array} \right] 10 \end{array} \right] 13$$

Observe that since the cosine function is decreasing, it is convenient to arrange the angles in increasing order on the left side, so that the function values .9001, .8998, and .8988 will be arranged in decreasing order. This will make it easy to do the subtractions on the right side.

The proportion is

$$\frac{x}{10'} = \frac{10}{13},$$

hence $x = 100/13 = 8'$. But angle C should lie between $25^\circ\ 50'$ and $26^\circ\ 0'$, so we must *subtract* $8'$ from $26^\circ\ 0'$, to get $C = 25^\circ\ 52'$.

Rule 2. *For the increasing functions, sin and tan always place the larger angle at the top. For the decreasing functions, cos and cot always place the smaller angle at the top. Then the numbers on the right side will always be arranged properly for subtraction.*

Example 8. Find sin $67^\circ\ 12'$.

$$10' \left[\begin{array}{l} \sin 67^\circ\ 20' = .9228 \\ 2' \left[\begin{array}{l} \sin 67^\circ\ 12' = \\ \sin 67^\circ\ 10' = .9216 \end{array} \right] x \end{array} \right] 12$$

$$\frac{2'}{10'} = \frac{x}{12}$$

Hence $x = 12 \times 2/10 = 2.4$ units in the last column, or $x = .0002$ to the nearest tenthousandth. Therefore $\sin 67^\circ\ 12' = .9216 + .0002 = .9218$ with 4-figure accuracy.

Example 9. Find cot $19^\circ\ 43'$.

$$10' \left[\begin{array}{l} \cot 19^\circ\ 40' = 2.798 \\ 7' \left[\begin{array}{l} \cot 19^\circ\ 43' = \\ \cot 19^\circ\ 50' = 2.773 \end{array} \right] x \end{array} \right] 25$$

$$\frac{7'}{10'} = \frac{x}{25}$$

Hence $x = 25 \times 7/10 = 17.5$ units in the last column. We round off so that the last digit in the *final answer* is even. In other words, we take $x = 17$, so that $\cot 19^\circ\ 43' = 2.773 + .0017 = 2.790$.

★ 10. The Theory Behind Interpolation. Let us imagine that $\sin \theta$ has been computed and tabulated for every value of the angle θ between 0° and 90°. Of course this is impossible because such a table would have an infinite number of entries. Still there is no harm in imagining such a table and the graph that might arise if the data were plotted. We use the horizontal axis, or x-axis, to represent the angle θ, and we use the vertical axis, or y-axis to represent $\sin \theta$. For each entry in our table we plot a point P with coordinates (x, y) in the usual manner; that is, $x = \theta$ is the distance from P to the vertical axis (with some suitable scale) and $y = \sin \theta$ is the distance from P to the horizontal axis (again with some suitable scale, which may be different from the scale used for x).

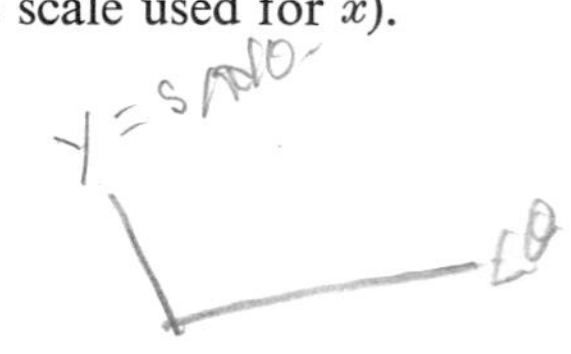

If we plot a few of the entries from Table B, the points will appear to lie on a smooth curve, as shown in Fig. 8, where we have plotted $\sin \theta$ for every 10-degree increment in θ. It can be rigorously proved that if all the entries of our hypothetical table were plotted, the points would indeed form a smooth curve,[1] but the proof cannot be given here. The

FIGURE 8

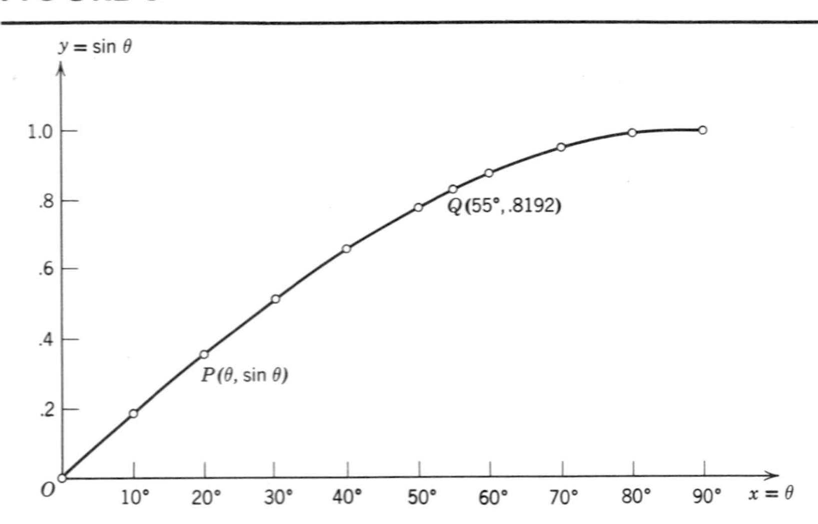

student may tentatively accept this fact, or if he wishes to test it, he may plot entries from Table B until he is convinced. Of course, the student should not accept such an experimental procedure as a proof, but this is the best that he can do with his present knowledge of mathematics.

Suppose now that we wish to find $\sin 55° 3'$. The graph in Fig. 8 is too small to be of much use in this problem, but if we enlarge it tremendously and look only at a small portion of the graph near Q: $(55°, .8192)$ then we will be able to estimate $\sin 55° 3'$.

In Fig. 9 we show this enlarged view of the neighborhood of the point Q. Of course the x and y axes have receded far out of sight, but this is remedied by showing some new axes, parallel to the old ones and intersecting at a new origin near Q. The markings on these new axes are consistent with those on the old ones. By this we mean that the markings on the new y-axis show the distances of those points from the old horizontal axis, which because of the enlargement no longer appears in the picture. The same thing holds for the markings on the new x-axis.

[1] The proof requires a knowledge of the calculus and is customarily presented in advanced calculus courses.

Finally, in Fig. 9 we have plotted the points $y = \sin\theta$ for θ running from 55° to 55° 10′, proceeding by increments of 1 minute. For this plot, we used more extensive tables, which give $\sin\theta$ to five significant figures. As a result of this increase in accuracy, the point A on the curve does not fall on Q, but as we shall see this is of no importance.

FIGURE 9

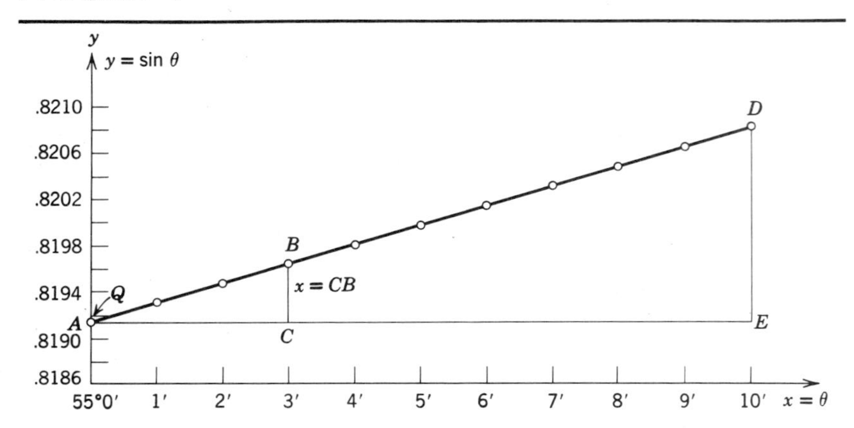

The most striking feature of Fig. 9 is that the points plotted seem to lie on a straight line AD, although in Fig. 8 the graph of $y = \sin\theta$ is certainly not a straight line. The fact is that in the enlarged view the points still form a curve, but the curvature is so gentle that it cannot be detected by the eye. For most practical computations it is therefore sufficient to assume that the straight line AD coincides with the curve $y = \sin\theta$, between $\theta = 55°$ and $\theta = 55°\ 10'$.

Assume now that AD is a straight line. Then triangle ABC is similar to triangle ADE and hence

$$\frac{AC}{AE} = \frac{CB}{ED} = \frac{x}{ED}. \tag{14}$$

But $AC = 3$, $AE = 10$, and $ED = \sin 55°\ 10' - \sin 55°\ 0'$. Using these values in (14) we can compute x and knowing x we can add this to sin 55° 0′ and obtain sin 55° 3′.

Suppose that only Table B is available. If we set up the usual scheme for computing sin 55° 3′ we have:

$$10'\left[\begin{array}{l} \sin 55°\ 10' = .8208 \\ 3'\left[\begin{array}{l}\sin 55°\ \ 3' = \\ \sin 55°\ \ 0' = .8192\end{array}\right] x \end{array}\right] .0016$$

and the proportion

$$\frac{3}{10} = \frac{x}{.0016}. \tag{15}$$

But (15) is the same as (14) when AC, AE, and ED are replaced by their numerical values. From (15) we have $x = .0016(3/10) = .0005$ (to the nearest tenthousandth) or $x = 5$ units in the last column. Finally sin $55° \ 3' = .8192 + .0005 = .8197$. If we consult a five-place table, we find sin $55° \ 3' = .81965$, so our interpolation does give four significant figures.

Summary. *Interpolation is based on the assumption that for a small range of the variable, the graph of the function is a straight line. When the interpolation scheme is used there is no need to draw the similar triangles.*

EXERCISE 6

In each of the following, find θ to the nearest minute by interpolation in Table B.

1. $\sin \theta = .1620$. **2.** $\cos \theta = .1776$. **3.** $\tan \theta = 1.812$.
4. $\cot \theta = 1.861$. **5.** $\cos \theta = .1898$. **6.** $\sin \theta = .1914$.
7. $\cot \theta = .1933$. **8.** $\tan \theta = .1984$. **9.** $\cos \theta = .4444$.
10. $\sin \theta = .5555$. **11.** $\tan \theta = 6.666$. **12.** $\cos \theta = .7777$.
13. $\cot \theta = 2.222$. **14.** $\tan \theta = 1.212$. **15.** $\sin \theta = .8888$.
16. $\cot \theta = .3333$.

In each of the following, find the indicated trigonometric function to four significant figures by interpolation in Table B.

17. sin 19° 41′. **18.** tan 41° 19′. **19.** cos 19° 14′. **20.** cot 14° 19′.
21. tan 25° 25′. **22.** sin 31° 31′. **23.** cot 84° 19′. **24.** cos 42° 42′.
25. cot 53° 53′. **26.** sin 25° 25′. **27.** tan 76° 56′. **28.** cos 8° 58′.
29. sin 8° 8′. **30.** tan 54° 32′. **31.** cos 41° 41′. **32.** cot 24° 24′.

11. Some Terminology from Surveying and Navigation. The *angle of elevation* (*depression*) of an object, is the angle the line of sight to the object makes with the horizontal plane. For example, in Fig. 10, A is the angle of elevation of the top of the flagpole as viewed from the point O, and B is the angle of depression of the base of the building as viewed from the same point.

The *bearing of a line* measures angles in a horizontal plane and is the acute angle this line makes with a north-south line. It is specified by writing first N or S, then the acute angle and E or W. For example in Fig. 11 the bearing of the line OA is N 10° E, the bearing of OB is N 30° W, for OC this bearing is S 50° W, and for the line OD it is S 70° E.

FIGURE 10

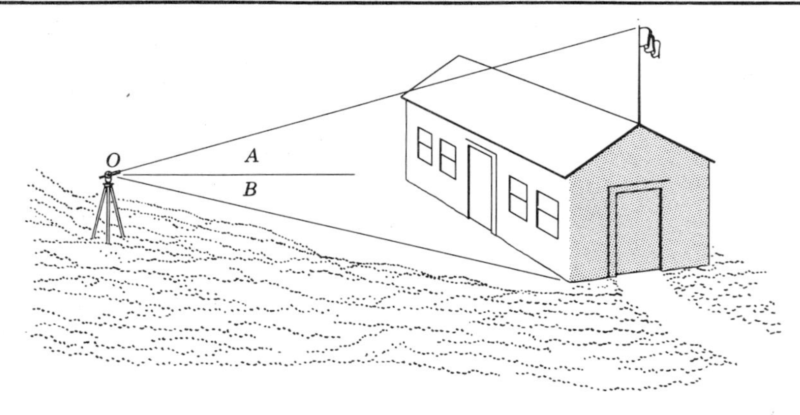

FIGURE 11

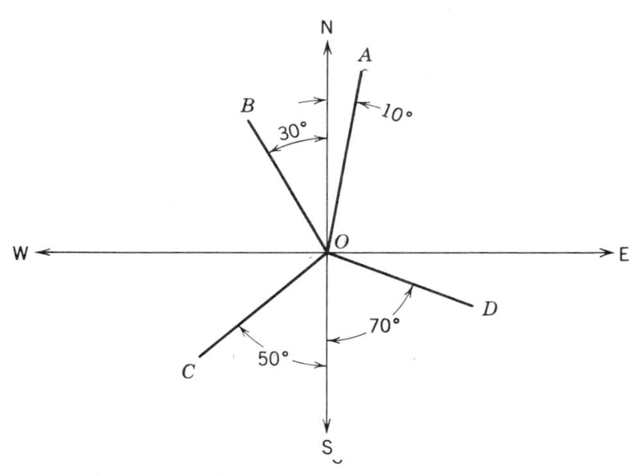

The bearing of a point B from a point A is just the bearing of the line AB.

If P and Q represent two extreme endpoints of an object viewed from a point O, then the angle POQ is said to be the *angle subtended by the object at the point O.* For example, a 36-in. baseball bat held horizontally across home plate subtends an angle of 3° at the eye of the pitcher 60 ft away.

12. Applications. In §§2 and 3 we have already seen two applications of trigonometry. We give four more examples to illustrate the great variety of situations where trigonometry is useful.

Example 10. In order to determine the height of clouds covering the sky over an airport, a searchlight is focused on a cloud directly overhead. From a point on the ground 720 ft away from the searchlight, the angle of elevation of the spot of light on the cloud is 53°. Find the height of the cloud.

Solution. If h denotes this height, then

$$\frac{h}{720} = \tan 53^\circ,$$

$$h = 720 \tan 53^\circ = 720 \times 1.327 = 955.44.$$

Since the data is given with two-figure accuracy, the answer should be given with the same accuracy, thus: The cloud is 960 ft above the airport.

Example 11. An airplane takes off from an airfield at a point 750 ft from a power line directly ahead. If the top wire of the power line is 70 ft high, and if the pilot wishes to clear these lines by 30 ft, what should be his angle of climb?

Solution. Let θ be the angle of climb. Then

$$\tan \theta = \frac{100}{750} = .1333.$$

Then from Table B, $\theta = 8^\circ$ to the nearest degree.

Example 12. The escalators in a certain department store travel 110 ft/min and make an angle of 31° 20′ with the horizontal. If the distance from the first floor to the second floor is 22 ft, find to the nearest second the time it takes for a shopper to go from the first floor to the second floor. Assume the shopper stands still on the escalator.

Solution. Let c denote the distance traveled by the shopper. Then c is the hypotenuse of a right triangle. The vertical leg is 22 ft and the angle opposite this side is 31° 20′. Hence

$$\frac{22}{c} = \sin 31^\circ 20', \qquad c = \frac{22}{\sin 31^\circ 20'} = \frac{22}{.5200.}$$

We postpone the arithmetic until the very end of the work in the hope that cancellation will make it easier. The shopper travels along c at the rate of 110 ft/min or

$$\frac{110 \text{ ft}}{\cancel{\text{min}}} \frac{1 \cancel{\text{min}}}{60 \text{ secs}} = \frac{11}{6} \text{ ft/sec.}$$

The formula, rate × time = distance, gives for the time t,

$$t = \frac{\text{distance}}{\text{rate}} = \frac{22 \text{ ft}/.5200}{11 \text{ ft}/6 \text{ sec}} = \frac{22 \cancel{\text{ft}}}{.5200}\,\frac{6 \text{ sec}}{11 \cancel{\text{ft}}} = \frac{3}{.13} \text{ sec.}$$

Therefore $t = 23$ sec to the nearest second.

The student should observe that in this example dimensions such as ft, min, and secs, have been treated as mathematical quantities, and canceled as such. This is a useful trick, and is sometimes quite helpful in revealing errors. For example, suppose in the last step of the solution, the student decided to multiply the two numbers and obtained

$$\frac{22}{.5200} \times \frac{11}{6} = 77.6$$

The student might then submit the answer 78 secs, realizing of course that this escalator is a rather slow one, built for shoppers who are not in a hurry. But using dimensions as a check he would have

$$\frac{22 \text{ ft}}{.5200} \times \frac{11 \text{ ft}}{6 \text{ sec}} = 77.6 \text{ ft}^2/\text{sec.}$$

Now this obviously does not have the dimensions that we wish, and hence must be wrong.

Example 13. From a window 31 ft above the ground, the two curbstones on either side of the street have the angles of depression 35° and 22°. How wide is the street?

FIGURE 12

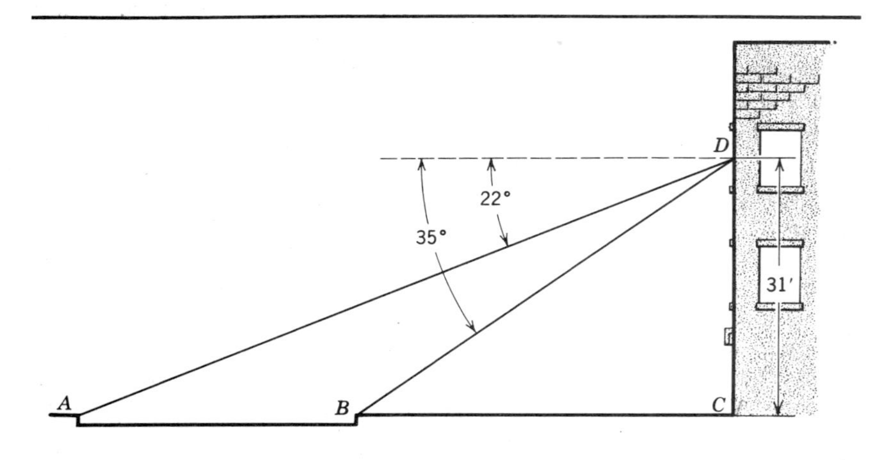

Solution. From Fig. 12:

$$\frac{AC}{DC} = \cot 22°, \qquad \frac{BC}{DC} = \cot 35°,$$

$$AC = DC \cot 22° = 31 \times 2.475 = 76.725, \qquad BC = DC \cot 35° = 31 \times 1.428 = 44.268.$$

$$AB = AC - BC = 76.725 - 44.268 = 32.457 = 32 \text{ ft}$$

(with 2-figure accuracy).

Notice that if we round off the lengths for AC and BC before subtraction we would obtain $AB = 77 - 44 = 33$ ft, a slightly different answer. For this reason, it is preferable not to round off until the last computation has been made.

EXERCISE 7

1. The largest tree in California is the General Sherman tree, estimated to be about 3500 years old. At a point 195 ft from the center of its base and on the same elevation, the angle of elevation of the top of the tree is 54° 30′. How tall is the tree?

2. The Eiffel Tower in Paris is 984.2 ft high. What will be the angle of elevation of the top from a point on the ground (assumed level) which is 300.0 ft from the center of its base?

3. A regular pentagon (five-sided figure) is inscribed in a circle of radius 15.00 What is the length of any one of its sides? What is the radius of the circle inscribed in this pentagon?

4. A regular decagon (ten-sided figure) is inscribed in a circle of radius 15.00. What is the length of any one of its sides? What is the radius of the circle inscribed in this decagon? Are the answers to this problem one-half the answers in Problem 3.

5. A trapeze artist stands with his eyes 72 ft above one edge of a net which is 120 ft long. What is the angle of depression of the other end of the net as viewed by this artist?

6. A trapeze of length 33.5 ft swings through an angle of 18° 30′ in reaching a vertical position. How far does a man sitting on the trapeze descend during this swing?

7. If the angle of swing in Problem 6 is doubled, how far does the man descend? Is this answer twice the answer in Problem 6?

8. Find to the nearest minute the angle between the diagonal of a cube and a diagonal of one of its faces, meeting the first diagonal at a corner.

9. A pilot flying due north estimates that the Washington Monument is 5.0 mi due east. After 3 min of flying the Washington Monument bears S 20° E. Estimate the speed of the airplane in miles per hour. How far is the airplane from the Washington Monument at the end of 3 min?

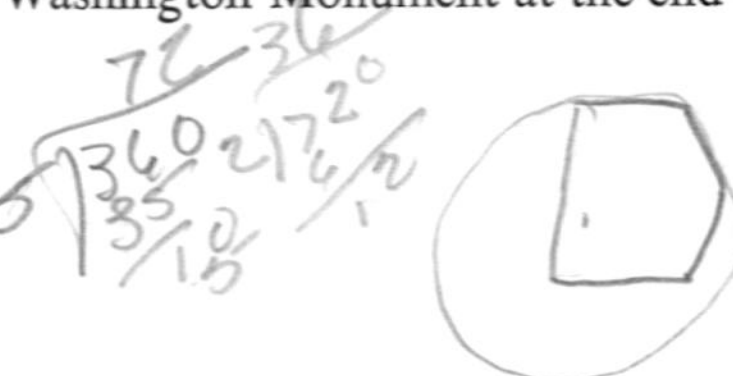

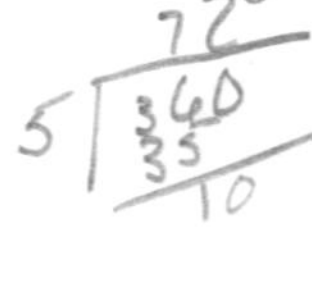

10. The University of Chicago is 222 mi north and 147 mi east of Washington University in St. Louis. What is the bearing of the University of Chicago from Washington University?

11. The University of Notre Dame in South Bend is 41 mi south and 126 mi west of the University of Michigan in Ann Arbor. The University of Michigan is 28 mi south and 36 mi east of Michigan State University in East Lansing. What is the bearing of Notre Dame from Michigan State University?

12. Find the angles of a rhombus if the two diagonals are 25.00 ft and 42.50 ft.

13. The angles of a rhombus are $70° 28'$ and $109° 32'$ and each side is 12.00 ft. How long are the two diagonals?

14. A fire truck has an extension ladder that is 70.0 ft long mounted on a swivel base 6.0 ft above the street level. Suppose that the closest the truck can approach the burning building puts the swivel base 15.0 ft from the wall. What is the highest point that the ladder can reach and still rest against the wall? How far does the top of the ladder descend if the fire forces the truck to move an additional 5.0 ft away from the building? What is the angle of elevation of the ladder in both positions?

★ **15.** Two observers stationed 1000 ft apart spot an approaching airplane. The angles of elevation of the airplane from these two points are $23° 40'$ and $25° 40'$. Assuming that the airplane and the two observers are in the same vertical plane, compute the altitude of the airplane with 3-figure accuracy.

13. The Special Angles 30°, 45°, and 60°. Although computation of the entries in the trigonometric tables is difficult and laborious, there are certain special angles for which this computation is quite simple.

Figure 13 shows an isosceles right triangle. Since $A = B$ and $A + B + C = 180°$, it follows that $A = 45°$. If we take each side to be 1 unit in length, then the hypotenuse is $\sqrt{2}$. Therefore,

FIGURE 13

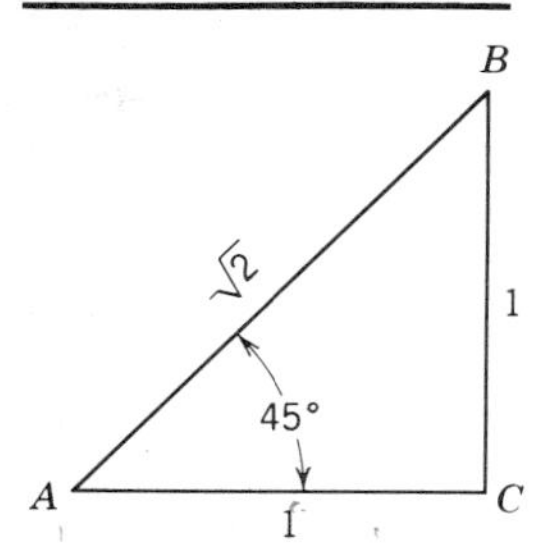

$$\sin 45° = \frac{1}{\sqrt{2}} = \frac{\sqrt{2}}{2}, \qquad \csc 45° = \frac{\sqrt{2}}{1} = \sqrt{2},$$

$$\cos 45° = \frac{1}{\sqrt{2}} = \frac{\sqrt{2}}{2}, \qquad \sec 45° = \frac{\sqrt{2}}{1} = \sqrt{2},$$

$$\tan 45° = \frac{1}{1} = 1, \qquad \cot 45° = \frac{1}{1} = 1.$$

If an equilateral triangle is divided, as shown in Fig. 14, by a line from one vertex to the midpoint of the opposite side, two 30°–60° right triangles are formed. If we take BC to be 1 unit in length, then $AB = 2$ and from the Pythagorean theorem $AC = \sqrt{4 - 1} = \sqrt{3}$. It is now easy to

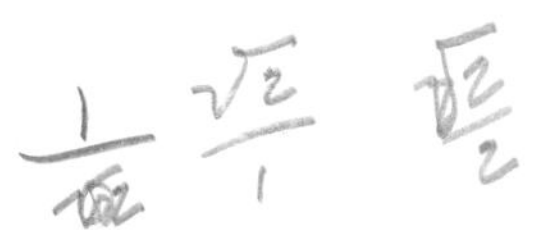

compute all of the trigonometric functions for both 30° and 60°.

$$\sin 30^\circ = \frac{1}{2} = \cos 60^\circ,$$

$$\cos 30^\circ = \frac{\sqrt{3}}{2} = \sin 60^\circ,$$

$$\tan 30^\circ = \frac{1}{\sqrt{3}} = \frac{\sqrt{3}}{3} = \cot 60^\circ,$$

$$\cot 30^\circ = \sqrt{3} = \tan 60^\circ,$$

$$\sec 30^\circ = \frac{2}{\sqrt{3}} = \frac{2\sqrt{3}}{3} = \csc 60^\circ,$$

$$\csc 30^\circ = 2 = \sec 60^\circ.$$

FIGURE 14

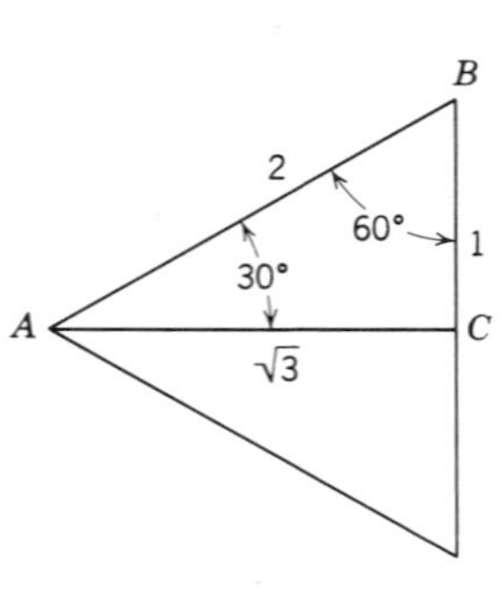

If we want the trigonometric functions of 0° and 90°, we must consider a degenerate triangle in which two of the sides coincide. Or if this seems to be objectionable, because such a figure is not admissable as a right triangle, we can consider a right triangle with a very small angle as is shown in Fig. 15, and examine the limiting behavior of these trigonometric functions as this small angle tends to zero.

If the student feels uneasy about this step, he can comfortably ignore the angles 0° and 90° for the present. In Chapter 4 we will give a definition of the trigonometric functions that will be meaningful for all real angles, including negative ones, as well as for angles greater than a right angle. When this is done, the angles 0° and 90° will cause no trouble.

In the meantime (just for fun) let us risk consideration of the triangles in Fig. 15. Here we suppose that in each triangle the base $b = AC$ is fixed at 1 unit in length. The hypotenuse consequently is greater than 1 unit, but as the angle at A becomes closer and closer to

FIGURE 15

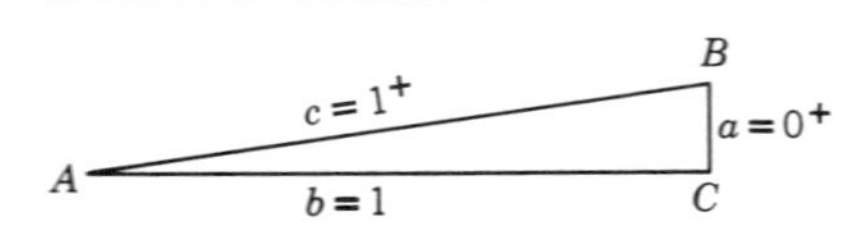

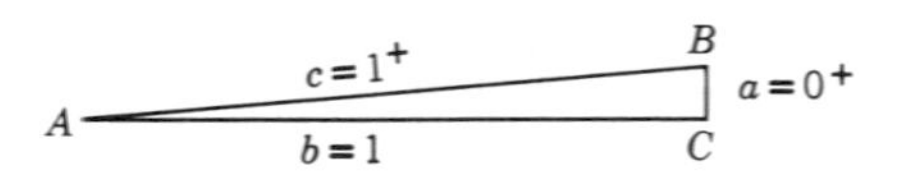

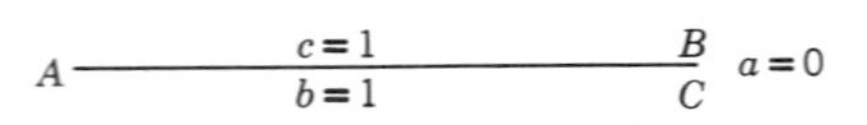

zero, the point B will move closer and closer to C. The limiting values will be $a = BC = 0$, $c = AB = 1$. Therefore we assert that:

$$\sin 0^\circ = \frac{0}{1} = 0 = \cos 90^\circ$$

$$\cos 0^\circ = \frac{1}{1} = 1 = \sin 90^\circ$$

$$\tan 0^\circ = \frac{0}{1} = 0 = \cot 90^\circ$$

$$\cot 0^\circ = \frac{1}{0} = \infty = \tan 90^\circ$$

$$\sec 0^\circ = \frac{1}{1} = 1 = \csc 90^\circ$$

$$\csc 0^\circ = \frac{1}{0} = \infty = \sec 90^\circ.$$

For convenience we tabulate the information we have just obtained.

TABLE 2

θ	sin	cos	tan	cot	sec	csc
0°	0	1	0	∞	1	∞
30°	$\frac{1}{2}$	$\frac{\sqrt{3}}{2}$	$\frac{\sqrt{3}}{3}$	$\sqrt{3}$	$\frac{2\sqrt{3}}{3}$	2
45°	$\frac{\sqrt{2}}{2}$	$\frac{\sqrt{2}}{2}$	1	1	$\sqrt{2}$	$\sqrt{2}$
60°	$\frac{\sqrt{3}}{2}$	$\frac{1}{2}$	$\sqrt{3}$	$\frac{\sqrt{3}}{3}$	2	$\frac{2\sqrt{3}}{3}$
90°	1	0	∞	0	∞	1

The student should memorize the derivations of the entries in this table so that he can, on demand, give any one of these entries by quickly sketching the appropriate triangle and computing the ratio in question. The angles in this list are favorites with the "quiz-masters of mathematics" because their trigonometric functions can be obtained without referring to the extensive Table B in the Appendix. They will occur repeatedly in problems both in this text and in more advanced mathematical books.

EXERCISE 8

1. Check that the entries in Table 2 are consistent with the assertions made about the trigonometric functions in §6.

2. Are the entries in Table 2 consistent with the entries in Table B of the Appendix?

3. For each of the six trigonometric functions plot the entries of Table 2 on coordinate paper, using the horizontal axis for the angle θ, and the vertical axis for the trigonometric function. Try to sketch a curve through the points plotted. If necessary plot more points from Table B in the Appendix.

4. Try to reproduce Table 2, without looking at the book. This should require not more than seven minutes. If the student finds that he is too slow, he should practice once a day until his "running time" is below that indicated. A really fast man can break three minutes without too much trouble.

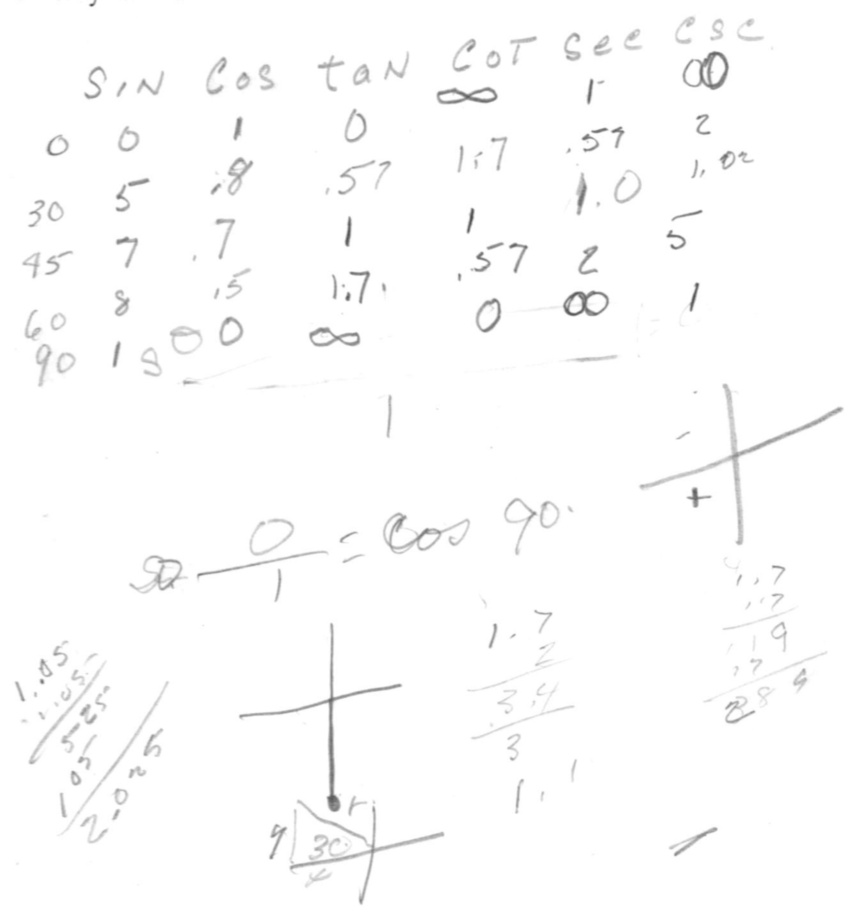

CHAPTER 2

LOGARITHMS

1. Objective. The student who has worked most of the problems in Chapter 1 has done so much arithmetic that he should be heartily sick of it. The time has come to learn a new method which will simplify computations and save the student's time and energy. Further, it will allow the student to do some computations that were previously beyond his power. For example, as matters now stand he may know how to extract a square root and he may have heard that there is a method for getting the cube root, but a problem like "find the $\sqrt[7]{200}$" will certainly seem to be horribly difficult. By the end of this chapter, this problem will appear very easy (Exercise 15, Problem 15).

Briefly (and inaccurately) described, logarithms allow us to do multiplication by addition, division by subtraction, powers by multiplication, and root extraction by division.

It may be argued by some pupils "there is no need to learn logarithms, since computing machines are available which are faster and more accurate than logarithms." The error in such an argument is readily seen by making the parallel argument "there is no need to learn to walk, since automobiles are available which go faster than any man can ever run." A man must first learn to crawl, then to stagger, then to walk, then to run, and finally after eighteen years of this he *may* be qualified to learn to drive a car.

Although John Napier (1550–1617), the inventor of logarithms, intended only to simplify computation and had no other objective in mind, time has shown that these logarithms have many very important applications in engineering, physics, and pure mathematics. Curiously enough Napier believed his reputation would rest on a religious book, *A Plaine Discouery of the whole Reuelation of Saint John*, in which, among other things, he tried to prove the world would end sometime between 1688 and 1700.

2. The Laws of Exponents. We recall that if $B > 0$ and if x and y are arbitrary real numbers then:

(1) $B^x B^y = B^{x+y}$, (4) $B^0 = 1$,

(2) $\dfrac{B^x}{B^y} = B^{x-y}$, (5) $B^{-x} = \dfrac{1}{B^x}$,

(3) $(B^x)^y = B^{xy}$, (6) $B^{x/y} = \sqrt[y]{B^x} = (\sqrt[y]{B})^x$.

As examples of each of these formulas we have:

(1e) $2^3 2^5 = 2^8 = 256$, (4e) $1{,}000{,}000^0 = 1$,

(2e) $\dfrac{5^7}{5^4} = 5^3 = 125$, (5e) $(.1)^{-2} = \dfrac{1}{(.1)^2} = 100$,

(3e) $(3^{1/4})^8 = 3^2 = 9$, (6e) $27^{4/3} = (\sqrt[3]{27})^4 = 3^4 = 81$.

3. Definition of the Logarithm of a Number. Briefly, the logarithm of a number is an exponent. What exponent is it? It is the exponent that must be used with a given base to produce the number in question. If we make this definition precise, it becomes rather complicated but here it is.

Definition 1. *The logarithm of a number N to a given base b, is the power x to which the given base b must be raised in order to produce the number N.*

Symbols can be used to simplify the expression of a complicated idea, and since this definition of a logarithm is quite complicated, it deserves the simplification that symbols can give it. First we introduce the symbol log N (read log of N) for the logarithm of the number N. To indicate the base b that is used, b is added as a subscript. Thus $\log_b N$ (read log of N to the base b) denotes the logarithm of the number N to the base b.

Definition 1 (with symbols).

(7) $$\log_b N = x,$$

if and only if

(8) $$b^x = N.$$

Clearly, in (8) x is the exponent that is used with b to obtain N. Therefore, by definition, x is the logarithm of N to the base b. But this is just equation (7).

Examples

$\log_2 8$	$= 3$	because	$2^3 = 8,$
$\log_2 16$	$= 4$	because	$2^4 = 16,$
$\log_{16} 16$	$= 1$	because	$16^1 = 16,$
$\log_5 25$	$= 2$	because	$5^2 = 25,$
$\log_5 1$	$= 0$	because	$5^0 = 1,$
$\log_4 2$	$= .5$	because	$4^{.5} = \sqrt{4} = 2,$
$\log_4 .5$	$= -.5$	because	$4^{-.5} = 1/\sqrt{4} = .5,$
$\log_4 .0625$	$= -2$	because	$4^{-2} = \frac{1}{16} = .0625,$
$\log_{10} 100$	$= 2$	because	$10^2 = 100,$
$\log_{64} 4$	$= \frac{1}{3}$	because	$64^{1/3} = \sqrt[3]{64} = 4.$

EXERCISE 9

Find each of the following logarithms.

1. $\log_{10} 10.$ **2.** $\log_{10} 1000.$ **3.** $\log_{10} 10{,}000.$ **4.** $\log_{10} 0.1.$
5. $\log_{10} .01.$ **6.** $\log_{10} .001.$ **7.** $\log_2 32.$ **8.** $\log_3 81.$
9. $\log_4 256.$ **10.** $\log_4 64.$ **11.** $\log_8 2.$ **12.** $\log_8 4.$
13. $\log_8 32.$ **14.** $\log_8 16.$ **15.** $\log_2 \frac{1}{16}.$ **16.** $\log_3 \frac{1}{81}.$
17. $\log_9 \frac{1}{3}.$ **18.** $\log_9 \frac{1}{27}.$ **19.** $\log_{1/2} 4.$ **20.** $\log_{1/3} 27.$

Find the unknown N, b, or x in each of the following equations.

21. $\log_b 32 = 5.$ **22.** $\log_b 81 = 4.$ **23.** $\log_9 N = \frac{1}{2}.$
24. $\log_8 N = \frac{2}{3}.$ **25.** $\log_4 32 = x.$ **26.** $\log_8 \sqrt{2} = x.$
27. $\log_{\sqrt{2}} 8 = x.$ **28.** $\log_{32} 8 = x.$ **29.** $\log_3 N = 4.$
30. $\log_4 N = 3.$ **31.** $\log_b \frac{1}{9} = -\frac{1}{2}.$ **32.** $\log_5 N = -2.$
33. $\log_4 N = -3.$ **34.** $\log_b \frac{1}{7} = -\frac{1}{3}.$ **35.** $\log_{\sqrt{3}} 81 = x.$
★**36.** $\log_4 (\log_4 16) = x.$ ★**37.** $\log_5 (\log_3 243) = x.$
★**38.** $\log_b (\log_b 27^3) = 2.$ ★**39.** $\log_2 (\log_2 N) = 3.$

4. The Three Laws of Logarithms. Using only the definition of a logarithm, and the laws of exponents, equations (1), (2), and (3), we can prove three very important theorems about logarithms. In these theorems the base b is assumed to be the same throughout. To simplify matters,

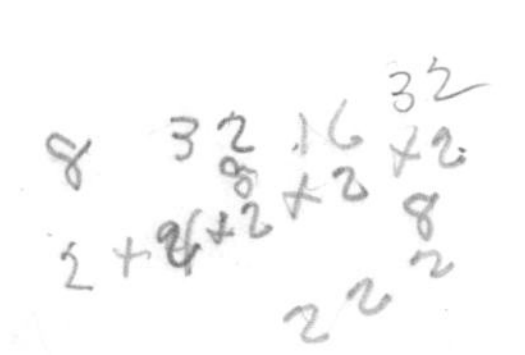

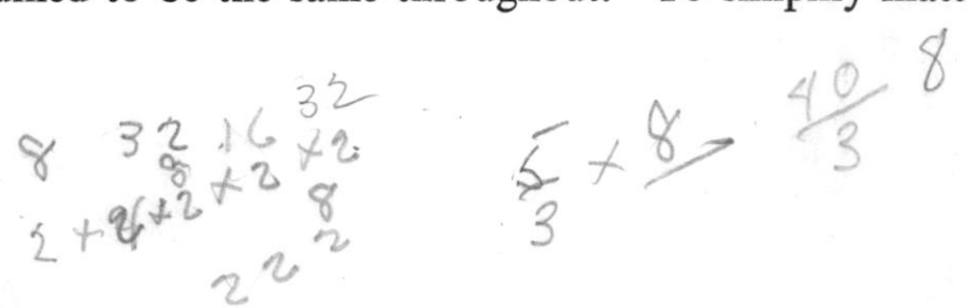

we omit mentioning the base, and we drop the subscript b. Furthermore, in what follows, we assume that M and N are positive.

Theorem 1. *The logarithm of a product is equal to the sum of the logarithms of its factors, i.e.,*

$$\log MN = \log M + \log N. \tag{9}$$

Theorem 2. *The logarithm of a fraction is equal to the logarithm of the numerator minus the logarithm of the denominator, i.e.,*

$$\log \frac{M}{N} = \log M - \log N. \tag{10}$$

Theorem 3. *The logarithm of the kth power of a number is equal to k times the logarithm of the number, i.e.,*

$$\log N^k = k \log N. \tag{11}$$

To prove the first theorem let

$$\log M = x, \qquad \log N = y. \tag{12}$$

Then by the definition of a logarithm

$$M = b^x, \qquad N = b^y. \tag{13}$$

If we multiply the two equations in (13) and use (1), the first law of exponents, we find

$$MN = b^x b^y = b^{x+y}. \tag{14}$$

But in (14) the exponent on b is $x + y$, so that by definition of the logarithm we must have

$$\log MN = x + y. \tag{15}$$

From equation (12), $x = \log M$ and $y = \log N$. Substituting these in (15) yields (9). Q.E.D.

The proof of Theorem 2 is the same, up to and including (13). If in (13) we divide the first equation by the second one and use (2), the second law of exponents, we find

$$\frac{M}{N} = \frac{b^x}{b^y} = b^{x-y}. \tag{16}$$

But in (16) the exponent on b is $x - y$, so that by the definition of the logarithm we must have

$$\log \frac{M}{N} = x - y. \tag{17}$$

From (12), $x = \log M$ and $y = \log N$. Substituting these in (17) yields (10). Q.E.D.

To prove Theorem 3, we again let $\log N = x$, and again have, by the definition of the logarithm, that

$$N = b^x. \tag{18}$$

If we raise both sides of (18) to the kth power and use (3), the third law of exponents, we find

$$N^k = (b^x)^k = b^{kx}. \tag{19}$$

But in (19) the exponent on b is kx, so that by the definition of the logarithm we must have

$$\log N^k = kx. \tag{20}$$

Finally, substituting for x its equivalent $x = \log N$ in (20) yields (11). Q.E.D.

One should learn these proofs, first as a good mental exercise, and second as an aid to a better understanding of logarithms.

Since each of the first three laws of exponents gave a corresponding theorem for logarithms, our curiosity should be aroused about the other three laws of exponents given by equations (4), (5), and (6). It turns out that:

Equation (4) gives

$$\log 1 = 0, \tag{21}$$

equation (5) gives

$$\log \frac{1}{N} = -\log N, \tag{22}$$

and equation (6) gives

$$M^{\log N} = N^{\log M}. \tag{23}$$

Equation (23) is never needed in elementary work and can safely be ignored by the student. The other two equations are important. Their proofs are posed as Problems 29 and 30 in Exercise 10.

EXERCISE 10

In Problems 1 to 20 all logarithms are to the base 10. Given that $\log 2 = .301$, $\log 3 = .477$, and $\log 7 = .845$, compute each of the following logarithms. *Hint:* Remember that $\log 10 = 1$ and that $5 = \frac{10}{2}$.

1. $\log 4$. **2.** $\log 5$. **3.** $\log 6$. **4.** $\log 8$.

5. $\log 9$. **6.** $\log 16$. **7.** $\log 81$. **8.** $\log \frac{1}{3}$.

9. $\log \frac{1}{2}$. **10.** $\log \sqrt{3}$. **11.** $\log \sqrt[4]{7}$. **12.** $\log \sqrt[6]{14}$.

13. $\log 70$. **14.** $\log 700$. **15.** $\log \frac{14}{3}$. **16.** $\log \frac{21}{2}$.

17. $\log \frac{3}{14}$. **18.** $\log \frac{2}{21}$. **19.** $\log \sqrt{3000}$. **20.** $\log \sqrt[3]{2000}$.

In Problems 21 through 28 identify each assertion (equation) as true or false. If it is false indicate how to correct the assertion to make it true.

21. $(\log A)^4 = 4 \log A$. **22.** $\log ABC^2 = \log A + \log B + 2 \log C$.

23. $\log X - \log Y = \dfrac{X}{Y}$. **24.** $\log \dfrac{A + B}{C} = \log A + \log B - \log C$.

25. $\log B = 2 \log \sqrt{B}$. **26.** $\log \dfrac{D}{EF} = \dfrac{\log D}{\log E + \log F}$.

27. $3 \log (\log B) = \log (\log B^3)$. **28.** $2 \log A^3 = \log A^8 - \log A^2$.

29. Prove that $\log 1 = 0$, by setting $N = 1$ in equation (9).

30. Prove equation (22) is valid by setting $M = 1$ in equation (10).

31. Starting with equation (9), prove that

$$\log MNP = \log M + \log N + \log P.$$

★ **32.** Starting with equation (6) prove that equation (23) is valid, *Hint:* Set $B^x = M$ and $B^{1/y} = N$.

5. Various Systems of Logarithms.

Before logarithms can be useful as an aid to computation, extensive tables must be prepared. And before these tables can be prepared, a suitable base must be selected.

If the base is $e = 2.7182 \cdots$, the logarithms are known as *natural logarithms*, or Napierian logarithms, after the inventor of logarithms.

If the base is 10, the logarithms are known as *common logarithms*, or Briggsian logarithms, after Henry Briggs (1561–1630), who first suggested the use of 10 as a base.

Since e is an irrational number, the student will raise his eyebrows at the name "natural" for logarithms with such a horrible base. After all, what number is more natural than 10? A course in differential calculus will help to explain this nomenclature. As the student pursues his study of mathematics deeper and deeper he will see why e is, along with π, one of the most important irrational numbers occurring in natural science, and why logarithms with this base are quite properly called natural logarithms.

For the rest of this text, however, the base will be 10, and the notation log N will mean the logarithm to the base 10.

★ In Exercise 10, we used log 2 = .301. This means that

$$2 = 10^{.301} = 10^{301/1000},$$

or that if 10 is raised to the power indicated by the numerator (301) and then if the root is extracted as indicated by the denominator (1000), the result should be 2. Strictly speaking, the result will not be 2, but will be an irrational number very close to 2. It can be proved that in order to get 2 exactly, the exponent must be an irrational number, and .301 represents just the first three digits of this number. This proof, and the methods used to obtain the approximations, such as log 2 = .301, are too difficult to be given in this book.

The student should feel quite pleased that all of the logarithms he will need have already been computed with 5-figure accuracy and recorded in Table C of the Appendix, so that all of the really difficult work connected with logarithms has been done for him. He has left only the *easy* task of learning how to use them.

6. A Table of Logarithms. Table C of the Appendix gives with 5-figure accuracy the logarithm of every four-digit number between 1 and 10. We will see shortly that with this table, the logarithm of any number can be obtained immediately.

Let us first examine Table C in detail. The *border* of the table, which consists of the first column and the top row, gives the number N. The first column gives the first three digits of N and the top row gives the fourth digit of N. The logarithm of N is found in the *body* of the table, the part to the right of the first column and below the first row.

Suppose that we want to find log 8.765. The first three digits 876 are located in the first column on page 219, and the fourth digit 5 is found in the top row on this same page. The entry in the body of the table under the 5, and in the same row with 876 is 275. These are the last three digits of the logarithm we are seeking. To pick up the first two digits, we must look for the nearest five-digit entry just preceding in the body of the table. This turns out to be 94002, so combining 94 and 275, we have from Table C

$$\log 8765 = 94275, \tag{24}$$

ignoring the decimal points temporarily.

To locate the decimal points, recall that for the base 10, log 1 = 0, log 10 = 1. Now

$$1 < 8.765 < 10$$

so we expect that

$$\log 1 < \log 8.765 < \log 10,$$

or

$$0 < \log 8.765 < 1. \quad (25)$$

Actually this inequality can be proved, but to do so would take us too far away from the subject. If we accept the fact that log N increases as N increases, then the inequality (25) is correct, and the decimal points in equation (24) must be placed thus:

$$\log 8.765 = .94275.$$

Everyone knows[1] that Table C is a log table for numbers N between 1 and 10, and for these numbers, log N lies between 0 and 1. Hence, in using Table C the decimal point goes just after the first nonzero digit of N, and just before the first digit of log N.

EXERCISE 11

In each of the following problems use Table C to find the logarithm of the number.

1. 3.456. **2.** 4.567. **3.** 5.678. **4.** 6.789.
5. 2.345. **6.** 1.234. **7.** 5.43. **8.** 4.

In each of the following problems use Table C to find N.

9. $\log N = .33345$. **10.** $\log N = .22220$. **11.** $\log N = .88880$.
12. $\log N = .31112$. **13.** $\log N = .50051$. **14.** $\log N = .95957$.
15. $\log N = .00775$. **16.** $\log N = .00000$.

7. The Characteristic and the Mantissa. We will now show how to find the logarithm of any number using Table C. First observe that when the base is 10:

$$\begin{array}{lcrll}
\log 1000 & = & 3 & \text{because} & 10^3 = 1000, \\
\log 100 & = & 2 & \text{because} & 10^2 = 100, \\
\log 10 & = & 1 & \text{because} & 10^1 = 10, \\
\log 1 & = & 0 & \text{because} & 10^0 = 1, \\
\log .1 & = & -1 & \text{because} & 10^{-1} = \frac{1}{10} = .1, \\
\log .01 & = & -2 & \text{because} & 10^{-2} = \frac{1}{100} = .01,
\end{array}$$

etc.

[1] How does everyone know this? In the same way that everyone knows to drive his car on the right side of a two-way street in North America. This practice is so common that there is no need to put signs on every street saying "Keep to the right." This saves money and reduces the number of unnecessary distractions. For the very same reasons decimal points are omitted in table C.

Suppose now that we wish to find log 876,500. Using scientific notation we can write

$$876{,}500 = 8.765 \times 10^5.$$

Then by Theorem 1 for the logarithm of a product

$$\log 876{,}500 = \log 8.765 + \log 10^5 = 5 + \log 8.765.$$

But from Table C, log 8.765 = .94275, hence log 876,500 = 5.94275.

This process is general. Before stating the rule for finding the logarithm of any number, we need

Definition 2. *When $N = A \times 10^m$ is in scientific notation, then log A is called the mantissa of the logarithm, and m is called the characteristic.*

Table C is a table of mantissas, and the mantissa is always between 0 and 1. The characteristic is always an integer.

Rule 1. *To find the logarithm of a number N, use Table C to find the fractional part of the logarithm (mantissa) using only the digits of N and ignoring the decimal point. Then add to this fraction, an integer m (the characteristic) determined from q, the number of places the decimal point must be moved to put it just after the first nonzero digit of N. Here*

$m = q > 0$	*if N is large*	$10 \leq N,$
$m = 0$	*if N is intermediate*	$1 \leq N < 10,$
$m = -q < 0$	*if N is small*	$N < 1.$

If we are given log N and wish to find N the procedure is reversed.

Example 1. Find log 13.57.
Solution. Mantissa: log 1.357 = .13258 (from Table C).
Characteristic: 1 . 3 . 5 7, $q = 1, m = 1.$
Hence log 13.57 = 1.13258.

Example 2. Find log 24,680,000.
Solution. Mantissa: log 2.468 = .39235 (from Table C).
Characteristic: 2 . 4 6 8 0 0 0 0 ., $q = 7, m = 7.$
Hence log 24,680,000 = 7.39235.

Example 3. Find N given that log N = 5.55558.
Solution. Mantissa: log 3.594 = .55558 (from Table C).
Characteristic: $m = 5$, 3 . 5 9 4 0 0 .
Hence N = 359,400.

Although we have written out all of the steps in detail, the student should do the problems in Exercise 12 mentally, writing only the answers.

EXERCISE 12

Write each of the following numbers in scientific notation, and then find its logarithm using Table C.

1. 345.6. **2.** 4567. **3.** 5,678,000. **4.** 67.89.
5. 23,450. **6.** 9.999. **7.** 93,330,000. **8.** 12.34.
9. 5430. **10.** 400,000,000,000.

Given log N, use Table C to find N in each of the following problems.

11. $\log N = 3.33345$. **12.** $\log N = 4.22220$. **13.** $\log N = 1.88880$.
14. $\log N = 2.31112$. **15.** $\log N = 6.50051$. **16.** $\log N = 7.95957$.
17. $\log N = .00775$ **18.** $\log N = 5.67888$. **19.** $\log N = .30103$.
20. $\log N = 2.00000$.

8. The Negative Characteristic. Suppose that we wish to find log .002. In scientific notation $.002 = 2 \times 10^{-3}$. Therefore

$$\log .002 = \log 2 + \log 10^{-3} = .30103 + (-3) = .30103 - 3.$$

$$\log .002 = -2.69897. \tag{26}$$

Although -2.69897 is the correct answer it turns out that when logarithms are used for computations, this is not a convenient form, because the fractional part, $-.69897$, is negative. The reason this form is inconvenient will be obvious to the student after he has finished studying §10. In the meantime we make the

Gentleman's Agreement. *Each logarithm will be written as a positive fraction (the mantissa) plus an integer which may be positive, negative, or zero.*

For example, in place of equation (26) we would write

$$\log .002 = .30103 - 3 \tag{27}$$

and then stop. Frequently it is convenient to standardize the negative integer which appears at the end of (27). If everyone agrees to use a -10, when the characteristic is negative, then (27) would be adjusted on the right side, by adding 7 in the front and subtracting 7 from the back. Thus,

$$\log .002 = 7.30103 - 10. \tag{28}$$

Still further modification is possible, for example

$$\log .002 = 27.30103 - 30, \tag{29}$$

$$\log .002 = 37.30103 - 40, \tag{30}$$

are both correct statements. It is best to postpone questions about why we wish to do these manipulations until after §10. At present, the student should assure himself that equations (26), (27), (28), (29), and (30) are all *equivalent*, that is, any one of them implies the others.

EXERCISE 13

In Problems 1 through 6 find the logarithm of the given number and express the answer in the form of equation (28).

1. .001492. **2.** .0001984. **3.** .7531.
4. .000005. **5.** .03339. **6.** .000000044.

In Problems 7 through 12, use Table C to find N.

7. $\log N = 9.28194 - 10$. **8.** $\log N = 8.34674 - 10$.
9. $\log N = 6.71600 - 10$. **10.** $\log N = 4.84111 - 10$.
11. $\log N = 17.90009 - 20$. **12.** $\log N = 19.87645 - 20$.

9. Interpolation. The logarithm of any number known with 4-figure accuracy can be read directly from Table C. If N is known with 5-figure accuracy, the logarithm can be obtained by interpolation. The theory of interpolation for logarithms is identical with the theory of interpolation for the trigonometric functions, already described in §9 of Chapter 1, so no further discussion is required.

Example 4. Find log 1776.2.
Solution. From Table C

$$10\left[\begin{array}{l}\log 1.7770 = .24969 \\ 2\left[\begin{array}{l}\log 1.7762 = \\ \log 1.7760 = .24944\end{array}\right]x\end{array}\right]25$$

$$\frac{2}{10} = \frac{x}{25}.$$

Hence $x = 25(2/10) = 5$ units in the fifth place. Therefore log 1776.2 = .24944 + .00005 = .24949, and since the characteristic is 3, we have log 1776.2 = 3.24949.

Observe that in the interpolation scheme, we have placed the decimal point after the 1, so that we are spared worrying about the characteristic while interpolating.

Example 5. If $\log N = 7.33333 - 10$, what is N?
Solution. From Table C

$$10\left[\begin{array}{l} \log 2.1550 = .33345 \\ x\left[\begin{array}{l}\log A \quad\;\; = .33333 \\ \log 2.1540 = .33325\end{array}\right]8 \end{array}\right]20$$

$$\frac{x}{10} = \frac{8}{20},$$

hence $x = 4$ units in the fourth place. Therefore $A = 2.1544$. Since the characteristic is -3, $N = .0021544$.

EXERCISE 14

In Problems 1 through 16, find the logarithm of the given number by interpolating in Table C.

1. 54,321. **2.** 765.43. **3.** .87654. **4.** .0097531.
5. 23.456. **6.** 34,567,000. **7.** .00030003. **8.** .019159.
9. 777.77. **10.** 88.088. **11.** .0066006. **12.** .23202.
13. 7.5075. **14.** .00090909. **15.** .011599. **16.** 1.9295.

In Problems 17 through 31, interpolate in Table C to find N to five significant figures.

17. $\log N = 5.43210$.
18. $\log N = 2.34567$.
19. $\log N = 1.23456$.
20. $\log N = 3.43434$.
21. $\log N = 6.56565 - 10$.
22. $\log N = 7.77777 - 10$.
23. $\log N = .70012 - 1$.
24. $\log N = .76006 - 1$.
25. $\log N = .90909$.
26. $\log N = 2.80808$.
27. $\log N = 2.03330 - 5$.
28. $\log N = .06060$.
29. $\log N = .12345 - 5$.
30. $\log N = 1.02320 - 3$.
31. $\log N = .86468$.

10. Logarithms as an Aid to Computation.

Example 6. Find the product $P = 2345 \times 5432$.
Solution. By Theorem 1, $\log P = \log 2345 + \log 5432$.

$$\begin{array}{r} \log 2345 = 3.37014 \\ \log 5432 = 3.73496 \\ \hline \log P = 7.10510 \\ P = 12{,}738{,}000. \end{array}$$

The student will find that the work will go more smoothly if he will do as much of the problem as possible before looking in the tables. This means that he should write the logarithmic equation, arrange the work in a column, fill in the characteristics—in short, write every part of the solution except the mantissas, and then turn to the tables.

The exact value of P is 12,738,040, so that for this problem logarithmic computation gives the answer correct to five significant figures.

Example 7. Find the quotient $Q = 2345/5432$ to five significant figures.

Solution. By Theorem 2, $\log Q = \log 2345 - \log 5432$.

$$\log 2345 = 3.37014$$
$$\log 5432 = 3.73496.$$

But log 5432 is larger than log 2345, so subtraction will yield a negative quantity. This will cause trouble, so to avoid this we adjust log 2345 by adding and subtracting 10. We have then

$$\begin{aligned} \log 2345 &= 13.37014 - 10 \\ \log 5432 &= 3.73496 \\ \hline \log Q &= 9.63518 - 10 \\ Q &= .43170 \end{aligned}$$

Direct computation gives $Q = .43170103 \cdots$, so again logarithmic computation gives the correct answer to five significant figures.

Example 8. Find $\sqrt{.1776}$ to five significant figures.

Solution. Let R be the desired root. Then by Theorem 3,

$$\begin{aligned} \log R &= \log (.1776)^{1/2} = \tfrac{1}{2} \log .1776, \\ \log .1776 &= 9.24944 - 10, \\ \tfrac{1}{2} \log .1776 &= 4.62472 - 5, \\ R &= .42143, \end{aligned}$$

with 5-figure accuracy. As a check we can square the answer. We find

$$.42142^2 = .1775948164,$$
$$.42143^2 = .1776032449,$$

hence logarithmic computation gives R correct to five significant figures.

Example 9. Find $\sqrt[3]{.1776}$ to five significant figures.

Solution. If we parallel the work of Example 3, we will run into trouble. Let us do so, and see what happens.

$$\log R = \tfrac{1}{3} \log .1776 = \tfrac{1}{3}(9.24944 - 10) = 3.08315 - 3.33333,$$

and this will give a negative fractional part after subtraction. To avoid this difficulty we may first alter the -10, which stands at the right in log .1776, so that the new integer is divisible by 3. There are many ways of doing this, but the standard way is to change -10 into -30 by adding 20 in front and subtracting it at the back. We then have

$$\log R = \tfrac{1}{3}(9.24944 - 10) = \tfrac{1}{3}(29.24944 - 30) = 9.74981 - 10,$$

$$R = .56210.$$

Example 10. Compute $\dfrac{.0044\sqrt[5]{666}}{5.6565\sqrt[3]{10{,}000}}$ to five significant figures.

Solution. Before using the tables, we make an outline showing the procedure we intend to follow. Let Q denote the quantity sought. Then

$$\log Q = \log .0044 + \tfrac{1}{5}\log 666 - (\log 5.6565 + \tfrac{1}{3}\log 10{,}000)$$

$\log 10{,}000 = 4.00000$	$\log 666 = 2.$
$\tfrac{1}{3}\log 10{,}000 = 1.33333$	$\tfrac{1}{5}\log 666 =$
$\log 5.6565 =$	$\log .0044 = 7. \qquad -10$
$\log D =$ →	$\log N =$
	$\log D =$
	$\log Q = \log N - \log D =$

The student is invited to fill in the blanks and show that $Q = .00013251$

Initially no name was given to the unknown quantity. We let N denote the numerator, D the denominator, and Q their quotient. The introduction of letters for unknown quantities makes it easier to think accurately about them. The student should form the habit of attaching names (letters) to any unnamed quantities that he meets in his scientific studies.

EXERCISE 15

In Problems 1 through 20 compute the answer to four significant figures using logs.

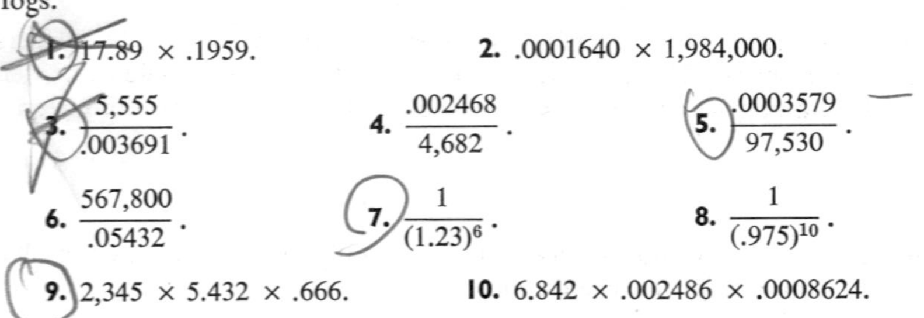

1. $17.89 \times .1959.$ **2.** $.0001640 \times 1{,}984{,}000.$

3. $\dfrac{5{,}555}{.003691}.$ **4.** $\dfrac{.002468}{4{,}682}.$ **5.** $\dfrac{.0003579}{97{,}530}.$

6. $\dfrac{567{,}800}{.05432}.$ **7.** $\dfrac{1}{(1.23)^6}.$ **8.** $\dfrac{1}{(.975)^{10}}.$

9. $2{,}345 \times 5.432 \times .666.$ **10.** $6.842 \times .002486 \times .0008624.$

11. $\dfrac{56.78 \times .0006785}{8765 \times 765.8 \times 6.421}$. **12.** $\dfrac{(42)^3 \times (23)^4}{(777)^2}$.

13. $(1{,}111)^{3/2}$. **14.** $(2{,}323)^{5/4}$. **15.** $\sqrt[7]{200}$.

16. $\sqrt[7]{2000}$. **17.** $\sqrt[7]{.02}$. **18.** $\sqrt[7]{.002}$.

19. $\sqrt[3]{\dfrac{243 \times .0888}{95.5}}$. **20.** $\sqrt[4]{\dfrac{832 \times .855}{88{,}800}}$

In Problems 21 through 47 compute the answer to five significant figures using logs.

21. $1111.3 \times .00022228$. **22.** $3210.2 \times .067876$.

23. $\dfrac{.0087654}{45.678}$. **24.** $\dfrac{.0000045829}{.00048521}$. **25.** $\dfrac{1}{(.013513)^{2/3}}$.

26. $\dfrac{10{,}001}{(2121)^3}$. **27.** $\dfrac{(130.5)^3}{.0355}$. **28.** $\dfrac{(210)^3}{.042424}$.

29. $\sqrt[7]{.009222}$. **30.** $\sqrt[6]{.0009876}$. **31.** $\sqrt{10{,}666}$.

32. $\sqrt{1066.6}$. **33.** $\left(\dfrac{24{,}682}{.012345}\right)^2$. **34.** $\dfrac{.3333\sqrt{44.4}}{\sqrt[3]{685 \times 48}}$.

35. $\sqrt{\dfrac{6321}{81.25\sqrt[3]{.16}}}$. **36.** $\sqrt{\dfrac{6123 \times 22.22}{81 \times 25 \times (.16)^3}}$.

37. $\dfrac{\sqrt{1623 \times 33.56}}{2.815 \times (.017)^2}$. **38.** $\dfrac{52 \times 51 \times 50 \times 49 \times 48}{5 \times 4 \times 3 \times 2 \times 1}$.

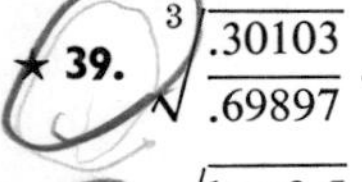

★ **39.** $\sqrt[3]{\dfrac{.30103}{.69897}}$.

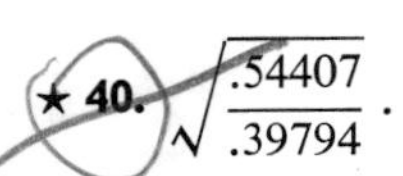

★ **40.** $\sqrt{\dfrac{.54407}{.39794}}$.

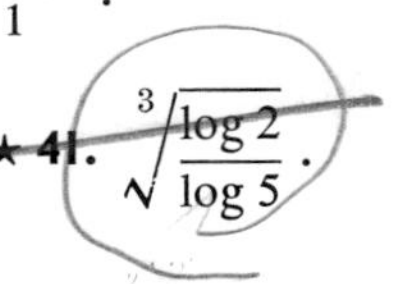

★ **41.** $\sqrt[3]{\dfrac{\log 2}{\log 5}}$.

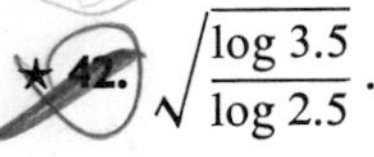

★ **42.** $\sqrt{\dfrac{\log 3.5}{\log 2.5}}$. ★ **43.** $(\log 1.776)(\log 1.984)$.

★ **44.** $(\log 25)(\log 50)$. ★ **45.** $\dfrac{\log 1.776}{\log 1.984}$. ★ **46.** $\dfrac{\log 50}{\log 25}$.

★ **47.** The notation $n!$ (read n factorial) means the product of all the integers from 1 to n inclusive. For example, in Problem 38 the quantity could be written $52!/(5!\,47!)$, and gives the number of possible poker hands. The expression

$$B = \frac{52!}{13!\;39!}$$

gives the number of possible bridge hands. Simplify the right side by cancellation and then use logarithms to estimate B.

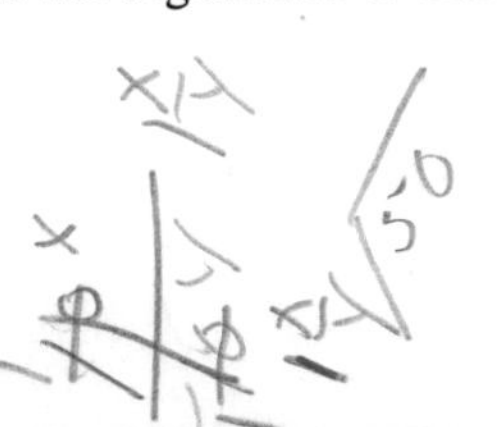

CHAPTER 3

LOGARITHMIC SOLUTION OF RIGHT TRIANGLES

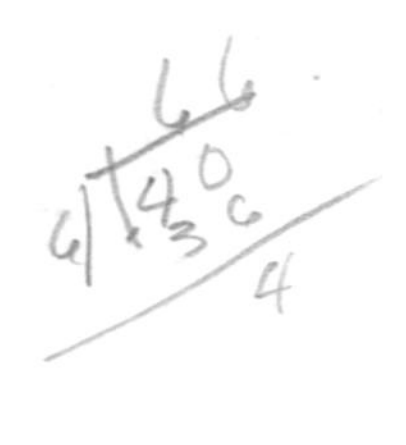

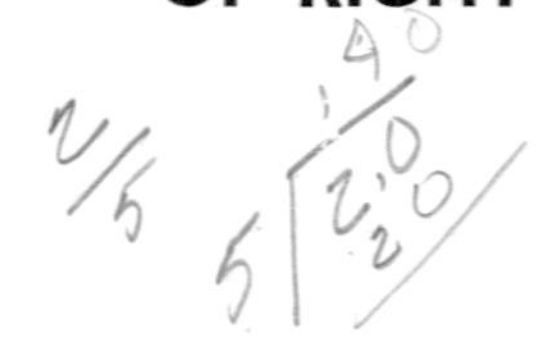

1. Objective. Now that we know how to use logarithms to shorten numerical computations, we will learn to use them to shorten the labor involved in trigonometry problems.

2. Logarithms of the Trigonometric Functions. Suppose that we are asked to solve the right triangle ABC, given $A = 17° \ 5'$ and the hypotenuse $c = 4567.0$. Since $a/c = \sin A$, we have $a = c \sin A$. The computation would be arranged thus:

$$\begin{array}{rl} \log c = \log 4567.0 & = 3.65963 \\ \log \sin A = \log \sin 17° \ 5' & = \\ \hline \log a & = \\ a & = \end{array}$$

To complete the computations, we might look in Table B and find that $\sin 17° \ 5' = .2938$, and then look for the logarithm of this number in Table C, finding $9.46805 - 10$. But even the labor of looking in two tables to find $\log \sin 17° \ 5'$, can be avoided, because in Table D these two tables are already combined. A portion of Table D is shown here, and an arrow marks the entry:

$$\log \sin 17° \ 5' = 9.46800 - 10.$$

The -10 is omitted from each entry to simplify the table and improve its appearance. Notice that using Tables B and C we found $\log \sin 17° \ 5' = 9.46805 - 10$, which differs by 5 units in the last place from the result obtained from Table D. Some such discrepancy may be expected, because Table B gives only four significant figures, and Table D is constructed with 5-figure accuracy. The student should complete the logarithmic computation and show that $a = 1342.6$.

17°

		L Sin	d	L Tan	cd	L Cot	L Cos	d	
	0	9.46 594	41	9.48 534	45	10.51 466	9.98 060	4	**60**
	1	9.46 635	41	9.48 579	45	10.51 421	9.98 056	4	59
	2	9.46 676	41	9.48 624	45	10.51 376	9.98 052	4	58
	3	9.46 717	41	9.48 669	45	10.51 331	9.98 048	4	57
	4	9.46 758	42	9.48 714	45	10.51 286	9.98 044	4	56
→	5	9.46 800	41	9.48 759	45	10.51 241	9.98 040	4	55
	6	9.46 841	41	9.48 804	45	10.51 196	9.98 036	4	54
	7	9.46 882	41	9.48 849	45	10.51 151	9.98 032	3	53
	8	9.46 923	41	9.48 894	45	10.51 106	9.98 029	4	52
	9	9.46 964		9.48 939		10.51 061	9.98 025		51

The theory of interpolation for Table D is just the same as for the other tables already studied. The only innovation in Table D is a column headed "d" in which the differences between successive entries are already tabulated. This saves the trouble of doing the subtractions. The letters "cd" at the top of the middle column abbreviate the phrase "common difference," and indicate that the difference between two successive entries is the same for both log tan and log cot.

Example 1. Find log sin 17° 5.2′.

Solution. From Table D, log sin 17° 5′ = 9.46800 − 10.
The difference located in the next column is 41 units in the fifth decimal place. For .2′ we must add $.2 \times 41 = 8.2$ or 8 units in the fifth decimal place. Therefore log sin 17° 5.2′ = 9.46808 − 10.

Example 2. Find θ if $\log \cot \theta = 10.51115 - 10$.

Solution. We find in Table D that log cot 17° 8′ = 10.51106 − 10.
But the cotangent function is decreasing, so our angle will be slightly smaller than 17° 8′. The entry under "cd" is 45, and our difference is $115 - 106 = 9$ units in the fifth decimal place. Since $9/45 = .2$, $\theta = 17° \, 7.8'$.

EXERCISE 16

Find the following logarithms:

1. log sin 25° 34′. **2.** log sin 55° 44′. **3.** log cos 81° 19′.

4. log cos 12° 34′. **5.** log tan 66° 44′. **6.** log tan 13° 57′.

7. $\log \cot 5^\circ 6'$. **8.** $\log \cot 75^\circ 31'$. **9.** $\log \sin 65^\circ 43.2'$.
10. $\log \sin 34^\circ 56.7'$. **11.** $\log \cos 23^\circ 45.6'$. **12.** $\log \cos 76^\circ 54.2'$.
13. $\log \tan 33^\circ 33.3'$. **14.** $\log \tan 82^\circ 22.8'$. **15.** $\log \cot 77^\circ 7.7'$.
16. $\log \cot 28^\circ 28.2'$.

Find the value of θ to the nearest tenth of a minute:

17. $\log \cos \theta = 9.94182 - 10$. **18.** $\log \cot \theta = 11.11052 - 10$.
19. $\log \tan \theta = 9.19889 - 10$. **20.** $\log \sin \theta = 9.53336 - 10$.
21. $\log \sin \theta = 9.92818 - 10$. **22.** $\log \cos \theta = 9.80428 - 10$.
23. $\log \cot \theta = 10.76543 - 10$. **24.** $\log \sin \theta = 9.35791 - 10$.
25. $\log \sin \theta = 9.55555 - 10$. **26.** $\log \cos \theta = 9.87654 - 10$.
27. $\log \cos \theta = 9.75310 - 10$. **28.** $\log \tan \theta = 11.11111 - 10$.
29. $\log \cot \theta = 9.09090 - 10$. **30.** $\log \cot \theta = 10.10101 - 10$.
31. $\log \tan \theta = 9.99888 - 10$. **32.** $\log \tan \theta = 9.88899 - 10$.

★ **33.** The fact that one column labeled "cd" can serve as the table of differences for both functions $\log \tan \theta$ and $\log \cot \theta$, depends on the identity

$$\log \tan (\theta + \alpha) - \log \tan \theta = -[\log \cot (\theta + \alpha) - \log \cot \theta]$$

which is valid when both θ and $\theta + \alpha$ are acute angles. Use the fact that $\tan \theta = 1/\cot \theta$ to prove this identity.

3. Applications. The following example illustrates the use of logarithms in trigonometric computations.

Example 3. Solve the right triangle given $a = 23{,}456$ and $b = 34{,}567$ (Fig. 1).

Solution. $\tan A = \dfrac{a}{b}$.

$$\begin{aligned}
\log a = \log 23{,}456 &= 14.37025 - 10 \\
\log b = \log 34{,}567 &= 4.53866 \\
\hline
\log \tan A &= 9.83159 - 10 \\
A &= 34^\circ 9.6' \\
B &= 90^\circ - A = 55^\circ 50.4'
\end{aligned}$$

FIGURE 1

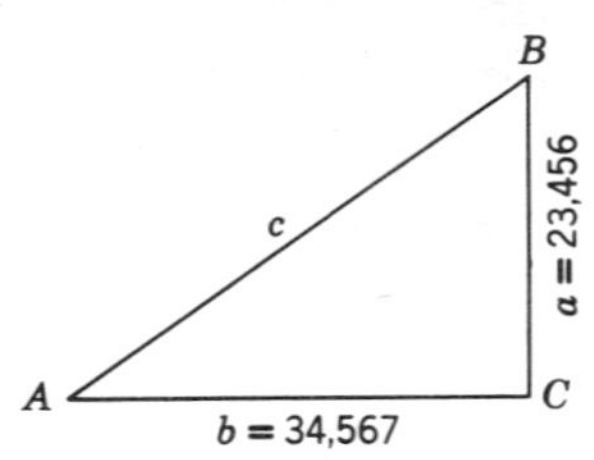

To find c: $\dfrac{a}{c} = \sin A$, so $c = \dfrac{a}{\sin A}$.

$$\begin{aligned}
\log a &= \log 23{,}456 = 14.37025 - 10 \\
\log \sin A &= \log \sin 34^\circ 9.6' = 9.74935 - 10 \\
\hline
\log c &= 4.62090 \\
c &= 41{,}774
\end{aligned}$$

Weds.

Check. We can compute b from the values for A and c we have just obtained, using $b = c \cos A$.

$$\begin{aligned} \log c &= \log 41{,}774 = 4.62090 \\ \log \cos A &= \log \cos 34^\circ 9.6' = 9.91776 - 10 \\ \hline \log b &= 14.53866 - 10 \\ b &= 34{,}567. \end{aligned}$$

An alternate algebraic check can be made by using the Pythagorean Theorem in the form

$$a^2 = c^2 - b^2 = (c + b)(c - b).$$

In this example the computations for a would appear thus:

$$\begin{aligned} c &= 41{,}774 \\ b &= 34{,}567 \\ \hline c + b &= 76{,}341 \\ c - b &= 7{,}207 \end{aligned} \qquad \begin{aligned} \log (c + b) &= \log 76{,}341 = 4.88276 \\ \log (c - b) &= \log 7{,}207 = 3.85775 \\ \hline \log a^2 &= 8.74051 \\ \log a &= 4.37026 \\ a &= 23{,}456 \end{aligned}$$

EXERCISE 17

In Problems 1 through 8, $\triangle ABC$ is a right triangle with the right angle at C. Use Tables C and D to solve the triangle with the appropriate accuracy.

1. $a = 1620$, $b = 1984$.

2. $a = 4321$, $b = 7654$.

3. $c = 9.876$, $A = 43^\circ 21'$.

4. $c = 6.789$, $B = 12^\circ 34'$.

5. $b = .043434$, $A = 28^\circ 28.2'$.

6. $a = .028282$, $B = 43^\circ 43.4'$.

7. $a = 13.579$, $c = 24.680$.

8. $b = 53.197$, $c = 86.024$.

Monday Jan 22.

Tan A = a/b

Sin A = a/c = Cos B = a/c

CHAPTER 4

TRIGONOMETRIC FUNCTIONS OF A GENERAL ANGLE

1. Objective. In this chapter we will change the definitions of the trigonometric functions so that they are defined for all angles. These new definitions must be chosen so that if the angle is an acute angle, the new definitions and the old definitions give the same result. This is the content of Theorem 5.

One might expect that after defining the trigonometric functions for general angles, we would then need larger tables to include the obtuse angles and the negative angles. One of the nice features of these new definitions is that Tables B and D of the Appendix do not need to be extended. This is the content of Theorems 6 and 7.

These new definitions require a rectangular coordinate system, so we will now review this topic.

2. Directed Distances and the Rectangular Coordinate System. Let AB in Fig. 1 be a line segment to which a particular direction has

FIGURE 1

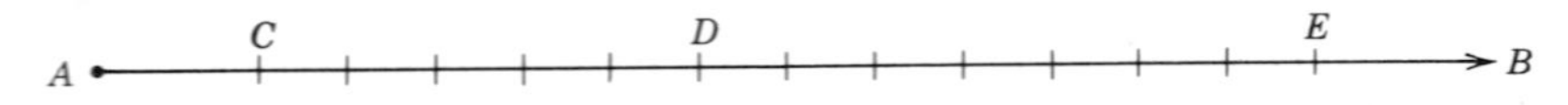

been assigned as indicated by the arrow, and let C and D be two points on this line segment 5 units apart. The distance between any two points is always understood to be a positive number, unless the points coincide. In this case the distance is zero.

If we wish to take into account the direction of travel, we may do this by attaching a positive or negative sign to the distance; positive when the direction coincides with that of AB, and negative when the direction opposes that of AB. Such distances are called *directed distances.* For example, CD denotes the directed distance from C to D in Fig. 1, and since this direction coincides with that of the directed line AB, we have $CD = 5$. On the other hand DC denotes the directed distance from D to C and hence $DC = -5$. As further examples we have in Fig. 1 that

$$CE = 12, \qquad EC = -12,$$
$$DE = 7, \qquad ED = -7,$$

Theorem I. *If P, Q, and R are any three points on a directed line, then for the directed distances,*

$$PQ + QR = PR. \tag{1}$$

To prove this theorem, one must consider all possible cases for the relative positions of the points. For example in Fig. 1, the equation

$$DE + EC = DC \tag{2}$$

is equivalent to

$$7 + (-12) = -5, \tag{3}$$

and this is obviously correct. The student should test Theorem 1, using Fig. 1 and letting Q be first C, then D, then E. There are six possible equations of the form (2) using points C, D, and E, and the student should show that each of these six equations leads to a correct numerical result similar to (3).

The rectangular coordinate system, already familiar to the student, is just two directed lines meeting at right angles, see Fig. 2. The point of intersection of these lines is called the *origin* and is usually lettered O. It is customary to take one of these lines to be horizontal and to take the direction to the right of O as the positive direction on this line. This horizontal line is called the *x-axis,* or the *horizontal axis.* The other directed line which is perpendicular to the x-axis, is called the *y-axis* or the *vertical axis,* and the positive direction is upward from O.

These two axes divide the plane into four quadrants, which are labeled Q.I, Q.II, Q.III, and Q.IV for convenience as indicated in Fig. 2.

Once a rectangular coordinate system has been chosen, any point in the plane can be located with respect to it. Suppose P is some point in the plane. Let PQ be a perpendicular to the x-axis and let PR be a perpendicular to the y-axis. The directed distance OQ is called the x-coordinate of P, and the directed distance OR is called the y-coordinate of P. In Fig. 2, $OQ = 1$ and $OR = 3$. It is customary to enclose this pair of numbers in parentheses, thus: (x, y) or $(1, 3)$, and these numbers are called the *coordinates* of the point P. Since the figure $OQPR$ is a rectangle $RP = OQ$ and $OR = QP$, so an alternate definition is possible, namely,

The x-coordinate of P is the directed distance of P from the y-axis,
The y-coordinate of P is the directed distance of P from the x-axis.

Figure 2 shows a number of other points with their coordinates. The reader should check each point to see if its coordinates appear to be consistent with the position of the point in the figure.

FIGURE 2

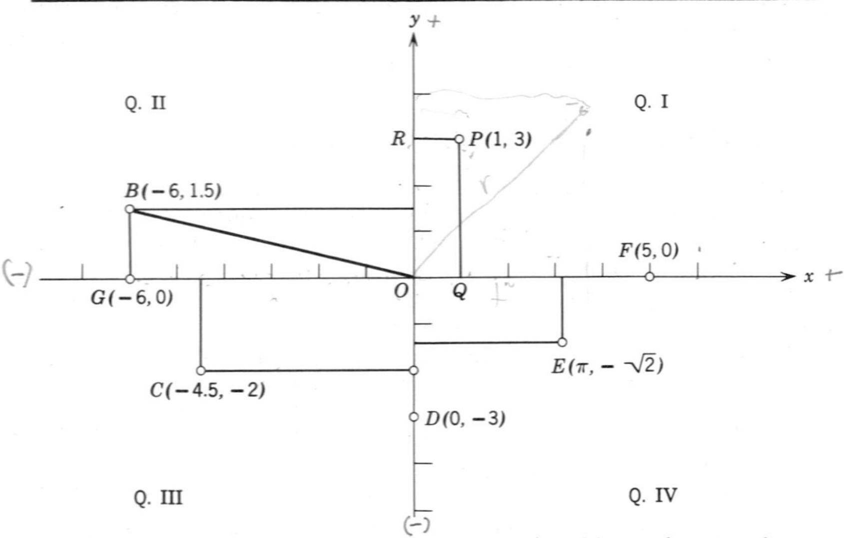

Of course, this procedure can be reversed. Given the coordinates $A(5, -8)$ for example, the point A can be located by moving 5 units to the right of O on the x-axis, and then proceeding downward 8 units along a line parallel to the y-axis. The preceding discussion proves

Theorem 2. *With a given rectangular coordinate system, each point P in the plane has a uniquely determined pair of coordinates (x, y). Conversely, each pair of coordinates (x, y) determines a unique point P with these coordinates.*

The distance of the point P from the origin O is usually denoted by r. Using the Pythagorean Theorem it is easy to prove that for any point P with coordinates (x, y)

$$r = \sqrt{x^2 + y^2}. \tag{4}$$

For example, in Fig. 2 the points OGB are the vertices of a right triangle and the distance of B from the origin is the hypotenuse. The directed distances are $OG = x = -6$, and $GB = y = 1.5$. The lengths of the sides of the triangle are the positive numbers 6 and 1.5. Thus, by the Pythagorean Theorem

$$r^2 = 6^2 + (1.5)^2 = (-6)^2 + 1.5^2 = x^2 + y^2 \tag{5}$$

and this illustrates equation (4). The distance r is not a directed distance; so in (4) the positive square root is indicated. Thus, for the point B in Fig. 2, we have $r = \sqrt{36 + 2.25} = 6.1847 \cdots$, an irrational number.

★ The rectangular coordinate system is frequently called the Cartesian coordinate system in honor of its inventor René Descartes (1596–1650). A brief but highly entertaining account of the life of this genius can be found in *Men of Mathematics* by E. T. Bell, Simon and Schuster, 1937.

EXERCISE 18

1. Let G, H, and J be three points in the order named, on a directed line. Let $GH = 4$ and $HJ = 11$. Write all the six possible equations of the form of equation (1) for these three points, and check by substituting numbers that each of these equations is valid.

2. Using coordinate paper plot the points $(-3, 4)$, $(4, -\sqrt{6})$, $(5, 0)$, and $(-5, -12)$. Find r for each of these points.

3. Using coordinate paper plot the points $(3, -4)$, $(\sqrt{5}, 2)$, $(-7, -7)$, $(-3, 0)$, and $(0, -5)$. Find r for each of these points.

In Problems 4 through 10 use the Pythagorean Theorem to find the missing coordinate of the point P.

4. $r = 5$, $x = 3$, P is in Q.IV.

5. $r = 13$, $x = -5$, P is in Q.III.

6. $r = 13$, $y = 12$, P is in Q.II.

7. $r = 5$, $y = 3$, P is in Q.II.

8. $r = \sqrt{13}$, $y = 2$, P is in Q.I.

9. $r = \sqrt{22}$, $x = \sqrt{13}$, P is in Q.IV.

10. $r = \sqrt{21}$, $x = -2\sqrt{3}$, P is in Q.III.

11. $r = \sqrt{13}$, $y = 3$, P is in Q.I.

12. In what quadrants are (*a*) $x < 0$, (*b*) $1/y > 0$, (*c*) $x/y > 0$?

13. In what quadrants are (*a*) $y > 0$, (*b*) $y/x < 0$, (*c*) $1/x > 0$?

14. What figure is formed from the set of all points which have (*a*) y coordinate equal to 3, (*b*) x coordinate equal to -4?

★ **15.** In each of the following, state what figure is formed by the set of all points whose coordinates (x, y) satisfy the given equation: (*a*) $x = y$, (*b*) $x = -y$, (*c*) $x^2 + y^2 = 16$, (*d*) $x^2 = y^2$.

★ **16.** Prove Theorem 1 by considering all six possible cases for the relative positions of the arbitrary points P, Q, and R. Is Theorem 1 still valid when some of the points coincide?

★ **17.** Prove that equation (4) is valid for any point $P(x, y)$.

3. The Trigonometric Angle. In plane geometry an angle is defined as the figure formed by two line segments meeting at a common end point. In trigonometry it is convenient to think of an angle as a figure generated by a rotation. In this case a line segment is rotated about one end point from a position OA to a new position OB. The segment OA is called the *initial side* of the angle, and the segment OB is called the *terminal side*. If the rotation is counterclockwise, the angle is

FIGURE 3

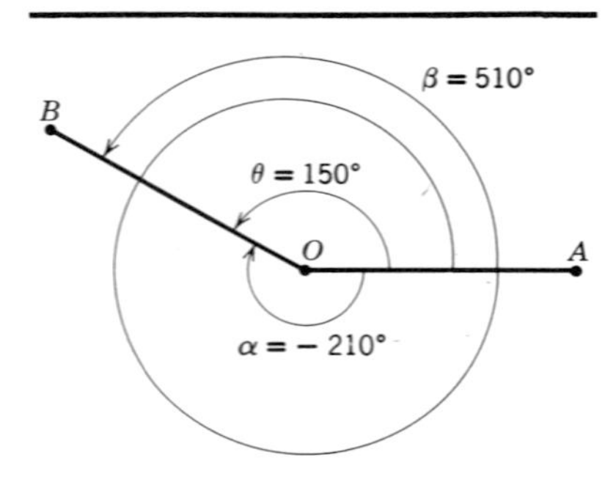

positive, and if the rotation is clockwise, the angle is negative. Thus in Fig. 3, $\theta = 150°$, and $\alpha = -210°$. Of course, there is nothing to prevent the rotating line from making more than one complete turn in either direction. This is illustrated in Fig. 3 by the angle β which is $\theta + 360°$, so that $\beta = 510°$. Thus, to give a trigonometric angle, one must specify which side is the initial side, which side is the terminal side, the direction of rotation, and the amount of rotation.

To define the trigonometric functions for any angle θ, the angle must be placed in standard position on a rectangular coordinate system. An angle is said to be in *standard position* if the vertex of the angle coincides with the origin and if the initial side of the angle falls on the positive x-axis.

Two angles are said to be *coterminal* if when placed in standard position, their terminal sides coincide. As examples the angles α and β of Fig. 3 are both coterminal with θ. It is easy to see that if two angles are coterminal they differ by some integral multiple of 360°. Hence we have

Theorem 3. *The angle α is coterminal with θ if and only if there is some integer n such that*

$$\alpha = \theta + n360°. \tag{6}$$

For example in Fig. 3, $n = -1$ for α, and $n = 1$ for β; that is $\alpha = -210° = 150° - 360°$, and $\beta = 510° = 150° + 360°$.

Instead of the long-winded statement "θ is an angle whose terminal side falls in Q.II when θ is placed in standard position" we will say briefly "θ is a second-quadrant angle" or "θ is in Q.II."

4. Definitions of the Trigonometric Functions for an Arbitrary Angle. We give the definitions in steps.

FIGURE 4

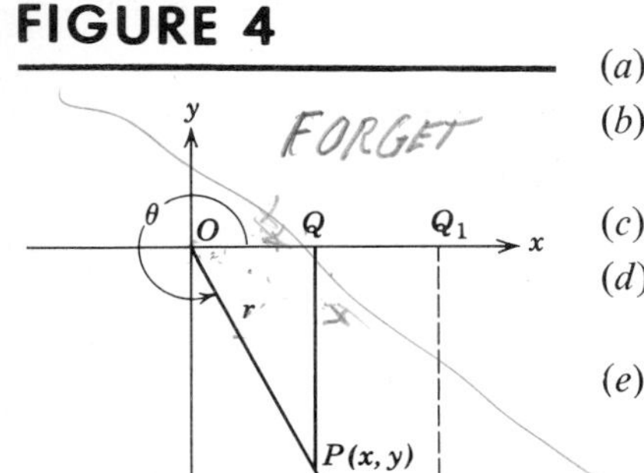

Definition I.

(*a*) *Place the angle θ in standard position.*

(*b*) *Select a point P on the terminal side of θ, not at the origin.*

(*c*) *Determine x and y the coordinates of P.*

(*d*) *Determine the distance $r > 0$ from P to the origin.*

(*e*) *Then,*

$$\sin\theta = \frac{y}{r}, \qquad \csc\theta = \frac{r}{y},$$

$$\cos\theta = \frac{x}{r}, \qquad \sec\theta = \frac{r}{x},$$

$$\tan\theta = \frac{y}{x}, \qquad \cot\theta = \frac{x}{y}.$$

Theorem 4. *The trigonometric functions are independent of the choice of the point P, as long as P is on the terminal side of θ.*

For simplicity we prove this only for the sine function. It will be clear from the proof that the result is also true for the other five trigonometric functions. Suppose that two different points P and P_1 have been taken on the terminal side of θ, as illustrated in Fig. 4. Clearly the triangles PQO and P_1Q_1O are similar, so the sides are proportional. If (x_1, y_1) are the coordinates for P_1 and if r_1 is the distance of P_1 to the origin, then this proportionality gives

$$\frac{|y|}{r} = \frac{|y_1|}{r_1}, \tag{7}$$

where we have used absolute value signs because the coordinates y and y_1 are negative, while the sides of the triangles have positive lengths. However, both y and y_1 are negative together, so from equation (7) we have

$$\frac{y}{r} = \frac{y_1}{r_1}. \tag{8}$$

Hence the ratio that defines $\sin\theta$ when P is the selected point is equal to the ratio that defines $\sin\theta$ when P_1 is the selected point. Q.E.D.

Example 1. Find all of the trigonometric functions for $\theta = -135°$.

Solution. Place the angle in standard position as illustrated in Fig. 5. Select P on the terminal side so that $r = \sqrt{2}$. Since the terminal side makes an angle of 45° with the negative y-axis, it is clear that P has the coordinates $(-1, -1)$. Hence

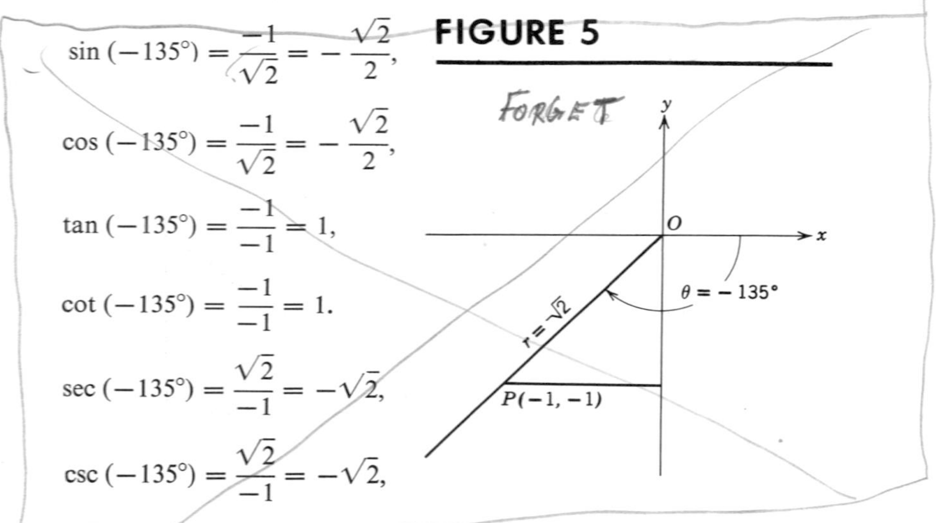

$$\sin(-135°) = \frac{-1}{\sqrt{2}} = -\frac{\sqrt{2}}{2},$$

$$\cos(-135°) = \frac{-1}{\sqrt{2}} = -\frac{\sqrt{2}}{2},$$

$$\tan(-135°) = \frac{-1}{-1} = 1,$$

$$\cot(-135°) = \frac{-1}{-1} = 1.$$

$$\sec(-135°) = \frac{\sqrt{2}}{-1} = -\sqrt{2},$$

$$\csc(-135°) = \frac{\sqrt{2}}{-1} = -\sqrt{2},$$

FIGURE 5

Example 2. Find all of the trigonometric functions for $\theta = 180°$.

Solution. If the angle 180° is placed in standard position, the terminal side will obviously coincide with the negative portion of the x-axis. We can take $(-1, 0)$ as a point on this terminal side. Then $r = 1$, and

$$\sin 180° = \frac{0}{1} = 0, \qquad \cos 180° = \frac{-1}{1} = -1, \qquad \tan 180° = \frac{0}{-1} = 0.$$

$$\csc 180° = \frac{1}{0} = \infty, \qquad \sec 180° = \frac{1}{-1} = -1, \qquad \cot 180° = \frac{-1}{0} = \infty.$$

How do these new definitions compare with those given in Chapter 1 for the trigonometric functions? The answer is contained in

Theorem 5. *If θ is an acute angle, then $\sin\theta$, given by Definition* 1 *of this chapter, is equal to $\sin\theta$ given by Definition* 1 *of Chapter* 1. *The same is true of each of the other five trigonometric functions.*

Proof. Let T be a right triangle as shown in Fig. 6, with $\theta = A$. Then by the definition of Chapter 1

$$\sin \theta = \frac{a}{c} \tag{9}$$

FIGURE 6

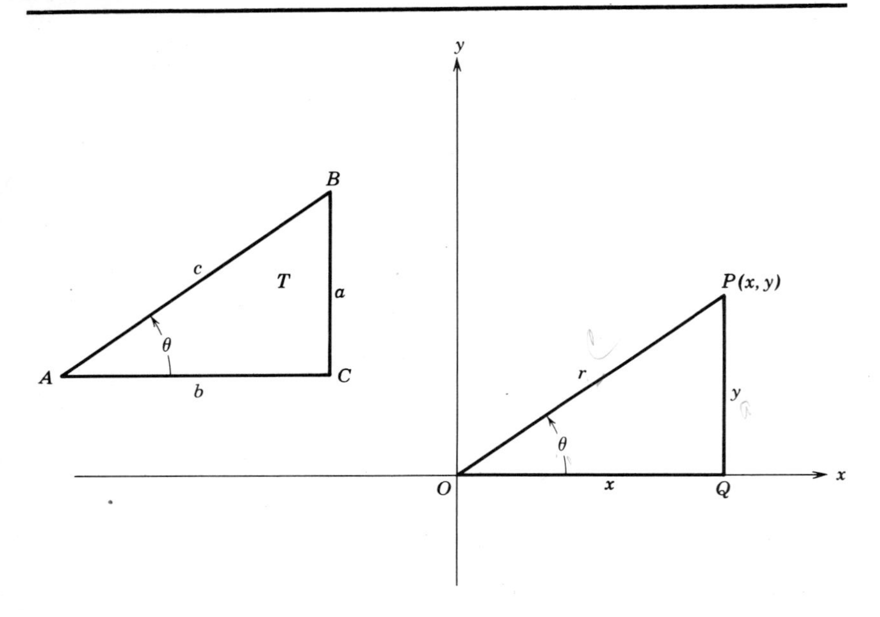

If we now place θ in standard position, the terminal side will fall in the first quadrant, because for an acute angle $0 < \theta < 90°$. Select P on this terminal side so that r, the distance of P from O, is c. The coordinates (x, y) of P are obviously both positive. From P drop a line PQ perpendicular to the x-axis. The triangles ABC and OPQ are clearly congruent and therefore $x = b$, and $y = a$. By Definition 1 of this chapter

$$\sin \theta = \frac{y}{r}. \tag{10}$$

But $y = a$ and $r = c$, so (9) and (10) give the same value for $\sin \theta$.

For the other five trigonometric functions we assert that since $x = b$, $y = a$, and $r = c$, any ratio formed with any two of the items on the right sides of these equations is equal to the ratio formed by the corresponding items on the left sides of these equations. Q.E.D.

EXERCISE 19

1. Give five angles each coterminal with $\theta = 30°$, and make a sketch showing each of these angles in standard position.

2. Do Problem 1 with $\theta = -45°$.

3. For each one of the trigonometric functions, state the quadrants in which the function is positive.

4. For each of the following angles find all the trigonometric functions: (*a*) 240°, (*b*) −30°, (*c*) 660°, (*d*) −225°, (*e*) 270°.

5. For each of the following angles find all the trigonometric functions: (*a*) 120°, (*b*) −45°, (*c*) 210°, (*d*) 720°, (*e*) −270°.

6. In each of the following problems the point (x, y) lies on the terminal side of θ when θ is in standard position. Make a sketch showing θ, $(0° < \theta < 360°)$ and find $\sin \theta$ and $\cos \theta$: (*a*) (3, 4), (*b*) (5, −12), (*c*) (−2, −3), (*d*) (−5, 3).

7. Do Problem 6 for the points: (*a*) (12, 5), (*b*) (−4, 3), (*c*) (−4, −5), (*d*) (1, −2).

5. Algebraic Signs of the Trigonometric Functions. Let us determine for each one of the trigonometric functions those quadrants in which the function is positive, and those in which it is negative. In $\sin \theta = y/r$, the denominator r is always positive, so it is sufficient to examine

TABLE 1

Quadrant	sin	cos	tan	cot	sec	csc
I	+	+	+	+	+	+
II	+	−	−	−	−	+
III	−	−	+	+	−	−
IV	−	+	−	−	+	−

the sign of y. Hence it is easy to see that $\sin \theta$ is positive if θ is in Q.I or in Q.II, and $\sin \theta$ is negative if θ is in Q.III or in Q.IV. This same type of analysis will do for the functions cosine, secant, and cosecant. For $\tan \theta = y/x$, we must watch the signs of both the numerator and the denominator. When both x and y are negative, as they are when θ is in Q.III, the quotient is positive. For θ in Q.II, x is negative and y is positive, so $\tan \theta$ is negative. In Q.IV it is y that is negative, while x is positive, but the quotient is still negative. The analysis for $\cot \theta$ is similar. The results are tabulated in Table 1 for convenience.

The student should verify that each entry of this table is correct. He should then close the book and reproduce this table without peeking.

6. Reduction to Functions of an Acute Angle. We next show how to reduce the problem of finding the trigonometric functions of any angle to that of finding the functions of an appropriate acute angle. This process requires two theorems and one new definition.

Theorem 6. *If two angles α and θ are coterminal then:*

$$\sin\alpha = \sin\theta, \qquad \cos\alpha = \cos\theta, \qquad \tan\alpha = \tan\theta,$$
$$\csc\alpha = \csc\theta, \qquad \sec\alpha = \sec\theta, \qquad \cot\alpha = \cot\theta.$$

The proof is obvious and is left for the student.

Example 3. Find tan 2200°.

Solution. $2200° = 6 \times 360° + 40°$, hence 2200° and 40° are coterminal. From Table B, $\tan 2200° = \tan 40° = .8391$.

If θ does not happen to be in Q.I then the related angle will be helpful.

Definition 2. *The related angle of θ is the smallest nonnegative angle that the terminal side of θ makes with the x-axis, when θ is in standard position.*

We will denote the related angle by ρ (rho) and by definition $0° \leqq \rho \leqq 90°$. In Fig. 7 we show a number of angles θ, together with their related angles ρ.

FIGURE 7

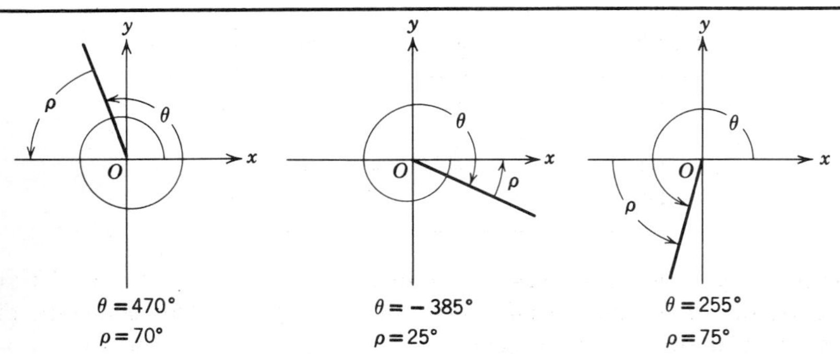

We will see in the next theorem that in order to find a trigonometric function of θ, we merely find the function of ρ and then attach the proper algebraic sign, as indicated by Table 1 of the preceding section.

Theorem 7. *If ρ is the related angle of θ, then:*

(11)	$\sin\rho = \lvert\sin\theta\rvert,$	(14)	$\csc\rho = \lvert\csc\theta\rvert,$
(12)	$\cos\rho = \lvert\cos\theta\rvert,$	(15)	$\sec\rho = \lvert\sec\theta\rvert,$
(13)	$\tan\rho = \lvert\tan\theta\rvert,$	(16)	$\cot\rho = \lvert\cot\theta\rvert.$

Proof. Let us consider the particular case of θ in Q.III as shown in Fig. 8. The coordinates for P are both negative. On the other hand, the sides of the triangle OPQ have positive length. If a and b denote these lengths then $a = |y|$, and $b = |x|$. For θ we have $\sin\theta = y/r$. Since $r > 0$, we can write

$$(17)\quad |\sin\theta| = \left|\frac{y}{r}\right| = \frac{|y|}{r} = \frac{a}{r} = \sin\rho,$$

and this proves (11). The other five equations are proved similarly. Finally, we leave it for the student to examine the situation when θ is in any one of the other three quadrants.

FIGURE 8

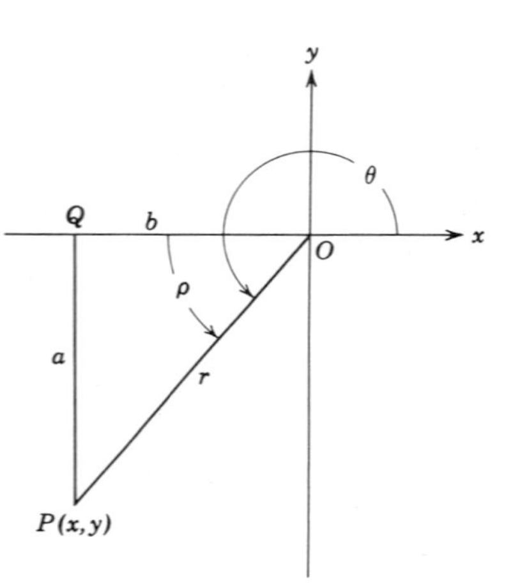

Example 4. Find sin 480° and tan 480°.

Solution. $480° = 360° + 180° - 60°$, hence θ in Q.II and $\rho = 60°$.

$\sin 60° = \sqrt{3}/2$, $\tan 60° = \sqrt{3}$.

Therefore $\sin 480° = \sqrt{3}/2$ and $\tan 480° = -\sqrt{3}$.

Example 5. Find θ $(0° < \theta < 360°)$ if the terminal side of θ goes through the point $(-1, 2)$ when θ is in standard position.

Solution. For the related angle $\tan\rho = 2$. From Table B, $\rho = 63°\,26'$.

Since $(-1, 2)$ is in Q.II, θ is in Q.II. Therefore $\theta = 180° - 63°\,26' = 116°\,34'$.

EXERCISE 20

In Problems 1 through 8 find the quadrant, and the related angle for each of the given angles.

1. 700°. **2.** 550°. **3.** 1500°. **4.** −750°.
5. −910°. **6.** −1000°. **7.** −1900°. **8.** 1210°.

In Problems 9 through 14 find sin, cos, and tan for each of the angles listed.

9. 170°. **10.** 255°. **11.** −145°.
12. 680°. **13.** −380°. **14.** −250°.

Oblig triangle

In Problems 15 through 20 find the angle θ to the nearest minute ($0° < \theta < 360°$) if the terminal side goes through the indicated point when θ is in standard position.

15. $(2, -3)$. **16.** $(-3, 7)$. **17.** $(-3, -\sqrt{7})$.

18. $(1, -2\sqrt{2})$. **19.** $(-\sqrt{5}, 2)$. **20.** $(-\sqrt{21}, -2)$.

7. The Trigonometric Functions of ($-\theta$). Let θ be any angle. Then $(-\theta)$ denotes the same amount of rotation but in the opposite direction. As a result, if θ and $-\theta$ are placed in standard position on the same rectangular coordinate system, the terminal sides of these two angles will be symmetrical with respect to the x-axis. This is shown in Fig. 9, which illustrates two of the many possible cases.

It is easy to see that if a line PQP' is drawn perpendicular to the x-axis, the two triangles formed will be congruent. Let a and b denote the lengths of the sides of these triangles. Since a and b are both positive, the coordinates of P and P' are as indicated in the figure. Suppose θ is in Q.II. Then from Fig. 9:

FIGURE 9

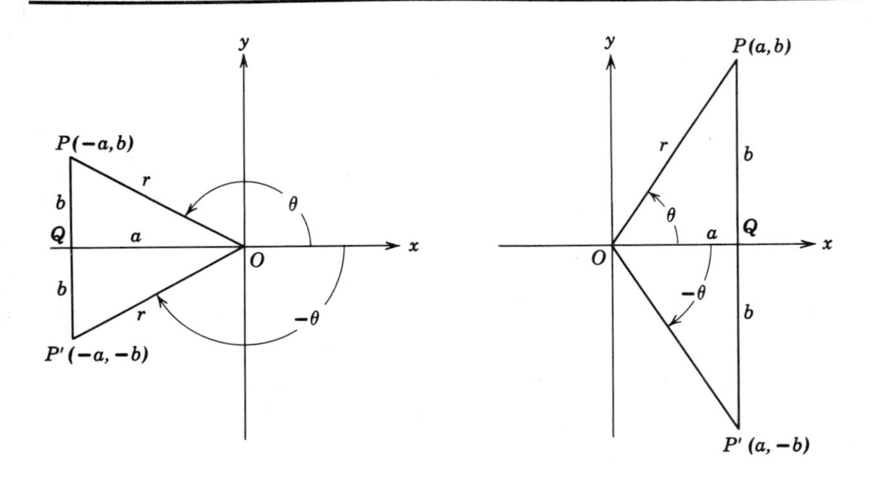

$$\text{(18)} \qquad \sin(-\theta) = \frac{-b}{r}, \qquad \sin\theta = \frac{b}{r},$$

hence

$$\text{(19)} \qquad \sin(-\theta) = -\sin\theta;$$

and

(20) $$\cos(-\theta) = \frac{-a}{r}, \qquad \cos\theta = \frac{-a}{r},$$

hence

(21) $$\cos(-\theta) = \cos\theta.$$

If θ is in Q.I we still have (18), but (20) is replaced by $\cos(-\theta) = a/r$, and $\cos\theta = a/r$. Nevertheless, these still lead to (21).

The student should draw the figures when θ is in Q.III or in Q.IV, and prove that (19) and (21) are valid for any angle. The same set of figures can be used to investigate the remaining trigonometric functions. This proves

Theorem 8. *For any angle* θ,

(19) $\sin(-\theta) = -\sin\theta$, (23) $\csc(-\theta) = -\csc\theta$,

(22) $\tan(-\theta) = -\tan\theta$, (24) $\cot(-\theta) = -\cot\theta$,

but

(21) $\cos(-\theta) = \cos\theta$, (25) $\sec(-\theta) = \sec\theta$.

Functions that behave like the top four functions in this list are known as *odd* functions. A change of sign in the variable gives a change of sign in the function. Functions that behave like the bottom two, are known as *even* functions. A change of sign in the variable leaves the function unchanged. As further examples, x^3 and $1/x$ are odd functions, but x^2 and x^4 are even functions. Using function notation[1] we can state the definitions more simply and accurately.

Definition 3. *A function* $f(\theta)$ *is called odd if* $f(-\theta) = -f(\theta)$ *for all* θ. *The function is called even if for all* θ, $f(-\theta) = f(\theta)$.

EXERCISE 21

1. Complete the proof of Theorem 8 by examining the remaining cases. What is the situation if θ is a negative angle?

2. Give two more examples of an odd function, and two more examples of an even function.

3. Give two examples of functions that are neither odd nor even functions.

★★ **4.** Prove that if $f(x)$ is an odd function and $g(x)$ is an even function, then the product $p(x) = f(x)g(x)$ is an odd function, and the quotient $q(x) = f(x)/g(x)$ is an odd function.

[1] See Chapter 0 § 9 for a discussion of function notation.

★★ **5.** Prove that if both $f(x)$ and $g(x)$ are odd functions then both $p(x)$ and $q(x)$ in Problem 4 are even functions.

★★ **6.** Prove that if $f(x)$ is an odd function, then the power $P(x) = [f(x)]^n$ is an odd function when n is an odd integer, and an even function when n is an even integer. What happens if $f(x)$ is an even function? The function $[f(x)]^n$ is frequently written $f^n(x)$ for brevity.

CHAPTER 5

ELEMENTARY TRIGONOMETRIC IDENTITIES

1. Objective. Our aim is to make clear the logical difference between an identity and a conditional equation. The student has already encountered both of these concepts in his previous mathematical work, but due, undoubtedly, to foggy conditions at the time of the meeting he is probably not aware of the distinction between the two.

The difference is easily illustrated by drawing on algebra. Once this distinction is grasped we can turn to trigonometric identities. The subject matter is extremely important for later mathematical work, but for the present the student should regard it merely as a good practice field in which he can display his talent for algebraic manipulation, using trigonometric functions.

Proving trigonometric identities should be fun for a person who has a normal, healthy, inquisitive mind. The converse, however, is not necessarily true.

2. Algebraic Identities. Let us begin by combining the two fractions as indicated

$$\frac{3+x}{1-x} - \frac{3-x}{1+x}$$

in the usual manner. We have

$$\frac{3+x}{1-x} - \frac{3-x}{1+x} = \frac{(3+x)(1+x) - (1-x)(3-x)}{(1-x)(1+x)}$$

$$= \frac{3+4x+x^2-(3-4x+x^2)}{1-x^2} = \frac{8x}{1-x^2}.$$

Thus we have proved that for all (?) x

$$\frac{3+x}{1-x} - \frac{3-x}{1+x} = \frac{8x}{1-x^2}. \tag{1}$$

On the other hand, the equation

$$x^4 - 2x^3 - x^2 + 2x = 0 \tag{2}$$

is true (valid) for $x = -1, 0, 1,$ and 2 but for no other values of x.

Definition 1. *An equation that is true for all values of the variables involved is called an identity.*

Equation (1) is an identity.

Definition 2. *An equation that is true only for certain special values of the variables involved is called a conditional equation.*

Equation (2) is a conditional equation. It is true only on the condition that $x = -1, 0, 1,$ or 2. The word *equation* is used loosely, to describe either type of relationship.

An alert student should rise up in protest, because the equal sign is used in both (1) and (2) where it has two different meanings. In defense of this practice we can say that identities are used in solving a conditional equation, so that an attempt to use different signs in (1) and (2) would be confusing. We give an illustration.

Solve the (conditional) equation

$$(x - 2y)^2 = x^2 - xy + y^2. \tag{3}$$

Since $(x - 2y)^2 = x^2 - 4xy + 4y^2$, for all values of x and y, (an identity) we can write the conditional equation (3) as

$$x^2 - 4xy + 4y^2 = x^2 - xy + y^2.$$

Hence $3y^2 - 3xy = 0$ or $3y(y - x) = 0$. Therefore (3) is satisfied (valid, true) if $y = 0$ or if $y = x$ and only in these cases.

Sometimes when it is convenient to use a symbol to distinguish between an identity and a conditional equation, the identity sign $\equiv$ consisting of three parallel lines is used. This same sign is also frequently used in definitions because they are really identities. For example, the definition of y^3 is $y^3 \equiv yyy$, and this is an identity because it is true for all values of y. In this book the identity sign will not be used. Rather we ask the student to be on guard. Whenever he sees the equal sign he should be able to answer the question "Is this equation an identity or a conditional equation?"

The student has already met a great many identities in his previous mathematical work, although probably they were not called by that name. Here are a few:

$$(x - 4)(x + 4) = x^2 - 16, \tag{4}$$

$$(y + 2)^3 = y^3 + 6y^2 + 12y + 8, \tag{5}$$

$$\frac{A}{B} + \frac{1}{2} = \frac{2A + B}{2B}, \tag{6}$$

$$\log MN = \log M + \log N. \tag{7}$$

Here are a few expressions that look like the above identities, but are in fact conditional equations:

$$(x - 4)(x + 4) = 6x, \tag{8}$$

$$(y + 2)^3 = y^3 + 5y^2 + 8y + 5, \tag{9}$$

$$\frac{A}{B} + \frac{1}{2} = \frac{A + 1}{B + 2}, \tag{10}$$

$$\log MN = 2 \log M + 3 \log N. \tag{11}$$

Equation (8) is true if and only if $x = -2$ or $x = 8$. For (9) the solution is $y = -1$ or $y = -3$. Equation (10) holds if and only if $A = -B^2/4$. For (11) the condition is $M = 1/N^2$ for this equation to be valid.

Let us reexamine the identity (1), and the definition of an identity. Is equation (1) really true for all values of x? If we set $x = 1$ in equation (1) we find

$$\frac{4}{0} - \frac{2}{2} = \frac{8}{0} \tag{12}$$

Now 4/0 is not a number so (12) is really meaningless. If one wishes to entertain himself by writing for (12)

$$\text{Not a number } -1 = \text{not a number}, \tag{13}$$

there is no great harm in doing so. The proper attitude is this: Equation (1) is meaningless if $x = 1$ or $x = -1$, but it is true for all values of x for which both sides of the equation have meaning. This is really as much as we could expect from the equation.

If we wish to be fussy about this matter, we should change Definition 1 by adding just after the word "involved" the phrase "for which both sides of the equation have meaning." However we offer the student this truce; we will not mention this fine point again throughout the rest of this book, if he in turn will also refrain from worrying about it.

In proving an identity, it is customary to work only on one side of the equation. As an example, the proper form for the proof of the identity (1) is illustrated below.

$$\frac{3+x}{1-x} - \frac{3-x}{1+x} = \frac{8x}{1-x^2}$$

$$= \frac{(3+x)(1+x) - (3-x)(1-x)}{(1-x)(1+x)}$$

$$= \frac{3+4x+x^2-(3-4x+x^2)}{1-x^2}$$

$$= \frac{3+4x+x^2-3+4x-x^2}{1-x^2}$$

$$= \frac{8x}{1-x^2} \qquad = \frac{8x}{1-x^2}.$$

The equal sign is said to be *reflexive*, because if $A = B$ then $B = A$. This means that in any given identity we may select the side on which we prefer to work. Quite naturally we choose to simplify the complicated side rather than complify the simplicated side.

EXERCISE 22

1. Check that the identity (1) is valid for $x = 0$, $x = 2$, $x = 3$, and $x = \frac{1}{2}$ by showing that both sides of this equation give respectively 0, $-\frac{16}{3}$, -6, and $\frac{16}{3}$.

2. Check that the identity (4) is valid for $x = 1, 3, 5,$ and 7 by showing that both sides of this equation give respectively -15, -7, 9, and 33.

3. Check that equation (2) is not valid when $x = -2$ or when $x = 3$.

4. Check that equation (8) is not valid when $x = 5$, or when $x = 6$.

5. Solve each of the equations (8), (9), (10), and (11).

In Problems 6 to 12 prove each of the identities. Work only on one side.

6. $(a+b)^2 - (a-b)^2 = 4ab$.

7. $(x+y)^3 - (x-y)^3 = 2y(3x^2+y^2)$.

8. $(A+B)^4 - (A-B)^4 = 8AB(A^2+B^2)$.

9. $\dfrac{1+x}{1-x} + \dfrac{1-x}{1+x} = 2 + \dfrac{4x^2}{1-x^2}$.

10. $\dfrac{3+x}{1-x} + \dfrac{3-x}{1+x} = 6 + \dfrac{8x^2}{1-x^2}$.

11. $\dfrac{\dfrac{3}{2} + \dfrac{(x-5)}{(x+4)}}{\dfrac{11}{4} - \dfrac{(3x+21)}{(2x+8)}} = 2$.

12. $\dfrac{\dfrac{5}{2} - \dfrac{(9x-8)}{(4x-3)}}{\dfrac{1}{4} + \dfrac{(x+3)}{(8x-6)}} = \dfrac{2}{3}$.

★ **13.** Prove that if n is an integer greater than 4, then $n^2 - 16$ is not a prime.

★ **14.** Prove that if n is a positive integer, then $n^2 + 6n + 5$ is not a prime.

★ **15.** Here is an old mind-reading trick. Joe Blow asks Jim Dim to: (*a*) Think of a number, but keep it secret. (*b*) Double the number. (*c*) Add 36. (*d*) Divide the result by 2. (*e*) Subtract the number he started with. Then Joe Blow proudly announces that the number Jim Dim has in his mind at the end of these steps is 18.

This trick depends on a simple algebraic identity. Find and prove this identity and thus expose the trick. In practical applications this trick frequently falls flat, because Jim Dim cannot do the arithmetic correctly.

★ **16.** What is the converse of the last statement in §1 of this chapter.

3. The Basic Trigonometric Identities. We begin by proving a theorem that gives the fundamental trigonometric identities. All of the other trigonometric identities in this chapter are proved by manipulation with these eight basic ones, so the student should memorize these equations, (14) through (21), as quickly as possible.

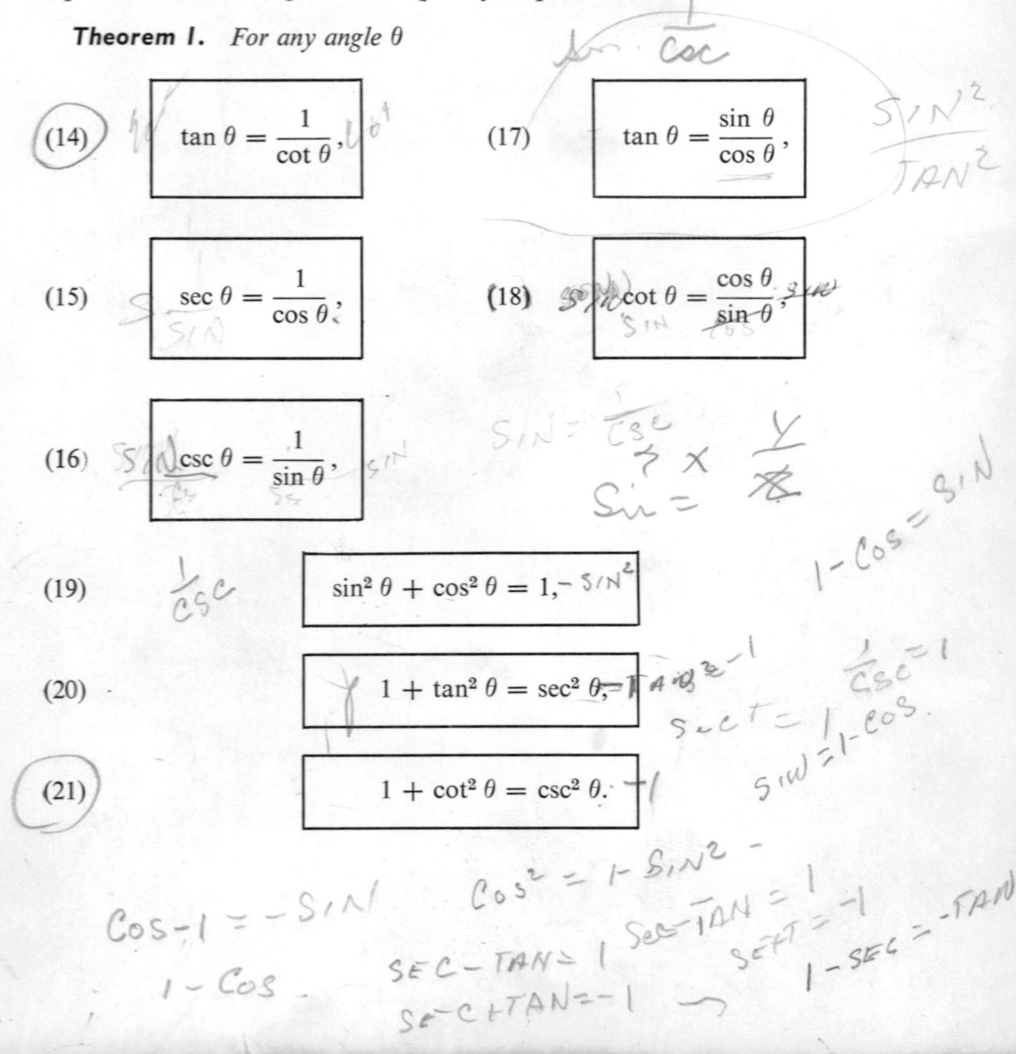

Theorem I. *For any angle* θ

(14) $\tan\theta = \dfrac{1}{\cot\theta}$, (17) $\tan\theta = \dfrac{\sin\theta}{\cos\theta}$,

(15) $\sec\theta = \dfrac{1}{\cos\theta}$, (18) $\cot\theta = \dfrac{\cos\theta}{\sin\theta}$,

(16) $\csc\theta = \dfrac{1}{\sin\theta}$,

(19) $\sin^2\theta + \cos^2\theta = 1$,

(20) $1 + \tan^2\theta = \sec^2\theta$,

(21) $1 + \cot^2\theta = \csc^2\theta$.

Proof. When θ is placed in the standard position, and the point $P(x, y)$ is a point on the terminal side, the definition gives $\cot \theta = x/y$. Then

$$\frac{1}{\cot \theta} = \frac{1}{x/y} = 1 \cdot \frac{y}{x} = \frac{y}{x} = \tan \theta,$$

hence (14) is valid for all angles θ.

To prove that (15) is also true for all angles θ we write

$$\frac{1}{\cos \theta} = \frac{1}{x/r} = 1 \cdot \frac{r}{x} = \frac{r}{x} = \sec \theta. \qquad \text{Q.E.D.}$$

The proof for (16) is similar, and we leave this as an exercise for the student.

In the same way we find for (17) that

$$\frac{\sin \theta}{\cos \theta} = \frac{y/r}{x/r} = \frac{y}{r} \cdot \frac{r}{x} = \frac{y}{x} = \tan \theta. \qquad \text{Q.E.D.}$$

Equation (18) can be handled in the same way as (17) but we wish to vary our technique. Since (14) and (17) are now proved for all θ, we can use these equations in proving new results. Indeed, taking reciprocals of both sides of (14) we have $\cot \theta = 1/\tan \theta$. Then using (17), we find

$$\cot \theta = \frac{1}{\sin \theta/\cos \theta} = 1 \times \frac{\cos \theta}{\sin \theta} = \frac{\cos \theta}{\sin \theta}. \qquad \text{Q.E.D.}$$

To prove (19) recall that for any point in the plane

$$r^2 = x^2 + y^2. \tag{22}$$

If we divide both sides of (22) by r^2 we have

$$1 = \frac{x^2}{r^2} + \frac{y^2}{r^2} = \left(\frac{x}{r}\right)^2 + \left(\frac{y}{r}\right)^2. \tag{23}$$

Now suppose that $P(x, y)$ is a point on the terminal side of θ. Then using Definition 1 in (23) we have

$$1 = (\sin \theta)^2 + (\cos \theta)^2$$

and this is just (19). Notice that this identity is just a disguised form of the Pythagorean Theorem. Equations (20) and (21) may be handled in the same way. To obtain (20), divide both sides of (22) by x^2. To obtain (21), divide both sides of (22) by y^2. We leave the details to the student.

The formulas of Theorem 1 can be written in a large variety of ways.

We give just a few illustrations:

(14) $\tan\theta = \dfrac{1}{\cot\theta}$ gives $\tan\theta\cot\theta = 1$, or $\cot\theta = \dfrac{1}{\tan\theta}$;

(17) $\tan\theta = \dfrac{\sin\theta}{\cos\theta}$ gives $\tan\theta\cos\theta = \sin\theta$, or $\cos\theta = \dfrac{\sin\theta}{\tan\theta}$;

(19) $\sin^2\theta + \cos^2\theta = 1$, gives $\sin^2\theta = 1 - \cos^2\theta$,

or $\sin^2\theta = (1 - \cos\theta)(1 + \cos\theta)$.

Further, (19) gives

$$\sin\theta = \pm\sqrt{1 - \cos^2\theta}. \tag{24}$$

It would be utterly ridiculous to memorize all of the various forms into which the equations of Theorem 1 can be thrown. It is much wiser, first, to memorize the identities (14) through (21), and second, to understand the algebraic manipulations used in the preceding illustrations. The only algebraic operation that is even slightly complicated is the factorization $A^2 - B^2 = (A - B)(A + B)$.

The radical sign, $\sqrt{\ }$, which occurs in (24) always means the positive root, so the $\pm$ sign is necessarily put in front of the radical sign because the trigonometric function on the left may on occasion be negative.

4. Examples of Simple Trigonometric Identities. We will give a few examples to show the wide variety of identities that can be proved using the basic ones of Theorem 1. Just as for algebraic identities we work only on one side.

Example 1. Prove that $\sec A \sin A = \tan A$.
Solution.

$$\sec A \sin A = \tan A$$

$$= \frac{1}{\cos A}\sin A$$

$$= \frac{\sin A}{\cos A}$$

$$= \tan A \qquad = \tan A.$$

Example 2. Prove that $5\sin^2 B + 3\cos^2 B - 2 = 2\sin^2 B + 1$.
Solution.

$$5\sin^2 B + 3\cos^2 B - 2 = 2\sin^2 B + 1$$

$$= 2\sin^2 B + 3\sin^2 B + 3\cos^2 B - 2$$

$$= 2\sin^2 B + 3(\sin^2 B + \cos^2 B) - 2$$

$$= 2\sin^2 B + 3 - 2 \qquad = 2\sin^2 B + 1.$$

Example 3. Prove that $\dfrac{2\sin^2 C - 1}{\sin C \cos C} = \tan C - \cot C.$

Solution.

$$\frac{2\sin^2 C - 1}{\sin C \cos C} \qquad = \tan C - \cot C$$

$$= \frac{2\sin^2 C - (\sin^2 C + \cos^2 C)}{\sin C \cos C}$$

$$= \frac{\sin^2 C - \cos^2 C}{\sin C \cos C}$$

$$= \frac{\sin^2 C}{\sin C \cos C} - \frac{\cos^2 C}{\sin C \cos C}$$

$$= \frac{\sin C}{\cos C} - \frac{\cos C}{\sin C} \qquad = \tan C - \cot C.$$

Example 4. Prove that $(\sin D + \cos D)(\sec D - \csc D)$
$= \tan D - \cot D.$

Solution.

$$(\sin D + \cos D)(\sec D - \csc D) \qquad = \tan D - \cot D$$

$$= \sin D \sec D + \cos D \sec D - \sin D \csc D - \cos D \csc D$$

$$= \frac{\sin D}{\cos D} + 1 - 1 - \frac{\cos D}{\sin D}$$

$$= \tan D - \cot D \qquad = \tan D - \cot D.$$

Notice that in this identity each one of the six trigonometric functions appears exactly once.

EXERCISE 23

Prove each of the following identities. The identities in this list are very simple and no one of the first 25 should require more than four minutes to prove.

1. $\sin A \cot A = \cos A.$

2. $\sin B \sec B \cot B = 1.$

3. $\csc C \tan C = \sec C.$

4. $\cos D \csc D = \cot D.$

5. $\cos^2 E \csc^2 E = \csc^2 E - 1.$

6. $\sec^2 F - \sec^2 F \sin^2 F = 1.$

7. $\dfrac{\sin^2 A}{\csc^2 A} = \sin^4 A.$

8. $\dfrac{\cos^3 B}{\cot^3 B} = \sin^3 B.$

9. $\dfrac{\cos^3 C}{\cot^2 C} = \cos C \sin^2 C.$

10. $\dfrac{\cos^3 D}{\tan^2 D} = \cos^5 D \csc^2 D.$

11. $\dfrac{\cot E}{\csc E} = \cos E.$

12. $\dfrac{\tan^2 F}{\sec^2 F} = \sin^2 F.$

13. $\csc^2 H \sec^5 H = \tan^5 H \csc^7 H.$

14. $\sin \alpha \cos \alpha(\tan \alpha + \cot \alpha) = 1.$

15. $(1 - \sec^2 \gamma)(1 - \csc^2 \gamma) = 1.$

16. $1 + \tan^4 \alpha + 2 \tan^2 \alpha = \sec^4 \alpha.$

17. $1 - 2 \sin^2 \theta = 2 \cos^2 \theta - 1.$

18. $\dfrac{\sin^4 B - \cos^4 B}{\sin^2 B - \cos^2 B} = 1.$

19. $\dfrac{\cos^2 C}{1 + \sin C} = 1 - \sin C.$

20. $\dfrac{\sec^2 D - \tan^2 D}{\csc^2 D} = \sin^2 D.$

21. $\dfrac{1 - \tan^2 E}{1 + \tan^2 E} = \cos^2 E - \sin^2 E.$

22. $\sin^3 G \cos^3 G = \tan^6 G \cos^9 G \csc^3 G.$

23. $\sec \beta \csc \beta(\sin \beta + \cos \beta) = \sec \beta + \csc \beta.$

24. $\dfrac{3 \cos \varphi + 5 \sin \varphi \cot \varphi}{2 \sin \varphi} = 4 \cot \varphi.$

25. $\dfrac{1 + \cot A + \sec A}{\csc A} = \sin A + \cos A + \tan A.$

The following identities are a little more difficult than the first 25, but no one of them should require more than six minutes to prove.

26. $2 \csc \alpha - \cot \alpha \cos \alpha = \sin \alpha + \csc \alpha.$

27. $2 \sin^2 \beta(\tan^2 \beta + 1) + 1 = \sec^2 \beta + \tan^2 \beta.$

28. $(1 + \tan \gamma)(1 - \cot \gamma) = \tan \gamma - \cot \gamma.$

29. $\sec \theta \csc \theta - 2 \cos \theta \csc \theta = \tan \theta - \cot \theta.$

30. $\tan A(1 + \csc A) = \sec A(1 + \sin A).$

31. $(1 - \sec B)(\cos^2 B + \cos B) = -\sin^2 B.$

32. $(1 + \sin C)(\sec C - \tan C) = \cos C.$

33. $\cos^2 D(1 + \tan D)^2 = \sin^2 D(1 + \cot D)^2.$

34. $(\sin E + 2 \cos E)^2 + (2 \sin E - \cos E)^2 = 5.$

35. $(\sec F + 3 \tan F)^2 - (3 \sec F + \tan F)^2 = -8.$

36. $\sec G \csc G(\tan G + \cot G) = \sec^2 G + \csc^2 G.$

37. $\cos^3 A \sin A + \sin^3 A \cos A = \sin A \cos A.$

38. $1 + \tan^2 B - \sin^2 B - \sin^2 B \tan^2 B = 1.$

39. $\sin^3 C(1 + \cot C) + \cos^3 C(1 + \tan C) = \sin C + \cos C.$

40. $D \sec^2 D + \csc D - D \tan^2 D - \cot D \cos D = D + \sin D.$

41. $\dfrac{\cos^3 E - \sin^3 E}{\cos E - \sin E} = 1 + \sin E \cos E.$

42. $\dfrac{\tan^3 F + 1}{\tan F + 1} = \sec^2 F - \tan F.$

43. $1 + \tan^6 \alpha = \sec^2 \alpha(3 - 3 \sec^2 \alpha + \sec^4 \alpha).$

44. $\sec^6 \beta - 1 = \tan^2 \beta(3 + 3 \tan^2 \beta + \tan^4 \beta).$

45. $\sin^6 \gamma + \cos^6 \gamma = 1 - 3 \sin^2 \gamma + 3 \sin^4 \gamma.$

46. $\dfrac{\cos^2 \theta}{\sin^2 \theta - 7 \sin \theta + 6} = \dfrac{1 + \sin \theta}{6 - \sin \theta}.$

47. $\dfrac{\tan^2\theta - 8}{\tan^2\theta + 2\sec\theta - 14} = \dfrac{3 + \sec\theta}{5 + \sec\theta}$.

★ **48.** $(\sec\varphi + \tan\varphi - 1)(\sec\varphi - \tan\varphi + 1) = 2\tan\varphi$.

★ **49.** $(1 + \tan\alpha + \cot\alpha)^2 = 1 + \sec^2\alpha + \csc^2\alpha + 2\sec\alpha\csc\alpha$.

★ **50.** $(1 + \cot\beta + \csc\beta)^2 = 2(1 + \csc\beta)(\cot\beta + \csc\beta)$.

5. More Complicated Trigonometric Identities. A knowledge of certain basic algebraic facts is necessary for proving the more complicated identities.

THE ADDITION OF FRACTIONS. The algebraic rule for adding two fractions is

$$\frac{A}{B} + \frac{C}{D} = \frac{AD + BC}{BD}. \tag{25}$$

This rule is also applicable when the quantities are trigonometric functions, for when the angle is fixed the trigonometric functions are just numbers.

Example 5. Prove that

$$\frac{\tan\theta}{\csc\theta - \cot\theta} - \frac{\sin\theta}{\csc\theta + \cot\theta} = \sec\theta + \cos\theta.$$

Solution. Working only on the left side we have

$$\frac{\tan\theta}{\csc\theta - \cot\theta} + \frac{-\sin\theta}{\csc\theta + \cot\theta}$$

$$= \frac{\tan\theta(\csc\theta + \cot\theta) - \sin\theta(\csc\theta - \cot\theta)}{(\csc\theta - \cot\theta)(\csc\theta + \cot\theta)} \qquad \text{[by (25)]}$$

$$= \frac{\tan\theta\csc\theta + 1 - 1 + \sin\theta\cot\theta}{\csc^2\theta - \cot^2\theta}$$

$$= \frac{\dfrac{\cancel{\sin\theta}}{\cos\theta}\dfrac{1}{\cancel{\sin\theta}} + \dfrac{\cancel{\sin\theta}}{1}\dfrac{\cos\theta}{\cancel{\sin\theta}}}{1}$$

$$= \frac{1}{\cos\theta} + \cos\theta,$$

$$= \sec\theta + \cos\theta.$$

THE REDUCTION OF COMPOUND FRACTIONS. The algebraic rule is

$$\frac{\dfrac{A}{B}}{\dfrac{C}{D}} = \frac{A}{B}\frac{D}{C} = \frac{AD}{BC}. \tag{26}$$

Sometimes when only three terms actually appear on the left, the fourth term must be inserted in the form of 1 in a convenient spot. Thus:

(27) $$\frac{A}{\frac{B}{C}} = \frac{A/1}{\frac{B}{C}} = \frac{A}{1}\frac{C}{B} = \frac{AC}{B},$$

but

(28) $$\frac{\frac{A}{B}}{C} = \frac{\frac{A}{B}}{C/1} = \frac{A}{B}\frac{1}{C} = \frac{A}{BC},$$

and the two results in (27) and (28) are quite different.

Example 6. Prove that

$$\frac{\csc\theta}{\cot\theta + \tan\theta} = \cos\theta.$$

Solution. Again we work only on the left side, but this time for convenience we arrange the work in a line rather than in a column.

$$\frac{\csc\theta}{\cot\theta + \tan\theta} = \frac{\frac{1}{\sin\theta}}{\frac{\cos\theta}{\sin\theta} + \frac{\sin\theta}{\cos\theta}} = \frac{\frac{1}{\sin\theta}}{\frac{\cos^2\theta + \sin^2\theta}{\sin\theta\cos\theta}}$$

$$= \frac{1}{\cancel{\sin\theta}}\,\frac{\cancel{\sin\theta}\cos\theta}{\cos^2\theta + \sin^2\theta} = \frac{\cos\theta}{1} = \cos\theta.$$

CANCELLATION AND ITS INVERSE. The algebraic rule is

(29) $$\frac{AD}{BD} = \frac{A}{B}.$$

Since the equality sign is reflexive, equation (29) (like any equation) can be read from left to right and also from right to left. Thus the fraction A/B can always be altered in form by introducing any factor D both in the numerator and in the denominator. When D is suitably selected, this operation can be very helpful.

Example 7. Prove that

$$\frac{1}{\sec X(1 - \sin X)} = \sec X + \tan X.$$

Solution. Working on the left side, we use (29) with $D = 1 + \sin X$.

This gives:

$$\frac{1}{\sec X(1 - \sin X)} = \frac{1 + \sin X}{\sec X(1 - \sin X)(1 + \sin X)} = \frac{1 + \sin X}{\sec X(1 - \sin^2 X)}.$$

We now see why the factor D was chosen to be $1 + \sin X$. Because it gives $1 - \sin^2 X = \cos^2 X$ in the denominator. Continuing, the left side is

$$\frac{1 + \sin X}{\sec X \cos^2 X} = \frac{1 + \sin X}{(\sec X \cos X) \cos X} = \frac{1 + \sin X}{\cos X} = \sec X + \tan X.$$

EXERCISE 24

all odd

Prove each of the following identities.

1. $\dfrac{\tan B \sin B}{\tan B - \sin B} = \dfrac{\sin B}{1 - \cos B}$.
2. $\dfrac{\cos C - \sin C}{\cos C + \sin C} = \dfrac{\cot C - 1}{\cot C + 1}$.
3. $\csc E = \dfrac{1 + \cot E}{\sin E + \cos E}$.
4. $\sec G \csc G = \tan G + \cot G$.
5. $\dfrac{1 + \sin \alpha}{1 - \sin \alpha} = -\dfrac{1 + \csc \alpha}{1 - \csc \alpha}$.
6. $\dfrac{\tan \theta - \cot \theta}{\sin \theta - \cos \theta} = \sec \theta + \csc \theta$.
7. $(\sec \theta + \tan \theta)^2 = \dfrac{1 + \sin \theta}{1 - \sin \theta}$.
8. $\dfrac{\sin^2 \theta}{\tan \theta - \sin \theta} = \dfrac{\sin \theta \cos \theta}{1 - \cos \theta}$.
9. $\dfrac{\tan \theta - 1}{1 - \cot \theta} = \tan \theta$.
10. $\dfrac{1 - \sin \theta}{\cos \theta} = \dfrac{\cos \theta}{1 + \sin \theta}$.
11. $\dfrac{\sin \theta + \cos \theta}{\sec \theta + \csc \theta} = \sin \theta \cos \theta$.
12. $\dfrac{\sin \theta}{\csc \theta - \cot \theta} = 1 + \cos \theta$.
13. $\dfrac{3}{1 + 2\cos^2 \theta} = \dfrac{3 \sec^2 \theta}{3 + \tan^2 \theta}$.
14. $\dfrac{\tan A \sin A}{1 + \cos A} = \sec A - 1$.
15. $\tan^2 B - \sin^2 B = \tan^2 B \sin^2 B$.
16. $\dfrac{\sec^4 D + \tan^4 D}{\sec^2 D \tan^2 D} - 2 = \dfrac{\cos^4 D}{\sin^2 D}$.
17. $\dfrac{1}{\cos E + \sin E \tan E} = \cos E$.
18. $\dfrac{\sec^2 F - \tan^2 F}{\sec F - \cos F} = \cot F \csc F$.
19. $\dfrac{2 - \cos^2 \alpha}{1 - \sin^2 \alpha} = \sec^4 \alpha - \tan^4 \alpha$.
20. $\dfrac{\csc \beta - \cot \beta}{\csc \beta + \cot \beta} = \dfrac{1 - \cos \beta}{1 + \cos \beta}$.
21. $\dfrac{1}{1 - 2\sin \gamma} = \dfrac{2 \sec \gamma + \tan \gamma}{2 \cos \gamma - 3 \tan \gamma}$.
22. $(\cot^2 \gamma - \cos^2 \gamma)^2 = \dfrac{\cos^8 \gamma}{\sin^4 \gamma}$.
23. $\dfrac{\cos A \cot A}{1 + \sin A} = \csc A - 1$.
24. $\dfrac{1}{1 + \cos^2 B} = \dfrac{\sec^2 B}{\tan^2 B + 2}$.
25. $\dfrac{\tan C - \sin C}{\sin^3 C} = \dfrac{\sec C}{1 + \cos C}$.
26. $\dfrac{\tan D - \cot D}{\tan D + \cot D} = 2\sin^2 D - 1$.

10

27. $\dfrac{1}{\sin E + \cos E \cot E} = \sin E.$

28. $\dfrac{\cos^2 \alpha \cot^2 \alpha}{\cot \alpha - \cos \alpha} = \cos \alpha + \cot \alpha.$

29. $\sec A = \dfrac{1 + \tan A}{\sin A + \cos A}.$

30. $\dfrac{\cos B}{1 - \sin B} = \dfrac{\cot B \cos B}{\cot B - \cos B}.$

★**31.** $\dfrac{\csc^4 D + \cot^4 D}{\csc^2 D \cot^2 D} = \dfrac{\sin^4 D}{\cos^2 D} + 2.$

★**32.** $\dfrac{\cot \theta \cos \theta}{\cot \theta + \cos \theta} = \dfrac{\cot \theta - \cos \theta}{\cot \theta \cos \theta}.$

★**33.** $\dfrac{1 + \sin \theta + \cos \theta}{1 + \sin \theta - \cos \theta} = \dfrac{\sin \theta}{1 - \cos \theta}.$

★**34.** $\dfrac{\sec \alpha + \tan \alpha}{\cos \alpha - \tan \alpha - \sec \alpha} = -\csc \alpha.$

35. $\dfrac{1}{1 + \sin A} + \dfrac{1}{1 - \sin A} = 2 \sec^2 A.$

36. $\dfrac{\sin D - \cos D}{\cos D} + \dfrac{\cos D + \sin D}{\sin D} = \sec D \csc D.$

37. $\dfrac{1}{\sec F - 1} - \dfrac{1}{\sec F + 1} = 2 \cot^2 F.$

38. $\dfrac{1 + \sin \beta}{\cos \beta} + \dfrac{\cos \beta}{1 + \sin \beta} = 2 \sec \beta.$

39. $\dfrac{1 - \cos \gamma}{\sin \gamma} - \dfrac{\sin \gamma}{1 - \cos \gamma} = -2 \cot \gamma.$

40. $\dfrac{\cos C}{\tan C + \sec C} - \dfrac{\cos C}{\tan C - \sec C} = 2.$

41. $(\tan G + \cot G)^2 = \sec^2 G \csc^2 G.$

42. $\dfrac{\tan \alpha}{\cos \alpha - 1} - \dfrac{\tan \alpha}{\cos \alpha + 1} = \dfrac{-2}{\sin \alpha \cos \alpha}.$

✓**43.** $\dfrac{\tan \beta}{1 - \cot \beta} + \dfrac{\cot \beta}{1 - \tan \beta} = 1 + \tan \beta + \cot \beta.$

44. $\cos^2 \beta + 2 \sin^2 \beta + \sin^2 \beta \tan^2 \beta = \sec^2 \beta.$

45. $\sin \gamma \cos \gamma (\sec \gamma + \csc \gamma)^2 - 2 = \sec \gamma \csc \gamma.$

46. $\dfrac{\sin^2 \theta}{\sin \theta - \cos \theta} - \dfrac{\sin \theta + \cos \theta}{\tan^2 \theta - 1} = \sin \theta + \cos \theta.$

47. $\dfrac{\cos \theta}{\sin \theta + \cos \theta} - \dfrac{\sin \theta}{\sin \theta - \cos \theta} = \dfrac{\cot^2 \theta + 1}{\cot^2 \theta - 1}.$

48. $\dfrac{\sin C}{\cot C + \csc C} - \dfrac{\sin C}{\cot C - \csc C} = 2.$

★**49.** $\left(\dfrac{\cos \theta}{\tan \theta} + \dfrac{\sin \theta}{\cot \theta}\right) \Big/ (\tan \theta + \cot \theta - 1) = \sin \theta + \cos \theta.$

★**50.** $\cos \beta + \cos \beta \cot \beta + \sin \beta \tan \beta + \sin \beta = \dfrac{1}{\cos \beta} + \dfrac{1}{\sin \beta}.$

★6. An Explanation. The tremendous number and variety of trigonometric identities certainly must leave the student surprised, if not absolutely stunned. However there is a simple explanation for this state of affairs.

Among the six trigonometric functions only one of them is really necessary.

By this statement we mean that if we pick one of them, such as the sine, all of the other trigonometric functions can be expressed in terms of it, hence special names for the other trigonometric functions are not really needed. In case $\sin\theta$ is chosen as the necessary function, the other five functions are obtained thus:

$$\cos\theta = \pm\sqrt{1-\sin^2\theta}, \qquad \sec\theta = \frac{1}{\cos\theta} = \pm\frac{1}{\sqrt{1-\sin^2\theta}},$$

$$\tan\theta = \frac{\sin\theta}{\cos\theta} = \pm\frac{\sin\theta}{\sqrt{1-\sin^2\theta}}, \qquad \csc\theta = \frac{1}{\sin\theta}.$$

$$\cot\theta = \frac{\cos\theta}{\sin\theta} = \pm\frac{\sqrt{1-\sin^2\theta}}{\sin\theta},$$

By similar manipulations it can be shown that any one of the other five trigonometric functions can be taken as the building block out of which the remaining ones can be constructed.

Why then do we have six trigonometric functions when just one would suffice? Because with just one trigonometric function many of the formulas and theorems from trigonometry would appear to be complicated and ugly. By using all six of the trigonometric functions the same formulas and theorems reveal themselves as simple and beautiful.

EXERCISE 25

Express each of the trigonometric functions of θ as a function of (*a*) $\cos\theta$, (*b*) $\tan\theta$, (*c*) $\cot\theta$, (*d*) $\csc\theta$, (*e*) $\sec\theta$.

★★7. A Principle of Duality for Trigonometric Identities. Let us consider the identity

$$\frac{\cos C - \sin C}{\cos C + \sin C} = \frac{\cot C - 1}{\cot C + 1} \tag{30}$$

which appears as Problem 2 in Exercise 24. If in this identity we replace each trigonometric function by its cofunction (see Definition 2 of Chapter 1) we have the equation

$$\frac{\sin C - \cos C}{\sin C + \cos C} = \frac{\tan C - 1}{\tan C + 1}. \tag{31}$$

Is this equation an identity? Of course we could try to settle this question by proving directly that (31) is an identity. But it would be much simpler and prettier if we could say that (31) is an identity because it was obtained from the known identity (30) by changing each trigonometric function into its cofunction. This is indeed the case, as we will shortly prove.

Definition 3. *If in an equation each trigonometric function which appears is replaced by its cofunction, the new equation obtained is called the dual of the original equation.*

Example 8. Equation (31) is the dual of (30), and (30) is the dual of (31).

Example 9. Theorem 1 of this chapter gives eight basic identities, equations (14) through (21). Referring to these equations:

Equation (16) is the dual of (15),
Equation (18) is the dual of (17),
Equation (21) is the dual of (20).

If we dualize (19), $\sin^2\theta + \cos^2\theta = 1$, we find $\cos^2\theta + \sin^2\theta = 1$ which is really identical with (19), except for the trivial interchange in the order of addition on the left side. Such an equation is called *self-dual.*

Definition 4. *If the dual of an equation differs only in a trivial way from the primitive (original) equation, then the equation is said to be self-dual.*

Example 10. Equation (14), $\tan\theta = 1/\cot\theta$, is self-dual because the dual of this equation is $\cot\theta = 1/\tan\theta$, and both of these equations are equivalent to $\cot\theta\tan\theta = 1$, so that they differ only in a trivial way.

Theorem 2 (The duality principle). *If an equation involving a single angle is an identity then its dual is also an identity.*

Thus the list of identities in Exercise 23 and 24 could easily be lengthened by merely including the dual of each identity (if it is not already in the list, and if it is not self-dual).

Proof of Theorem 2. We first remark that in Theorem 1, which gives the eight basic identities, two of these identities are self-dual and the remaining six can be paired into three sets of dual pairs. Thus if we take any one of these basic identities, its dual is also an identity.

Now suppose that A is an identity and D is its dual. The proof of A can be given, using only the identities of Theorem 1, since all identities in a single angle can be proved on the basis of these eight basic ones. If we dualize each equation in each step of this proof, we again get a valid chain of steps, because the dual of each of the identities of Theorem 1 is again an identity. But this dualized proof is just the proof of D, the dual of the identity A. Q.E.D.

Example 11. Let us consider a proof and its dual.

$$\begin{aligned}
(32) \qquad & \sin^4 A - \cos^4 A + \frac{2\cot^2 A}{\csc^2 A} = 1, \\
&= (\sin^2 A)^2 - \cos^4 A + 2\frac{\cos^2 A}{\sin^2 A}\sin^2 A \\
&= (1 - \cos^2 A)^2 - \cos^4 A + 2\cos^2 A \\
&= 1 - 2\cos^2 A + \cos^4 A - \cos^4 A + 2\cos^2 A \\
&= 1 \qquad\qquad = 1.
\end{aligned}$$

Now if we dualize this identity and its proof we have:

$$\begin{aligned}
(33) \qquad & \cos^4 A - \sin^4 A + \frac{2\tan^2 A}{\sec^2 A} = 1, \\
&= (\cos^2 A)^2 - \sin^4 A + 2\frac{\sin^2 A}{\cos^2 A}\cos^2 A \\
&= (1 - \sin^2 A)^2 - \sin^4 A + 2\sin^2 A \\
&= 1 - 2\sin^2 A + \sin^4 A - \sin^4 A + 2\sin^2 A \\
&= 1 \qquad\qquad = 1.
\end{aligned}$$

The principle of duality states that it is not necessary to prove that (33) is an identity. Once (32) has been proved to be an identity, then (33) must also be one, and a separate proof is not needed.

★★ EXERCISE 26

In all of the following problems, the statement "(x)" means the identity of Problem number (x) in Exercise 24.

1. Prove that (23) is the dual of (14), (27) is the dual of (17), and (29) is the dual of (3).

2. Prove that (30) is the dual of (1), (48) is the dual of (40), and (31) is the dual of (16)

3. Prove that each one of the identities (6), (11), (41), and (43) is self-dual.

4. Find any other identities that are self-dual in Exercise 24.

5. Show that (8) can be obtained from (1) by multiplying both sides of (1) by $\cos B$.

6. Show that squaring both sides of (4) gives (41).

7. Show that (32) can be obtained from (10) by multiplying both the numerator and the denominator on both sides by $\cot \theta$.

8. Show that (23) can be obtained from (10) by multiplying both sides by $\cot \theta$.

CHAPTER 6

OBLIQUE TRIANGLES

1. Objective. In Chapters 1 and 3 we learned how to solve a right triangle. Of course not all triangles have a right angle, so we must learn how to solve a triangle when it is not a right triangle. Such triangles are called *oblique* triangles. In this chapter we will prove two useful and very pretty theorems, (1) the law of cosines and (2) the law of sines. Together these two theorems will enable us to solve any triangle.

As a rough working rule, a triangle can be solved if any three items are known. Table 1 shows the various possibilities.

TABLE 1

Case	Symbol	Items Given	Law to Be Used in Solving the Triangle	Discussed in Section
I	*SSS*	Three sides	Cosine law	3
II	*SAS*	Two sides and the included angle	Cosine law	3
III	*SSA*	Two sides and the angle opposite one of the sides	Sine law	5
IV	*ASA*	Two angles and the included side	Sine law	4
V	*AAA*	Three angles	Cannot be solved	

In Case V one should not expect to solve for the sides, because two triangles can have the same angles (say 20°, 50°, and 110°) and still not be congruent. Of course they must be similar triangles. Our inability to solve the triangle in this case can also be explained by the fact that *three* items were not really given but only *two*, because knowing any two angles of a triangle, the third angle is automatically determined by the equation $A + B + C = 180°$, valid for the angles of any triangle.

2. A Distance Formula from Analytic Geometry. Let $P(2, 1)$ and $Q(6, 4)$ be two points in the plane, and suppose that we wish to compute the distance between P and Q. If lines are drawn parallel to

FIGURE 1

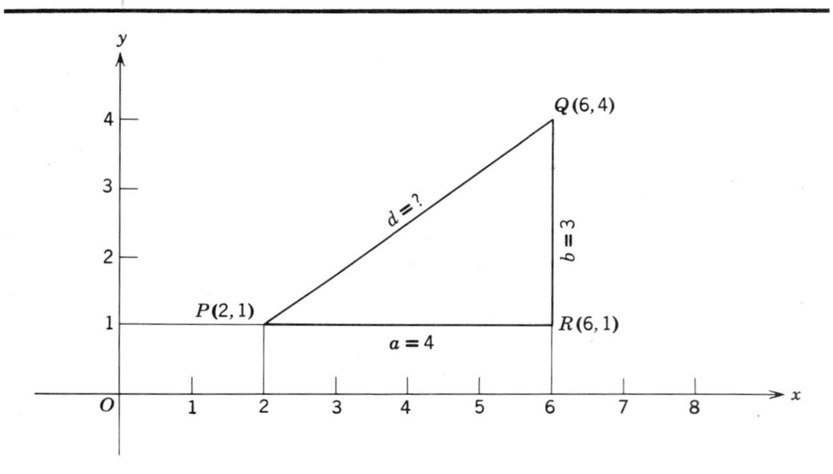

the coordinate axes through P and Q as indicated in Fig. 1, then the triangle PQR is a right triangle. Further, the sides have lengths

$$a = PR = 6 - 2 = 4$$

and

$$b = RQ = 4 - 1 = 3.$$

Therefore the distance between P and Q is the hypotenuse of triangle PQR and is given by

$$d = \sqrt{(6 - 2)^2 + (4 - 1)^2} = \sqrt{16 + 9} = 5.$$

The only thing left is to replace the numbers with letters, obtaining a general formula, and then to prove that the formula is valid for any pair of points P and Q.

Theorem 1. *If $P(x_1, y_1)$ and $Q(x_2, y_2)$ are arbitrary points in a plane, then the distance between P and Q is given by*

$$d = \sqrt{(x_2 - x_1)^2 + (y_2 - y_1)^2}. \tag{1}$$

Proof. As shown in Fig. 2, draw a vertical line through P and a horizontal line through Q, and let R be their point of intersection. Let S be the intersection point with the x-axis of PR (extended if necessary) and let T be the intersection point with the y-axis of the line QR (extended if necessary). Then by Theorem 1 of Chapter 4, on directed distances, the sides of the triangle PQR are given by

FIGURE 2

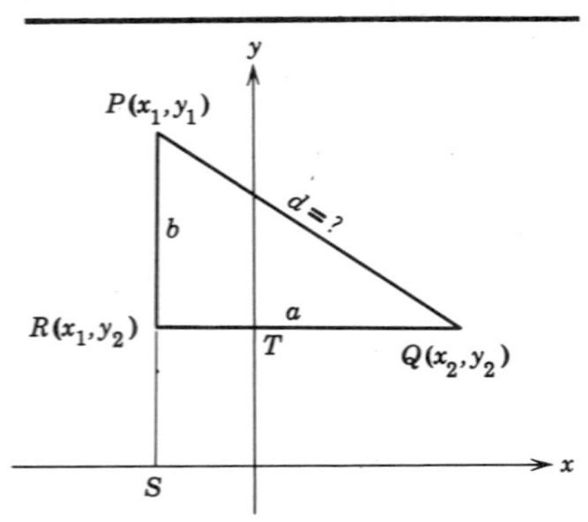

$$(2) \qquad a = RQ = RT + TQ = -TR + TQ,$$

and

$$(3) \qquad b = RP = RS + SP = -SR + SP.$$

But the coordinates are merely directed distances, so that $TR = x_1$, $TQ = x_2$, $SR = y_2$, and $SP = y_1$. Whence (2) and (3) give

$$(4) \quad a = -x_1 + x_2 = x_2 - x_1, \qquad \text{and} \qquad b = -y_2 + y_1 = y_1 - y_2.$$

Since $d = \sqrt{a^2 + b^2}$ and since $(y_1 - y_2)^2 = (y_2 - y_1)^2$, equation (4) gives equation (1). Q.E.D.

The formula (1) is easy to remember because it is just a disguised form of the Pythagorean Theorem.

EXERCISE 27

In each of the first 14 problems find the distance between the two points *without* making a drawing. Then make a careful drawing to scale, and check your answer by measuring the distance with a ruler.

1. (1, 1) and (6, 13).
2. (7, 6) and (4, 2).
3. (2, −4) and (−1, 0).
4. (−5, 1) and (−1, 4).
5. (−2, −2) and (4, 6).
6. (10, 1) and (−8, 1).
7. (−3, −1) and (−9, −1).
8. (5, 5) and (−6, −6).
9. (8, 10) and (1, 5).
10. (−2, −3) and (−3, −2).
11. (4, −3) and (−7, −8).
12. (9, 11) and (2, 6).
13. (−4, −5) and (−5, −4).
14. (2, −3) and (−3, −5).
15. Is formula (1) still valid, if the subscripts 1 and 2 are interchanged?
16. Is it always possible to select the letters P and Q so that $x_2 \geqq x_1$ and $y_2 \geqq y_1$?
17. How does formula (1) simplify if the point P is at the origin?

3. The Law of Cosines. This law is given by

Theorem 2. *In any triangle*

$$c^2 = a^2 + b^2 - 2ab \cos C. \tag{5}$$

This states that the square of one side is equal to the sum of the squares of the other two sides minus twice the product of these two sides and the cosine of their included angle. In (5) the angle C is of course the angle opposite the side c.

FIGURE 3

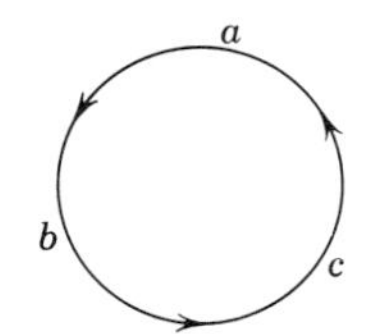

Since the unknown side could be either a, b, or c, there are two other forms for (5), namely:

$$a^2 = b^2 + c^2 - 2bc \cos A, \tag{6}$$

and

$$b^2 = c^2 + a^2 - 2ca \cos B. \tag{7}$$

These two formulas can be obtained from formula (5) by cyclic permutations of the letters a, b, and c. In a *cyclic permutation* of these letters, a is changed into b, b is changed into c, and c is changed into a, and the same sort of changes are also made on the letters A, B, and C. The diagram of Fig. 3 should prove helpful in making these changes. Observe that by a cyclic permutation of the letters, (5) will give (6) and (6) will give (7). Thus these last two formulas will be proved valid once we have proved (5).

FIGURE 4

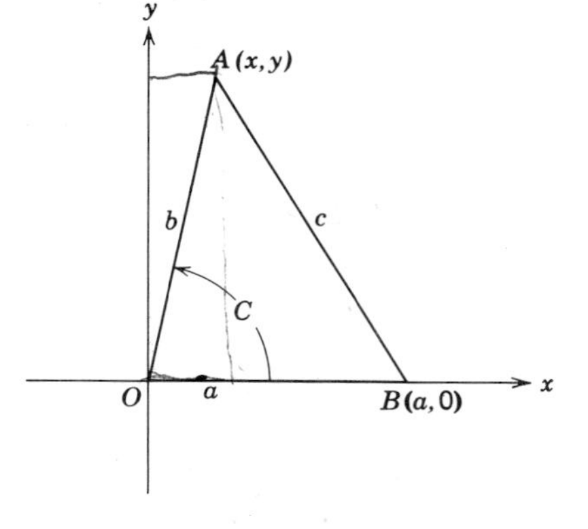

Proof of Theorem 2. Place the triangle on a rectangular coordinate system with the vertex C at the origin and the side a running along the positive x-axis as shown in Fig 4. Obviously the coordinates of B are $(a, 0)$. To find the coordinates (x, y) of A, recall that by the definition of the trigonometric functions

$$\sin C = \frac{y}{r}, \qquad \text{and} \qquad \cos C = \frac{x}{r}. \tag{8}$$

In this case $r = b$ so (8) yields $x = b \cos C$, and $y = b \sin C$. Thus the coordinates for A are $(b \cos C, b \sin C)$. Now apply formula (1) of

b cos C = a/b

Theorem 1 to find the square of the distance from B to A. We find from (1)

$$\begin{aligned} c^2 &= (b\cos C - a)^2 + (b\sin C - 0)^2 \\ &= b^2\cos^2 C - 2ab\cos C + a^2 + b^2\sin^2 C \\ &= a^2 + b^2(\cos^2 C + \sin^2 C) - 2ab\cos C \\ &= a^2 + b^2 - 2ab\cos C. \end{aligned}$$

Q.E.D.

If three sides of a triangle are given, then the angle C can be found using

Theorem 3. *In any triangle*

$$\cos C = \frac{a^2 + b^2 - c^2}{2ab}. \tag{9}$$

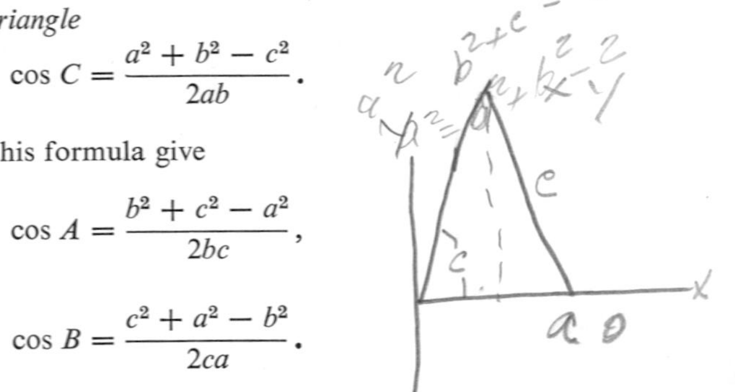

Cyclic permutations of this formula give

$$\cos A = \frac{b^2 + c^2 - a^2}{2bc}, \tag{10}$$

and

$$\cos B = \frac{c^2 + a^2 - b^2}{2ca}. \tag{11}$$

Proof. By transposing terms in (5) we find $2ab\cos C = a^2 + b^2 - c^2$. Then dividing both sides of this equation by $2ab$ yields (9). Q.E.D.

Formula (5) is easy to remember because it is a generalization of the Pythagorean Theorem. Indeed this formula differs from $c^2 = a^2 + b^2$,

FIGURE 5

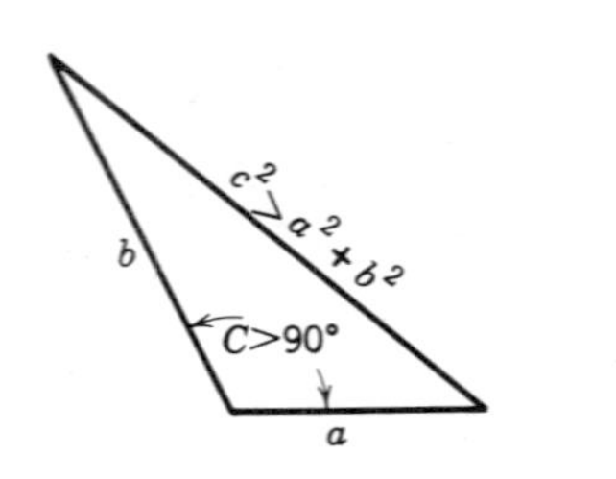

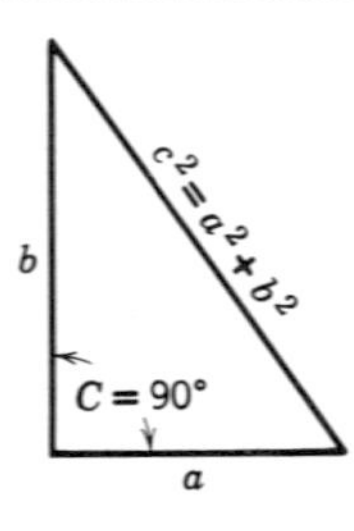

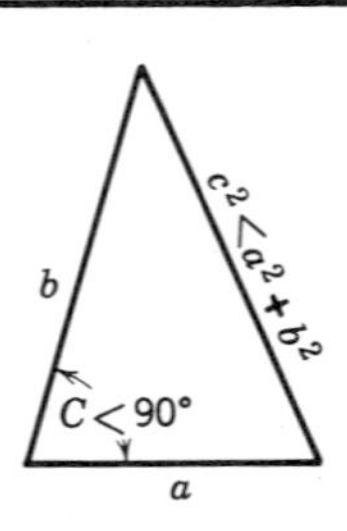

only in the extra term tacked on at the end. When $C = 90°$, $\cos C = 0$ and equation (5) *is* the Pythagorean Theorem for a right triangle. When $0 < C < 90°$, $\cos C$ is positive and something must be *subtracted* from $a^2 + b^2$ to get c^2. When $90° < C < 180°$, $\cos C$ is negative and now something is *added* to $a^2 + b^2$. These possibilities are illustrated in Fig. 5.

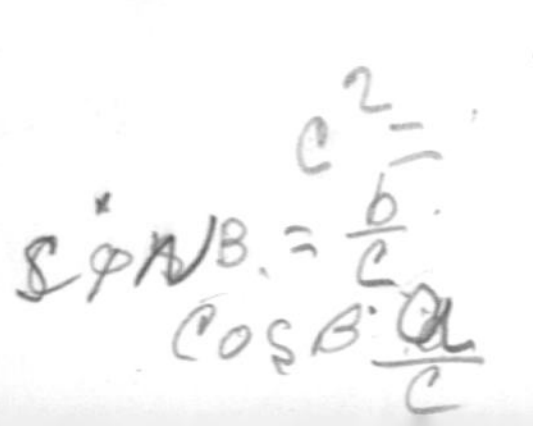

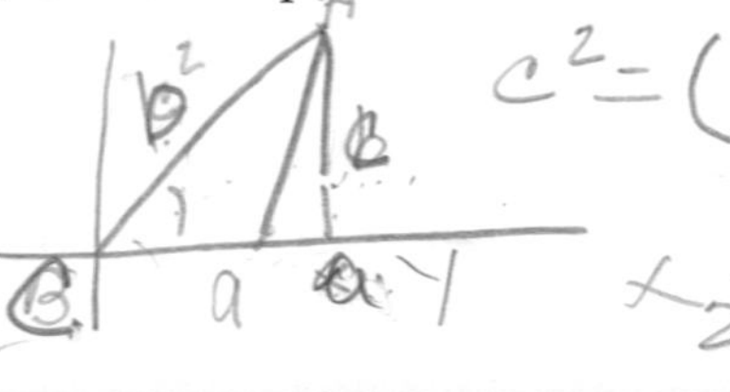

Example 1. Given that $a = 5$, $b = 8$, $C = 60°$ find the third side c of the triangle.

Solution.

$$\begin{aligned} c^2 &= a^2 + b^2 - 2ab \cos C \\ &= 5^2 + 8^2 - 2 \times 5 \times 8 \cos 60 \\ &= 25 + 64 - 40 = 49, \\ c &= 7. \end{aligned}$$

Example 2. Find to the nearest minute the angles A and B in the triangle of the preceding example.

Solution.

$$\cos A = \frac{b^2 + c^2 - a^2}{2bc} = \frac{8^2 + 7^2 - 5^2}{2 \times 8 \times 7} = \frac{64 + 49 - 25}{112} = \frac{88}{112} = .7857,$$

$$A = 38°\ 13'.$$

$$\cos B = \frac{c^2 + a^2 - b^2}{2ca} = \frac{7^2 + 5^2 - 8^2}{2 \times 7 \times 5} = \frac{49 + 25 - 64}{70} = \frac{10}{70} = .1429,$$

$$B = 81°\ 47'.$$

Check. $A + B + C = 38°\ 13' + 81°\ 47' + 60° = 180°\ 0'$.

EXERCISE 28

1. How does equation (5) simplify when $C = 180°$? Draw the triangle in this case. Is (5) still valid?

2. Do Problem 1 with $C = 0°$.

In Problems 3 through 8 find the unknown side.

3. $a = 7$, $b = 8$, $C = 120°$.

4. $a = 10$, $b = 6$, $C = 120°$.

5. $b = 5\sqrt{2}$, $c = 7$, $A = 135°$.

6. $b = 17$, $c = 7\sqrt{2}$, $A = 135°$.

7. $a = .012$, $c = .023$, $B = 24°\ 30'$.

8. $a = .080$, $c = .070$, $B = 72°$.

In Problems 9 and 10 find all of the angles of the triangle to the nearest 10 minutes.

9. $a = 5$, $b = 7$, $c = 11$.

10. $a = 600$, $b = 700$, $c = 1200$.

★ **11.** There are exactly six different nondegenerate triangles with integer sides, for which $a = 16$ and $B = 60°$. Find them.

★ **12.** There are exactly three different nondegenerate triangles with integer sides, for which $c = 18$ and $A = 60°$. Find them.

13. In Washington, D.C., Constitution Avenue and Pennsylvania Avenue intersect at an angle of 19°. The White House is on Pennsylvania Avenue 5600 ft from this point of intersection. The National Academy of Sciences is on Constitution Avenue 8600 ft from this intersection. Both buildings lie on the same side of 4th Street which runs perpendicular to Constitution Avenue at the intersection. How far is the White House from the National Academy of Sciences?

14. The Lincoln Memorial in Washington, D.C. is 4300 ft due west of the Washington Monument. The Pentagon is 7100 ft S 15° W from the Lincoln Memorial. How far is the Pentagon from the Washington Monument?

15. Two cars start at the same time from an intersection of two highways. The car on one highway averages 32 mph while the car on the other highway is driven steadily at 44 mph. If the highways are straight and the angle of intersection is 28°, how far apart are the cars at the end of 1 hr and 15 min?

16. If in Problem 15 the slower car left the intersection at noon and the faster car left the intersection at 12:30 P.M., how far apart would they be at 3 P.M. of the same day?

★ **17.** Starting from the law of cosines prove that in any triangle

$$a^2 + b^2 + c^2 = 2(ab \cos C + bc \cos A + ca \cos B).$$

★ **18.** Prove that in any triangle

$$\frac{\cos A}{a} + \frac{\cos B}{b} + \frac{\cos C}{c} = \frac{a^2 + b^2 + c^2}{2abc}.$$

4. The Law of Sines. This law is given by

Theorem 4. *In any triangle*

$$\frac{a}{\sin A} = \frac{b}{\sin B} = \frac{c}{\sin C}. \tag{12}$$

This states that in any triangle the sides are proportional to the sines of the opposite angles.

Since the lettering of the sides of an oblique triangle is arbitrary it is sufficient to prove only the first half of the theorem, namely

$$\frac{a}{\sin A} = \frac{b}{\sin B}. \tag{13}$$

There are two cases to consider, either (1) both of the angles A and B are acute, or (2) one of the angles is obtuse, and in this case we label the obtuse angle A. The two possibilities are shown in Fig. 6.

We first drop a perpendicular from the vertex of the angle C to the opposite side, which in Case 2 must be extended. Let h be the length of this perpendicular line segment, and let D be the point of intersection with the opposite side.

FIGURE 6

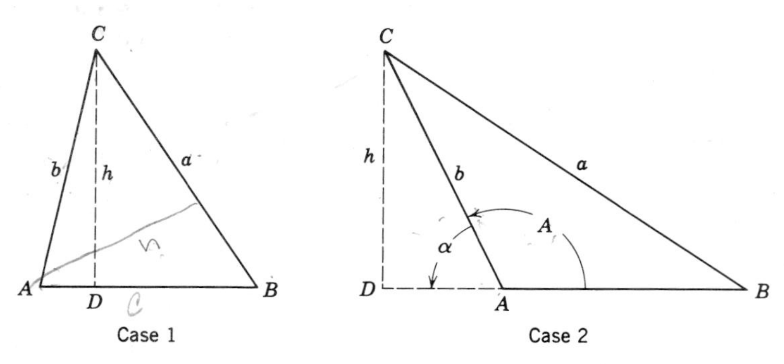

Case 1. Triangles ADC and BDC are right triangles. Therefore

$$\frac{h}{a} = \sin B, \qquad \frac{h}{b} = \sin A. \tag{14}$$

Hence

$$h = a \sin B, \qquad h = b \sin A. \tag{15}$$

Since h is the same in both equations,

$$a \sin B = b \sin A. \tag{16}$$

If we divide both sides of (16) by the product $\sin A \sin B$, we obtain (13).

Case 2. In this case triangles ADC and BDC are still right triangles, but instead of (14) we must write

$$\frac{h}{a} = \sin B, \qquad \frac{h}{b} = \sin \alpha, \tag{17}$$

since α is the angle in triangle ADC. However, $\alpha + A = 180°$, so α is the related angle of A. Since A is in Q.II, $\sin A$ is positive and therefore $\sin \alpha = \sin A$. When this substitution is made in the second equation of the set (17), this set is identical with the set (14). Then the rest of the proof in Case 2 proceeds exactly as in Case 1. Q.E.D.

Example 3. Solve the triangle if $a = 28$, $A = 135°$, and $B = 30°$.
Solution. By the law of sines $b/\sin B = a/\sin A$. Therefore,

$$b = \frac{a \sin B}{\sin A} = \frac{28 \sin 30°}{\sin 135°} = \frac{28 \times 1/2}{\sqrt{2}/2} = \frac{28}{\sqrt{2}} = 14\sqrt{2} = 20.$$

(with 2-figure accuracy).

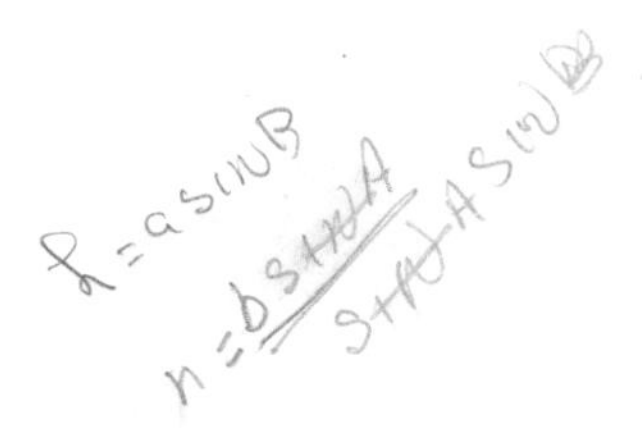

Since $C = 180° - (A + B) = 180° - 165° = 15°$, then

$$c = \frac{a \sin C}{\sin A} = \frac{28 \sin 15°}{\sin 135°} = \frac{28 \times .2588}{\sqrt{2}/2} = 28\sqrt{2} \times .2588 = 10\,.$$

(with 2-figure accuracy).

As a check we can compute c using b, thus

$$c = \frac{b \sin C}{\sin B} = \frac{20 \sin 15°}{\sin 30°} = \frac{20 \times .2588}{1/2} = 10\,.$$

(with 2-figure accuracy).

Example 4. Solve the triangle, given $b = 1984.0$, $A = 19°\ 14.0'$, and $C = 25°\ 51.8'$.

Solution. Here the data is given with 5-figure accuracy so it is desirable to use logarithms. First we find the third angle.

$$B = 180° - (A + C) = 180° - 45°\ 5.8' = 134°\ 54.2'.$$

$$a = \frac{b \sin A}{\sin B} = \frac{1984.0 \sin 19°\ 14.0'}{\sin 134°\ 54.2'}.$$

$\log 1984.0$	$= 3.29754$
$\log \sin 19°\ 14.0'$	$= 9.51774 - 10$
$\log$ numerator	$= 12.81528 - 10$
$\log \sin 45°\ 5.8'$	$= 9.85022 - 10$
$\log a$	$= 2.96506$
a	$= 922.70$

$$c = \frac{b \sin C}{\sin B} = \frac{1984.0 \sin 25°\ 51.8'}{\sin 134°\ 54.2'}$$

$\log 1984.0$	$= 3.29754$
$\log \sin 25°\ 51.8'$	$= 9.63971 - 10$
$\log$ numerator	$= 12.93725 - 10$
$\log \sin 45°\ 5.8'$	$= 9.85022 - 10$
$\log c$	$= 3.08703$
c	$= 1221.9$

EXERCISE 29

In Problems 1 through 4 find the sides of the triangle to two significant figures without using logarithms. Check your results by making an accurate drawing.

1. $a = 100$, $B = 60°$, $C = 45°$.

2. $a = 80$, $B = 45°$, $C = 30°$.

3. $b = 50$, $C = 120°$, $A = 45°$.

4. $c = 25$, $A = 130°$, $B = 20°$.

In Problems 5 through 8 use logarithms to find the sides of the triangle to five significant figures.

5. $b = .046464$, $A = 28°\ 39.0'$, $C = 39°\ 28.0'$.

6. $b = 888.88$, $A = 12°\ 34.5'$, $B = 23°\ 45.6'$.

7. $c = 25.252$, $A = 43°\ 21.0'$, $B = 54°\ 32.1'$.

8. $c = 7676.7$, $B = 19°\ 59.0'$, $C = 18°\ 12.0'$.

9. A vertical building stands on a street that slopes downward at an angle of $8°\ 20'$. At a point 125 ft down this street from the base of the building, the angle of elevation of the top of the building is $59°\ 30'$. How tall is the building?

10. A tree on a sloping hill casts a shadow 135 ft straight down the hill. If the hill slopes downward at an angle of 12° 30′ and the angle of elevation of the sun is 25° 40′, how tall is the tree?

11. The angles of elevation of an approaching airplane from two antiaircraft guns are 78° 15′ and 53° 25′. If these guns are 878 ft apart, and if the airplane is in a vertical plane with these guns, how far is the airplane from the nearest gun?

12. Two lookout towers A and B are 5.00 miles apart with A due west of B. A column of smoke is sighted from A with a bearing N 75° 10′ E, and from B with a bearing N 53° 20′ E. How far is the fire from the nearest tower?

13. Two points A and B on one bank of a river are 95 ft apart. A point C across the river is located so that angle CAB is 75° and angle CBA is 80°. How far is C from A?

5. The Ambiguous Case. Suppose that we are asked to solve a triangle, given two sides and the angle opposite one of them. To be specific, suppose that we are given $a = 35.00$, $b = 50.00$, and $A = 30° 0′$, as illustrated in Fig. 7. Our attempt to draw this figure is shown in Fig. 8. We first draw angle A with the base line extended. We then lay off the known side $b = AC = 50.00$. Then to locate the side opposite the angle A, we take point C as a center and with a radius $a = 35.00$ we describe an arc of a circle. This circular arc represents all possible positions for the end point B of the line segment opposite the angle A. But B must also be on the base line, so B is at the point of intersection of this circular arc and the base line. In this case there are two such points of intersection which we denote by B and B' (read B prime).

FIGURE 7

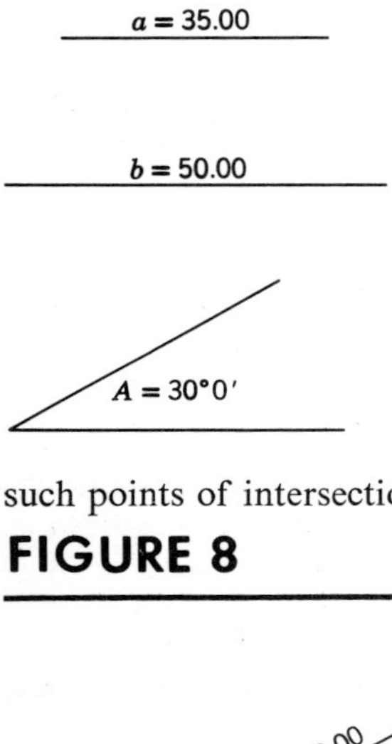

$a = 35.00$

$b = 50.00$

$A = 30°0′$

FIGURE 8

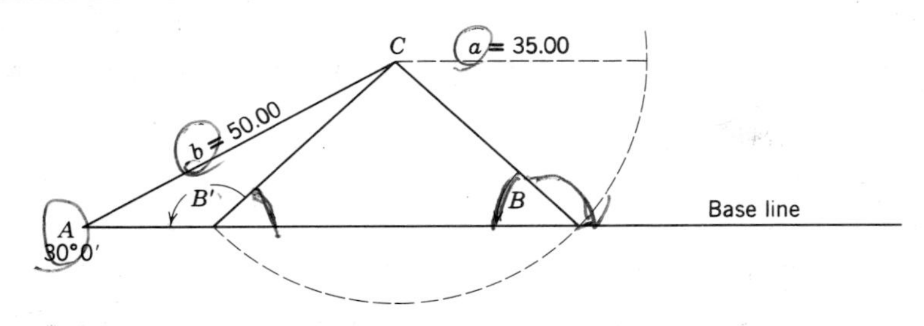

Therefore (to our great surprise) there are two triangles, ABC and $AB'C$, not congruent to each other and each one has $a = 35.00$, $b = 50.00$ and

$A = 30° 0'$. To complete the solution of this problem, we must solve each of these triangles.

Case 1. Triangle ABC. From (13) we have

$$\sin B = \frac{b \sin A}{a} \tag{18}$$

$$= \frac{50.00 \sin 30°}{35.00} = .7143\,.$$

Since in this case the angle B is acute, we find $B = 45° \ 35'$. Then $C = 180° - (30° \ 0' + 45° \ 35') = 104° \ 25'$. Finally

$$c = \frac{a \sin C}{\sin A} = \frac{35.00 \sin 104° \ 25'}{\sin 30°} = 70.00 \times .9685 = 67.80.$$

Case 2. Triangle $AB'C$. In this case the angle B' is obtuse. The law of sines is still applicable, so with B' replacing B, equation (18) is still valid. In other words, without any new computation $\sin B' = \sin B$. Therefore B is the related angle of B'. This can also be seen from the fact that the triangle $B'CB$ is isosceles. Then $B' = 180° - B = 180° - 45° \ 35' = 134° \ 25'$. Finally $C = 180° - (A + B') = 180° - 164° \ 25' = 15° \ 35'$, so that

$$c = \frac{a \sin C}{\sin A} = 70.00 \times .2686 = 18.80.$$

Now that we have solved this specific example in complete detail, let us return to the general situation. Suppose again that we are given the sides a and b and the angle A, and we are to determine the number of different (noncongruent) triangles with the given sides and angle. Figure 9 shows the various possibilities when the angle A is acute. The important thing to observe is that the number of triangles depends on the magnitude of the side a.

1. If a is too short there will be no triangles.
2. If a is just right there will be one triangle.
3. If a is somewhat longer there will be two triangles.
4. If a is too long there will be one triangle.

Of course, these statements about the magnitude of a are vague, but it is easy to make them precise.

Consider Case 2 where a is "just right." This means that the circular arc is tangent to the base line so that the triangle ABC is a right triangle. Then $a/b = \sin A$ and "just right" means $a = b \sin A$. Consequently in Case 1 "too short" means $a < b \sin A$, and in Cases 3 and 4, $a > b \sin A$.

Obviously, in Case 4, $a \geqq b$, so in Case 3 we have $b \sin A < a < b$. These results are summarized in Table 2. Because the number of triangles may be none, one, or two depending on a, the case *SSA* is called the ambiguous case.

FIGURE 9

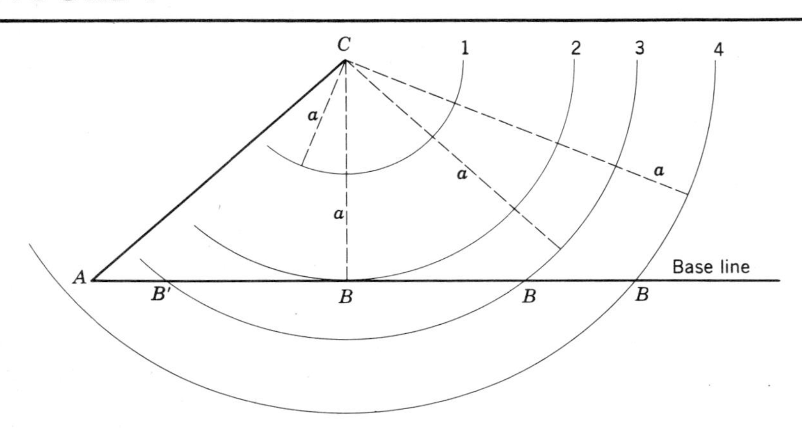

The situation is considerably simpler if the angle A is obtuse. We leave it to the student to examine Fig. 10 which shows the two possibilities in this case, and to convince himself that Table 3 is correct.

TABLE 2

If angle A is acute:

Case	Condition on a	Number of Triangles
1	$a < b \sin A$	None
2	$a = b \sin A$	One right triangle
3	$b \sin A < a < b$	Two
4	$b \leqq a$	One

TABLE 3

If angle A is obtuse:

Case	Condition on a	Number of Triangles
1	$a \leqq b$	None
2	$b < a$	One

FIGURE 10

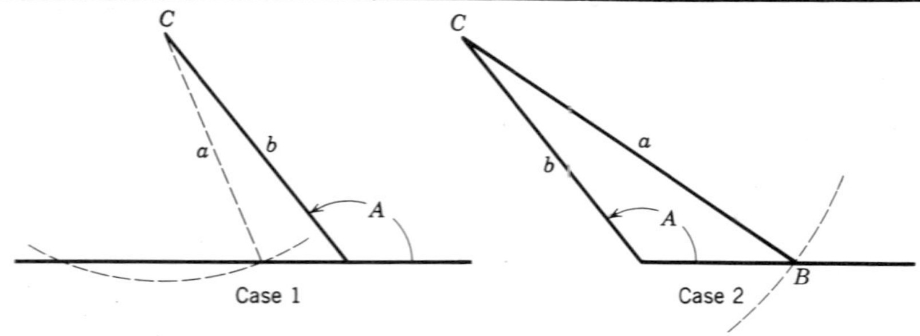

Example 5. How many different (noncongruent) triangles can be drawn with $A = 76° \, 10'$, $a = 107.5$, and $b = 111.1$.

Solution.

$$b \sin A = 111.1 \times .9710 = 107.9,$$
$$a = 107.5 < 107.9 = b \sin A.$$

Therefore there are no triangles with the given angle and sides.

It is not really necessary to memorize the condition $a < b \sin A$, because if we try to solve the triangle in this case we will soon run into a dead end which automatically signals to us that there are no triangles. If we try to solve the triangle of this example we have

$$\sin B = \frac{b \sin A}{a} = \frac{111.1 \times \sin 76° \, 10'}{107.5}$$

log 111.1	=	2.04571
log sin 76° 10′	=	9.98722 − 10
log numerator	=	12.03293 − 10
log 107.5	=	2.03141
log sin B	=	10.00152 − 10

Since $\log \sin B = .00152$, a positive number, $\sin B > 1$, and therefore the angle B does not exist.

Example 6. How many different triangles can be drawn with $A = 45°$, $b = \sqrt{5}$, $a = 3\sqrt{2/7}$.

Solution. Since $18/7 < 5$, taking square roots on both sides gives $3\sqrt{2/7} < \sqrt{5}$, or $a < b$, so Case 4 is ruled out.

We next examine Case 1, putting the equation in the form of a question:

$$a \overset{?}{<} b \sin A \tag{19}$$

(read, is a less than $b \sin A$?). Making the appropriate substitutions we have

$$3\sqrt{\frac{2}{7}} \overset{?}{<} \sqrt{5}\,\frac{\sqrt{2}}{2}, \tag{20}$$

or on squaring

$$\frac{18}{7} \overset{?}{<} \frac{10}{4} \tag{21}$$

But $18 \times 4 > 7 \times 10$. Since all of our steps are reversible the inequality signs in (19), (20), and (21) should be reversed. Thus we have Case 2, and there are two triangles.

EXERCISE 30

In Problems 1 through 10 determine the number of different (noncongruent) triangles that can be drawn with the given data. Whenever the angle B exists, compute it to the nearest minute.

1. $a = 75, \quad b = 85, \quad A = 135°$. **2.** $a = 50, \quad b = 70, \quad A = 120°$.

3. $a = 90, \quad b = 45, \quad A = 150°$. **4.** $a = 75, \quad b = 50\sqrt{2}, \quad A = 135°$.

5. $a = 40, \quad b = 70, \quad A = 30°$. **6.** $a = 30, \quad b = 25\sqrt{2}, \quad A = 45°$.

7. $a = 7\sqrt{13}, b = 16\sqrt{5}, A = 45°$. **8.** $a = 9\sqrt{17}, b = 12\sqrt{13}, A = 60°$.

9. $a = 11\sqrt{3}, b = 19, \quad A = 60°$. **10.** $a = 15, \quad b = 14, \quad A = 30°$.

In Problems 11 through 14 determine the number of different triangles that can be drawn with the given data, and solve each triangle completely, using logarithms.

11. $b = 4646.4, \quad c = 8080.0, \quad B = 33° 33.3'$.

12. $b = 2020.2, \quad c = 5555.7, \quad B = 18° 18.1'$.

13. $a = 5.5557, \quad c = 1.9302, \quad C = 20° 20.2'$.

14. $a = .0050127, c = .0019966, C = 23° 27.8'$.

15. A vertical tree 68.5 ft tall grows on a sloping hill. From a point 157 ft from the base of this tree, measured straight down the hill, the tree subtends an angle of 21° 20′. Find the angle that the sloping hill makes with the horizontal plane.

16. In order to measure the angle a sloping hill makes with the horizontal plane, a man sights his transit on a small stone S lying on the hill and finds the angle of elevation to be 7° 40′. The transit is 5.00 ft above a point T on the ground, and the distance TS straight up the hill is 123 ft. What is the angle that the hill makes with the horizontal plane?

17. If the angle subtended at the earth by a line joining Venus and the sun is 31°, and if Venus is 6.8×10^7 mi from the sun, and the earth is 9.3×10^7 mi from the sun, what is the distance from the earth to Venus? (Two answers are possible.)

18. A lighthouse is 23 mi N 55° E of a dock. A ship leaves the dock at 1:00 P.M. and sails due east at a speed of 15 mph. Find the time to the nearest minute when the ship will be 18 mi from the lighthouse. (Two answers are possible.)

19. The sides of a parallelogram are 15.0 in. and 11.0 in. and the longer diagonal makes an angle of 18° 50′ with the longer side. Find the length of the longer diagonal.

CHAPTER 7

ADDITION FORMULAS AND RELATED TOPICS

1. Objective. The student knows that if A, B, and C are any numbers then

$$C(A + B) = CA + CB. \tag{1}$$

Hence he expects by analogy, that if A and B are any angles then

$$\cos (A + B) = \cos A + \cos B. \tag{2}$$

Unfortunately formula (2) is **FALSE.** To prove that (2) is not an identity, we need only one counterexample; that is, one pair of angles A and B for which the two sides of this equation are not equal. Suppose we take $A = 0°$ and $B = 0°$. Then, since $\cos 0° = 1$, the left side of (2) gives

$$\cos (0° + 0°) = \cos 0° = 1,$$

while the right side of (2) gives

$$\cos 0° + \cos 0° = 1 + 1 = 2.$$

Since $1 \neq 2$, equation (2) is not an identity. Our first objective in this chapter is to replace the false identity (2) by the correct one:

$$\cos (A + B) = \cos A \cos B - \sin A \sin B. \tag{3}$$

From this identity it is easy to derive a large number of other important identities. The rest of this chapter is devoted to proving these identities and examining some of their applications. For example, formula (3) can be used to compute $\cos 75°$ by setting $A = 45°$ and $B = 30°$.

Indeed [by formula (3)]

$$\begin{aligned}\cos 75^\circ &= \cos(45^\circ + 30^\circ)\\ &= \cos 45^\circ \cos 30^\circ - \sin 45^\circ \sin 30^\circ\\ &= \frac{\sqrt{2}}{2}\frac{\sqrt{3}}{2} - \frac{\sqrt{2}}{2}\frac{1}{2} = \frac{\sqrt{6}-\sqrt{2}}{4}\\ &= \frac{2.4495 - 1.4142}{4} = \frac{1.0353}{4} = .2588,\end{aligned}$$

and this coincides with the value given in Table B for cos 75°.

The student is warned that in this chapter new and important formulas will come thick and fast, so he should memorize them as they are proved, or he will soon find himself snowed under.

2. The Formula for cos $(A + B)$. The formula in question is given in

Theorem 1. *For all angles A and B*

$$\cos(A + B) = \cos A \cos B - \sin A \sin B. \tag{3}$$

Proof. For simplicity we suppose first that the angles A and B are positive. Draw a circle of radius 1 unit with center at the origin of a rectangular coordinate system (see Fig. 1). Such a circle is called the *unit circle* for brevity. Place the angle A in standard position, and place the angle B so that the vertex of B is also at the origin, and the initial side of the angle B falls on the terminal side of the angle A. Let the radial lines which form the sides of the angles A and B intersect the unit circle at the points P, Q, and R as indicated in the figure. The key to the proof of Theorem 1 lies in the following obvious fact:

If the figure consisting of the unit circle and the three radial lines OP, OQ, and OR is rotated about the origin through any angle, the distance d between the points P and R remains unchanged.

To compute this distance we need the coordinates of the points in question. Clearly we have for P the coordinates (1, 0), since the unit circle has radius 1. Let θ be any angle in standard position and let (x, y) be the coordinates of the point of intersection of the terminal side with the unit circle. Then by definition:

$$\cos\theta = \frac{x}{r}, \qquad \text{and} \qquad \sin\theta = \frac{y}{r}. \tag{4}$$

But for any point on the unit circle, $r = 1$, hence

(5) $$x = \cos \theta, \qquad \text{and} \qquad y = \sin \theta.$$

Applying (5) to the point Q we find the coordinates are $(\cos A, \sin A)$. For the point R the angle in question is $A + B$, so the coordinates of R are $(\cos (A + B), \sin (A + B))$.

FIGURE 1

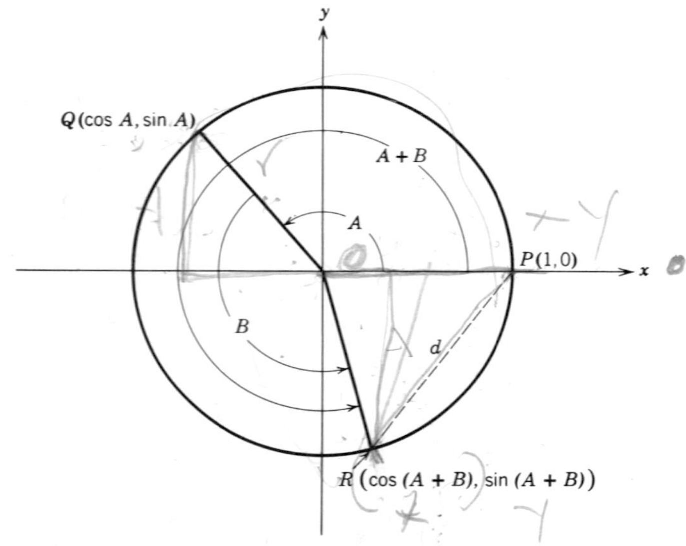

If d denotes the distance from P to R, then formula (1) of Chapter 6 gives

$$d^2 = (x_2 - x_1)^2 + (y_2 - y_1)^2 = [\cos (A + B) - 1]^2 + [\sin (A + B) - 0]^2$$
$$= \cos^2 (A + B) - 2 \cos (A + B) + 1 + \sin^2 (A + B).$$

But $\sin^2 (A + B) + \cos^2 (A + B) = 1$, so the expression for d^2 simplifies to

(6) $$d^2 = 2 - 2 \cos (A + B).$$

We now rotate the figure consisting of the unit circle and the three radial lines OP, OQ, and OR, in a clockwise direction about O, through an angle A. The resulting figure is shown in Fig. 2. Since the rotation was through an angle A, the point Q now falls on the positive x-axis, the radial line OP now makes an angle $-A$ with the positive x-axis, and the radial line OR now makes an angle B with the positive x-axis. Applying (5) to this figure we have $(\cos B, \sin B)$ for the coordinates of R and $(\cos (-A), \sin (-A))$ for the coordinates of P. But, by Theorem 8 of

Chapter 4, $\cos(-A) = \cos A$, and $\sin(-A) = -\sin A$, so the coordinates of P are $(\cos A, -\sin A)$.

FIGURE 2

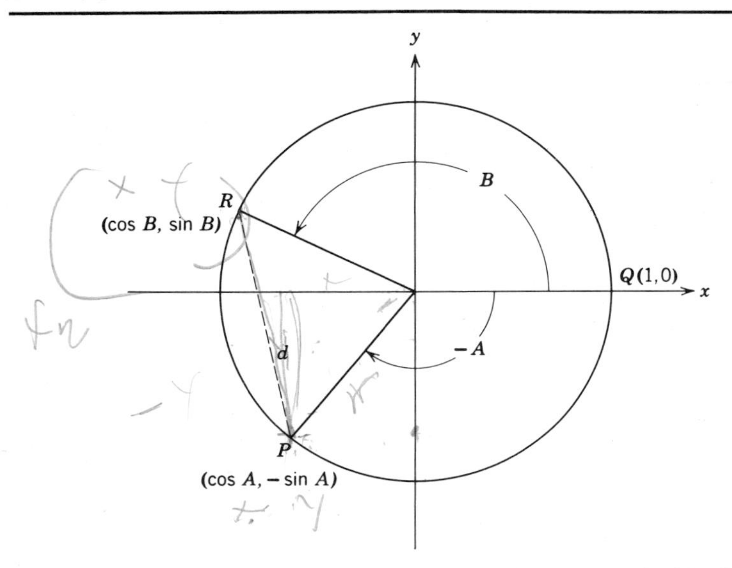

We again compute the distance d from P to R. Formula (1) of Chapter (6) gives

$$d^2 = (x_2 - x_1)^2 + (y_2 - y_1)^2 = (\cos B - \cos A)^2 + (\sin B + \sin A)^2$$
$$= \cos^2 B - 2\cos B\cos A + \cos^2 A + \sin^2 B + 2\sin B\sin A + \sin^2 A.$$

But $\cos^2 B + \sin^2 B = 1$ and $\cos^2 A + \sin^2 A = 1$, so we have for d^2

$$(7) \qquad d^2 = 2 - 2\cos A\cos B + 2\sin A\sin B.$$

The distance squared, as given by (6) and (7), is the same for both figures, since this distance did not change during the rotation. Equating the right sides of (6) and (7) gives

$$(8) \qquad 2 - 2\cos(A + B) = 2 - 2\cos A\cos B + 2\sin A\sin B.$$

If we subtract 2 from both sides of (8) and then divide both sides by -2, we obtain (3). Thus, Theorem 1 is proved when A and B are both positive angles.

Now suppose A is a negative angle or B is a negative angle, or perhaps both of the angles are negative. Select integers m and n so that $A + m\,360° > 0$, and $B + n\,360° > 0$. Then Theorem 1 is valid for these new positive angles, so we can write

(9) $\cos [(A + m\,360°) + (B + n\,360°)] =$
$$\cos (A + m\,360°) \cos (B + n\,360°) - \sin (A + m\,360°) \sin (B + n\,360°).$$

The angles A and $A + m\,360°$ are coterminal, so $\cos (A + m\,360°) = \cos A$, and $\sin (A + m\,360°) = \sin A$. A similar result is true for the angles B and $B + n\,360°$, and so the right side of (9) simplifies to

(10) $$\cos A \cos B - \sin A \sin B.$$

On the other hand, the angle on the left side of (9) can be written as

$$(A + m\,360°) + (B + n\,360°) = A + B + (m + n)\,360°$$

and is thus coterminal with the angle $A + B$. Hence, the left side of (9) is

(11) $$\cos (A + B).$$

Substituting (10) and (11) in (9) gives (3), and this completes the proof of Theorem 1.

Theorem 2. *For all angles A and B*

(12) $$\boxed{\cos (A - B) = \cos A \cos B + \sin A \sin B.}$$

Proof. Since Theorem 1 has been established for all angles, we may apply it to the angle $A + (-B) = A - B$. Thus we have

$$\cos (A - B) = \cos [A + (-B)] = \cos A \cos (-B) - \sin A \sin (-B),$$
(by Theorem 1)
$$= \cos A \cos B - \sin A(-\sin B),$$ (by Theorem 8 of Chapter 4)
$$= \cos A \cos B + \sin A \sin B.$$ Q.E.D.

Since "subtracting an angle B" may be regarded as "adding the angle $-B$" the two formulas (3) and (12) are called the *addition formulas for the cosine function.*

Theorem 3. *For any angle C*

(13) $\boxed{\cos (90° - C) = \sin C,}$ and (14) $\boxed{\sin (90° - C) = \cos C.}$

Proof. In Theorem 2, set $A = 90°$. This gives

(15) $$\cos (90° - B) = \cos 90° \cos B + \sin 90° \sin B.$$

But $\cos 90° = 0$ and $\sin 90° = 1$, so (15) becomes

(16) $$\cos (90° - B) = \sin B.$$

If we replace B by C, then (16) gives (13). If in (16) we set $90° - B = C$, then we must also set $B = 90° - C$. With these substitutions (16) gives (14). Q.E.D.

Example 1. Compute cos 15° using the angles 45° and 30°.

Solution. By Theorem 2

$$\cos 15° = \cos (45° - 30°) = \cos 45° \cos 30° + \sin 45° \sin 30°$$

$$= \frac{\sqrt{2}}{2}\frac{\sqrt{3}}{2} + \frac{\sqrt{2}}{2}\frac{1}{2} = \frac{\sqrt{6}+\sqrt{2}}{4} = \frac{2.4495 + 1.4142}{4} = .9659\,,$$

and this coincides with the value given in Table B.

Example 2. Prove that $\cos(-20°) = \sin 110°$.

Solution. In equation (14) of Theorem 3, set $C = -20°$. This gives

$$\cos(-20°) = \sin[90° - (-20°)] = \sin(90° + 20°) = \sin 110°.$$

Example 3. Simplify the expression $E = \cos\frac{3\theta}{5}\cos\frac{\theta}{3} - \sin\frac{3\theta}{5}\sin\frac{\theta}{3}$.

Solution. It is easy to recognize that this expression has the same form as the right side of (3) with $A = 3\theta/5$ and $B = \theta/3$. Whence E is just the cosine of the sum of these angles, that is $E = \cos(14\theta/15)$.

FIGURE 3

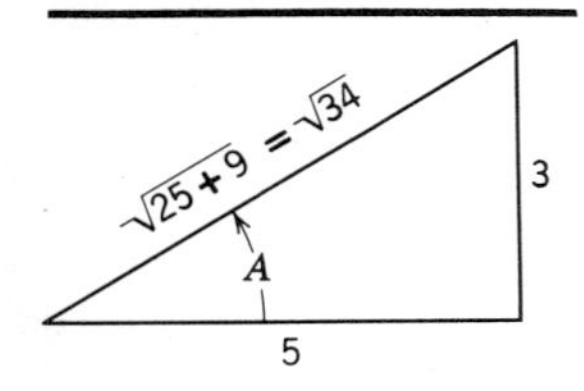

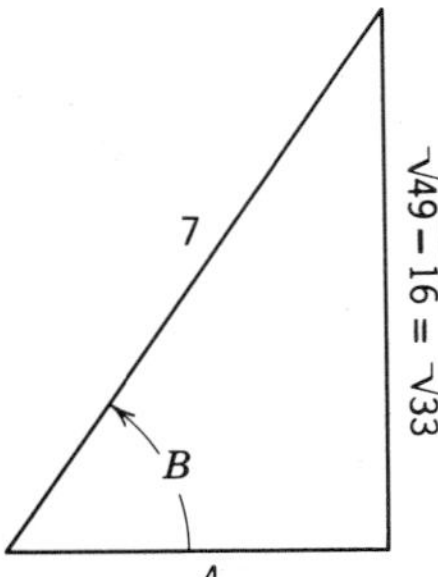

Example 4. If A and B are acute angles with $\tan A = 3/5$ and $\cos B = 4/7$, compute $\cos(A + B)$. Is $A + B$ in Q.I or Q.II?

Solution. From Fig. 3 we can read off the various trigonometric functions of A and B. We find

$$\cos A = \frac{5}{\sqrt{34}}, \qquad \sin A = \frac{3}{\sqrt{34}},$$

$$\cos B = \frac{4}{7}, \qquad \sin B = \frac{\sqrt{33}}{7},$$

$$\cos(A + B) = \cos A \cos B - \sin A \sin B$$

$$= \frac{5}{\sqrt{34}}\frac{4}{7} - \frac{3}{\sqrt{34}}\frac{\sqrt{33}}{7} = \frac{20 - 3\sqrt{33}}{7\sqrt{34}}.$$

Since A and B are acute, $A + B$ must lie either in Q.I or Q.II. To determine the quadrant, it is sufficient to find the sign of $\cos(A + B)$. Now $20^2 = 400$ and $(3\sqrt{33})^2 = 9 \times 33 = 297$. Since $400 > 297$ then $20 > 3\sqrt{33}$ and therefore $\cos(A + B) > 0$. Hence $A + B$ is in Q.I.

Example 5. Prove that for any angle C, $\tan(90^\circ - C) = \cot C$.
Solution.

$$\tan(90^\circ - C) = \frac{\sin(90^\circ - C)}{\cos(90^\circ - C)} = \frac{\cos C}{\sin C} = \cot C.$$

EXERCISE 31

In Problems 1 through 8 simplify each of the expressions by reducing it to a single term. Wherever possible, obtain a numerical value without using the tables.

1. $\cos 15^\circ \cos 5^\circ + \sin 15^\circ \sin 5^\circ$.
2. $\cos 1500^\circ \cos 500^\circ + \sin 1500^\circ \sin 500^\circ$.
3. $\cos 950^\circ \cos 550^\circ - \sin 950^\circ \sin 550^\circ$.
4. $\cos 102^\circ \cos 48^\circ - \sin 48^\circ \sin 102^\circ$.
5. $\cos 25^\circ \cos 185^\circ - \sin 25^\circ \sin 185^\circ$.
6. $\cos 140^\circ \cos 5^\circ + \sin 140^\circ \sin 5^\circ$.
7. $\cos 3A \cos 2A - \sin 3A \sin 2A$.
8. $\sin 4A \sin 6A + \cos 6A \cos 4A$.

9. Find $\cos 165^\circ$ using the angles 135° and 30°.
10. Find $\cos 195^\circ$ using the angles 150° and 45°.
11. Find $\cos 105^\circ$ using the angles 315° and 210°.
12. Find $\cos 165^\circ$ using the angles 300° and 135°.

In problems 13 through 24 prove that the given equations are identities.

13. $\cos(180^\circ + \theta) = -\cos\theta$.
14. $\cos(180^\circ - \theta) = -\cos\theta$.
15. $\cos(30^\circ + A) + \cos(150^\circ - A) = 0$.
16. $\cos(60^\circ + B) - \cos(300^\circ - B) = 0$.
17. $\dfrac{\cos 5B}{\sin 2B} - \dfrac{\sin 5B}{\cos 2B} = \cos 7B \sec 2B \csc 2B$.
18. $\dfrac{\cos 4B}{\sin 3B} + \dfrac{\sin 4B}{\cos 3B} = \sec 3B \cos B \csc 3B$.
19. $\cos(C + D)\cos D + \sin(C + D)\sin D = \cos C$.
20. $\cos(3F + 4G)\cos(2F + 5G) + \sin(3F + 4G)\sin(2F + 5G)$
$= \cos(F - G)$.
21. $-2\cos(135^\circ - H) = \sqrt{2}(\cos H - \sin H)$.
22. $\cos(A + B) + \cos(A - B) = 2\cos A \cos B$.
23. $\cos(A + B) - \cos(A - B) = -2\sin A \sin B$.
24. $\dfrac{\cos(A + B)}{\cos(A - B)} = \dfrac{1 - \tan A \tan B}{1 + \tan A \tan B}$.

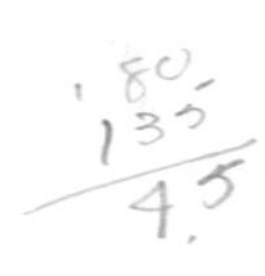

25. Is Theorem 3 of this chapter already contained in Theorem 1 of Chapter 1? If so, it was unnecessary to give a proof of Theorem 3. Explain.

26. Prove that for any angle C: (*a*) $\cot(90° - C) = \tan C$, (*b*) $\sec(90° - C) = \csc C$, (*c*) $\csc(90° - C) = \sec C$.

27. If A and B are complementary angles prove that

$$\cos(7A + 5B) = -\sin 2B.$$

28. If A and B are complementary angles prove that

$$\cos(5A - 2B) = \sin 7B.$$

29. If A and B are acute angles with $\sin A = \frac{2}{3}$ and $\sin B = \frac{3}{4}$, find $\cos(A + B)$. Is $A + B$ in Q.I or is it in Q.II? Do not use tables.

30. If A and B are Q.I angles and if $\sin A = \frac{2}{5}$ and $\sin B = \frac{10}{11}$, find $\cos(A + B)$. Is $A + B$ in Q.I or in Q.II? Do not use tables.

31. If A and B are Q.III angles and if $\tan A = \frac{2}{3}$ and if $\tan B = \frac{4}{3}$, find $\cos(A + B)$ and determine the quadrant for the angle $A + B$.

★ **32.** Let n be a positive integer and suppose that A and B are acute angles with $\tan A = (n - 1)/n$ and $\tan B = (n + 1)/n$. Find $\cos(A + B)$ and determine the quadrant for the angle $A + B$.

★ **33.** If C and D are acute angles with $\tan C = 3\sqrt{3}$ and $\tan D = \sqrt{3}/2$, prove that $C + D = 120°$.

★ **34.** If E, F, and G are acute angles with $\tan E = \frac{2}{3}$, $\tan F = \frac{3}{4}$ and $\tan G = \frac{11}{23}$ prove that $E + F = G + 45°$.

3. The Addition Formulas for the Sine and Tangent. These formulas are given in

Theorem 4. *For all angles A and B*

$$\sin(A + B) = \sin A \cos B + \cos A \sin B, \tag{17}$$

$$\sin(A - B) = \sin A \cos B - \cos A \sin B, \tag{18}$$

$$\tan(A + B) = \frac{\tan A + \tan B}{1 - \tan A \tan B}, \tag{19}$$

$$\tan(A - B) = \frac{\tan A - \tan B}{1 + \tan A \tan B}. \tag{20}$$

Proof. By Theorem 3

$$\begin{aligned}\sin(A+B) &= \cos[90^\circ-(A+B)] = \cos[(90^\circ-A)+B],\\ &= \cos(90^\circ-A)\cos B + \sin(90^\circ-A)\sin B, \quad \text{(by Theorem 2)}\\ &= \sin A\cos B + \cos A\sin B, \quad \text{(by Theorem 3)}\end{aligned}$$

hence (17) is proved. We can now use (17) to prove 18). Indeed

$$\begin{aligned}\sin(A-B) &= \sin[A+(-B)] = \sin A\cos(-B) + \cos A\sin(-B), \text{[by (17)]}\\ &= \sin A\cos B + \cos A(-\sin B), \quad \text{(by Theorem 8 of Chapter 4)}\\ &= \sin A\cos B - \cos A\sin B. \qquad \text{Q.E.D.}\end{aligned}$$

We can now use (17) and (18) to prove (19).

$$\tan(A+B) = \frac{\sin(A+B)}{\cos(A+B)} = \frac{\sin A\cos B + \cos A\sin B}{\cos A\cos B - \sin A\sin B}.$$

The next step is to divide both the numerator and denominator of this fraction by $\cos A\cos B$, in order to convert to tangent functions. This gives

$$\tan(A+B) = \frac{\dfrac{\sin A\cos B + \cos A\sin B}{\cos A\cos B}}{\dfrac{\cos A\cos B - \sin A\sin B}{\cos A\cos B}}$$

$$= \frac{\dfrac{\sin A\cancel{\cos B}}{\cos A\cancel{\cos B}} + \dfrac{\cancel{\cos A}\sin B}{\cancel{\cos A}\cos B}}{\dfrac{\cancel{\cos A\cos B}}{\cancel{\cos A\cos B}} - \dfrac{\sin A\sin B}{\cos A\cos B}} = \frac{\tan A + \tan B}{1 - \tan A\tan B}.$$

Finally the technique used in going from (17) to (18), can be used to derive (20) from (19). We leave this as an exercise for the student.

Example 6. Compute $\tan 75^\circ$.
Solution.

$$\tan 75^\circ = \tan(30^\circ + 45^\circ) = \frac{\tan 30^\circ + \tan 45^\circ}{1 - \tan 30^\circ\tan 45^\circ}$$

$$= \frac{\sqrt{3}/3 + 1}{1 - 1\sqrt{3}/3} = \frac{\sqrt{3}+3}{3-\sqrt{3}} = \frac{\sqrt{3}+3}{3-\sqrt{3}}\,\frac{3+\sqrt{3}}{3+\sqrt{3}}$$

$$= \frac{9 + 6\sqrt{3} + 3}{9-3} = 2 + \sqrt{3} = 3.732.$$

Example 7. Simplify the expression $\dfrac{\sin(\alpha+\beta)-\sin(\alpha-\beta)}{\sin(\alpha+\beta)+\sin(\alpha-\beta)}$.

Solution. For the numerator we have

$$N = \sin\alpha\cos\beta + \cos\alpha\sin\beta - (\sin\alpha\cos\beta - \cos\alpha\sin\beta)$$
$$= 2\cos\alpha\sin\beta.$$

For the denominator we add the material in the parentheses rather than subtract. This gives $D = 2\sin\alpha\cos\beta$. Therefore

$$\frac{\sin(\alpha+\beta)-\sin(\alpha-\beta)}{\sin(\alpha+\beta)+\sin(\alpha-\beta)} = \frac{N}{D} = \frac{2\cos\alpha\sin\beta}{2\sin\alpha\cos\beta} = \cot\alpha\tan\beta.$$

EXERCISE 32

In Problems 1 through 8 simplify each of the expressions by reducing it to a single term. Wherever possible, obtain a numerical value without using the tables.

1. $\sin 335^\circ \cos 305^\circ - \cos 335^\circ \sin 305^\circ$.

2. $\sin 215^\circ \cos 170^\circ - \cos 215^\circ \sin 170^\circ$.

3. $\sin 535^\circ \cos 545^\circ + \cos 535^\circ \sin 545^\circ$

4. $\sin 405^\circ \cos 505^\circ + \sin 505^\circ \cos 405^\circ$.

5. $\dfrac{\tan 62^\circ - \tan 17^\circ}{1 + \tan 62^\circ \tan 17^\circ}$.

6. $\dfrac{\tan 435^\circ - \tan 300^\circ}{1 + \tan 435^\circ \tan 300^\circ}$.

7. $\dfrac{\tan(C+D) + \tan(C-D)}{1 - \tan(C+D)\tan(C-D)}$.

8. $\dfrac{\tan(2E+F) + \tan 2(F-E)}{1 - \tan(2E+F)\tan 2(F-E)}$.

9. Find sin 105° and tan 105°, using the angles 45° and 60°.

10. Find sin 15° and tan 15° using the angles 45° and 60°.

11. Find sin 75° and tan 75° using the angles 315° and 240°.

12. Find sin 15° and tan 15° using the angles 150° and 225°.

13. Find $\tan(A+B)$ and $\tan(A-B)$ if $\tan A = \frac{3}{7}$ and $\tan B = \frac{4}{7}$.

14. Find $\tan(A+B)$ and $\tan(A-B)$ if $\tan A = 2$ and $\tan B = 3$.

15. Find $\sin(A+B)$ and $\sin(A-B)$ for the angles of Problem 13, assuming that A and B are acute angles.

16. Find $\sin(A+B)$ and $\sin(A-B)$ for the angles of Problem 14, assuming that A and B are acute angles.

★ **17.** Given that $\sin 1^\circ = .017452$ and $\cos 1^\circ = .999848$ compute sin 2° and cos 2° to six decimal places.

★ **18.** Using the data and results of Problem 17 compute sin 3° and cos 3° to six decimal places.

Prove the following identities.

19. $\sin(90° + \alpha) = \cos\alpha$

20. $\sin(270° + \beta) = -\cos\beta.$

21. $\tan(45° + \gamma) = \dfrac{1 + \tan\gamma}{1 - \tan\gamma}.$

22. $\tan(135° - \theta) = -\dfrac{1 + \tan\theta}{1 - \tan\theta}.$

23. $\sin(\alpha + 30°) + \sin(\alpha - 30°) = \sqrt{3}\sin\alpha.$

24. $\sin(\alpha + 45) - \sin(\alpha - 135°) = \sqrt{2}(\sin\alpha + \cos\alpha).$

25. $\dfrac{\cos(C + D) - \cos(C - D)}{\cos(C + D) + \cos(C - D)} = -\tan C \tan D.$

26. $\dfrac{\sin 3A}{\sin 2A} + \dfrac{\cos 3A}{\cos 2A} = \sin 5A \sec 2A \csc 2A.$

27. $\dfrac{\sin 3B}{\sin 2B} - \dfrac{\cos 3B}{\cos 2B} = \sec 2B \sin B \csc 2B.$

★**28.** $\cos(A + B + C) = \cos A \cos B \cos C - \sin A \sin B \cos C - \sin A \cos B \sin C - \cos A \sin B \sin C.$

★**29.** $\sin(A + B + C) = \sin A \cos B \cos C + \cos A \sin B \cos C + \cos A \cos B \sin C - \sin A \sin B \sin C.$

★**30.** $\tan(A + B + C) = \dfrac{\tan A + \tan B + \tan C - \tan A \tan B \tan C}{1 - \tan A \tan B - \tan B \tan C - \tan C \tan A}.$

4. The Double-Angle Formulas.

These formulas are given in

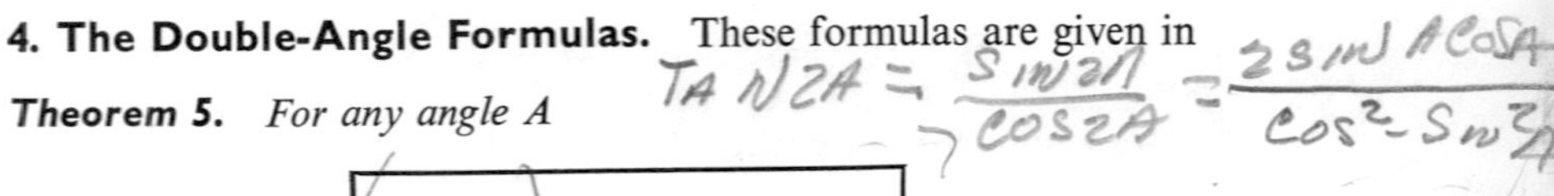

Theorem 5. *For any angle A*

$$\sin 2A = 2 \sin A \cos A, \tag{21}$$

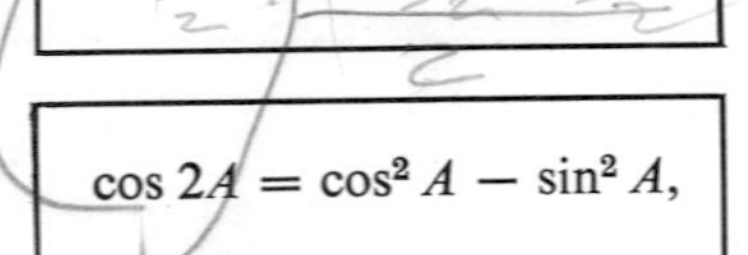

$$\cos 2A = \cos^2 A - \sin^2 A, \tag{22}$$

$$\tan 2A = \frac{2 \tan A}{1 - \tan^2 A}. \tag{23}$$

Each of these formulas is proved by setting $B = A$ in the appropriate addition formula. If we set $B = A$ in (17) we find

$$\sin(A + A) = \sin A \cos A + \cos A \sin A$$

$$\sin 2A = \sin A \cos A + \sin A \cos A = 2 \sin A \cos A,$$

and this proves (21). Similarly if we set $B = A$ in (3) we find (22), and if we set $B = A$ in (19) we obtain (23). Q.E.D.

Example 8. Prove the identity $\cos 2A = 1 - 2\sin^2 A$.
Solution. Since $\cos^2 A = 1 - \sin^2 A$ we can use this in (22). Indeed

$$\cos 2A = \cos^2 A - \sin^2 A = (1 - \sin^2 A) - \sin^2 A = 1 - 2\sin^2 \mathrm{A}.$$

Example 9. Given that $\sin 15° = (\sqrt{6} - \sqrt{2})/4$ and $\cos 15° = (\sqrt{6} + \sqrt{2})/4$, compute $\sin 30°$.
Solution.

$$\sin 30° = 2 \sin 15° \cos 15° = 2\,\frac{\sqrt{6} - \sqrt{2}}{4}\,\frac{\sqrt{6} + \sqrt{2}}{4}$$

$$= 2\,\frac{(\sqrt{6})^2 - (\sqrt{2})^2}{16} = \frac{6 - 2}{8} = \frac{1}{2}.$$

Example 10. Express $\sin 3A$ in terms of trigonometric functions of A.
Solution.

$$\sin 3A = \sin(2A + A) = \sin 2A \cos A + \cos 2A \sin A$$

$$= 2 \sin A \cos A \cos A + (\cos^2 A - \sin^2 A) \sin A$$

$$= 3 \sin A \cos^2 A - \sin^3 A.$$

5. The Half-Angle Formulas. These formulas are given in

Theorem 6. *For any angle θ*

(24) $$\sin\frac{\theta}{2} = \pm\sqrt{\frac{1 - \cos\theta}{2}},$$

(25) $$\cos\frac{\theta}{2} = \pm\sqrt{\frac{1 + \cos\theta}{2}},$$

(26) $$\tan\frac{\theta}{2} = \frac{\sin\theta}{1 + \cos\theta}.$$

Proof. If we add the two identities

$$\cos^2 A + \sin^2 A = 1 \tag{27}$$

and

$$\cos^2 A - \sin^2 A = \cos 2A \tag{22}$$

we obtain

$$2\cos^2 A = 1 + \cos 2A, \tag{28}$$

and if we subtract (22) from (27) we obtain

$$2\sin^2 A = 1 - \cos 2A. \tag{29}$$

If in each of these last two equations we divide by 2 and take the square root on both sides we find from (28):

$$\cos A = \pm\sqrt{\frac{1 + \cos 2A}{2}}, \tag{30}$$

and from (29)

$$\sin A = \pm\sqrt{\frac{1 - \cos 2A}{2}}, \tag{31}$$

Finally if we set $2A = \theta$, and hence $A = \theta/2$ in (30) and (31) we obtain (25) and (24) respectively.

To prove formula (26) notice that

$$\frac{\sin 2A}{1 + \cos 2A} = \frac{2\sin A\cos A}{\sin^2 A + \cos^2 A + \cos^2 A - \sin^2 A}$$

$$= \frac{2\sin A\cos A}{2\cos^2 A} = \tan A.$$

The same substitutions, $2A = \theta$, and $A = \theta/2$ will transform this identity into (26). Q.E.D.

The $\pm$ sign in (24) is unavoidable, because the radical sign always means the positive (or zero) square root, while $\sin(\theta/2)$ may be negative. A similar remark applies to equation (25). By taking the quotient of (24) and (25) we find

$$\tan\frac{\theta}{2} = \pm\sqrt{\frac{1 - \cos\theta}{1 + \cos\theta}}. \tag{32}$$

However this formula is not as nice as (26) because in (26) the nuisance $\pm$ sign does not appear.

Example 11. (*a*) Compute $\cos 120°$ from $\cos 240°$. (*b*) Compute $\cos 60°$ from $\cos 120°$.

Solution. (*a*) We assume as known that $\cos 240° = -\frac{1}{2}$. Then from (25)

$$\cos 120° = \pm\sqrt{\frac{1 + \cos 240°}{2}} = \pm\sqrt{\frac{1 - 1/2}{2}} = \pm\sqrt{\frac{1}{4}} = \pm\frac{1}{2}.$$

But we select the answer $-\frac{1}{2}$ because in Q.II the cosine is negative.
(*b*) We assume as known that $\cos 120° = -\frac{1}{2}$. Then from (25)

$$\cos 60° = \pm\sqrt{\frac{1 + \cos 120°}{2}} = \pm\sqrt{\frac{1 - 1/2}{2}} = \pm\sqrt{\frac{1}{4}} = \pm\frac{1}{2}.$$

But we select the answer $+\frac{1}{2}$ because in Q.I the cosine is positive. Observe that in (*a*) and (*b*) the computation is exactly the same. The determination of the sign in (25) must be made on the basis of some knowledge of the quadrant for $\theta/2$.

Example 12. Compute $\cos 7° 30'$.
Solution. By Example 1, $\cos 15° = (\sqrt{6} + \sqrt{2})/4$. Hence by (25)

$$\cos 7° 30' = \sqrt{\frac{1 + (\sqrt{6} + \sqrt{2})/4}{2}} = \frac{1}{2}\sqrt{\frac{4 + \sqrt{6} + \sqrt{2}}{2}} = .9914.$$

Example 13. Simplify the expression $\sqrt{1 - \cos 6A}$.
Solution. We can write

$$\sqrt{1 - \cos 6A} = \sqrt{2}\sqrt{\frac{1 - \cos 6A}{2}} = \sqrt{2} \sin 3A,$$

if both sides are positive (or zero). However the radical on the left side is never negative (by definition) so the right side must be adjusted in an appropriate way. This can be done using the absolute value sign. Indeed, for all angles A, $\sqrt{1 - \cos 6A} = \sqrt{2}\,|\sin 3A|$.

EXERCISE 33

In Problems 1 to 8 simplify each expression.

1. $\dfrac{2 \tan 20°}{1 - \tan^2 20°}$.

2. $\cos^2 5° - \sin^2 5°$.

3. $2 \sin 76° \cos 76°$.

4. $\sqrt{\dfrac{1 - \cos 426°}{2}}$.

5. $\sqrt{\dfrac{1 + \cos 200°}{2}}$.

6. $\dfrac{\sin 284°}{1 + \cos 284°}$.

7. $\dfrac{\sin A \cos A}{\cos^2 A - \sin^2 A}$.

8. $\dfrac{\tan 8B}{1 - \tan^2 8B}$.

9. Find $\sin 15°$ and $\cos 15°$ using $\cos 30° = \sqrt{3}/2$.

10. If A is an acute angle and $\cos A = \frac{3}{5}$ find $\sin (A/2)$ and $\cos (A/2)$.

11. If B is an acute angle and $\cos B = \frac{4}{5}$ find $\sin (B/2)$ and $\cos (B/2)$.

12. Find $\sin 2A$ and $\cos 2A$ for the angle A of Problem 10.

13. Find $\sin 2B$ and $\cos 2B$ for the angle B of Problem 11.

14. Given $\tan (A/2) = \frac{1}{3}$, find $\sin A$ and $\cos A$.

15. If $180° < A < 270°$ and $\tan A = \frac{3}{4}$, find $\sin (A/2)$ and $\cos (A/2)$.

16. If $270° < B < 360°$ and $\cos B = \frac{5}{13}$, find $\sin (B/2)$ and $\cos (B/2)$.

★ **17.** If $n > 1$, $\cos C = 2n/(1 + n^2)$, and if C is an acute angle, find $\sin (C/2)$ and $\cos (C/2)$.

★ **18.** Find $\sin 2C$ and $\cos 2C$ for the angle C of Problem 17.

★ **19.** Prove that $\sin 2A < 2 \sin A$ if $0 < A < 90°$.

★ **20.** Prove that if $0 < B < 45°$ then $\tan 2B > 2 \tan B$. What happens to this inequality if $45° < B < 90°$?

21. Express $\cos 3C$ in terms of $\cos C$.

22. Express $\tan 4D$ in terms of $\tan D$.

Prove the following identities.

23. $2 \cos^2 E - \cos 2E = 1.$

24. $\cos^2 2F - 4 \sin^2 F \cos^2 F = \cos 4F.$

25. $\dfrac{1 - 2 \sin^2 G}{\sin G \cos G} = 2 \cot 2G.$

26. $\dfrac{\sin 4H}{2 \sin 2H} = \cos^4 H - \sin^4 H.$

27. $\dfrac{\cos \alpha}{\cos \alpha - \sin \alpha} - \dfrac{\sin \alpha}{\cos \alpha + \sin \alpha} = \sec 2\alpha.$

28. $\dfrac{\cos \beta}{\cos \beta - \sin \beta} + \dfrac{\sin \beta}{\cos \beta + \sin \beta} = 1 + \tan 2\beta.$

29. $\dfrac{1 - \tan \gamma}{1 + \tan \gamma} = \dfrac{1 - \sin 2\gamma}{\cos 2\gamma}.$

30. $\dfrac{1 - \tan^2 \theta}{1 + \tan^2 \theta} = \cos 2\theta.$

31. $\dfrac{1 + \sin 2A + \cos 2A}{1 + \sin 2A - \cos 2A} = \cot A.$

32. $\dfrac{\sin B + \sin 2B}{1 + \cos B + \cos 2B} = \tan B.$

33. $\dfrac{\tan (C/2) + \cot (C/2)}{\cot (C/2) - \tan (C/2)} = \sec C.$

34. $\dfrac{2}{\tan (D/2) + \cot (D/2)} = \sin D.$

★ **35.** Prove that $\sin \theta$ and $\cos \theta$ are both rational if and only if $\tan (\theta/2)$ is either rational or does not exist.

★★ **36.** Show that the duality principle developed in §7 of Chapter 5 is not valid for identities involving multiples of an angle by considering the dual of equation (21).

6. Product to Sum Formulas; Sum to Product Formulas. Let us compare the two addition formulas for the sine function, namely

$$\sin (A + B) = \sin A \cos B + \cos A \sin B, \tag{17}$$

and

$$\sin (A - B) = \sin A \cos B - \cos A \sin B. \tag{18}$$

The fact that the right sides of these two equations differ only by the connecting sign suggests that adding them, or taking their difference ought to lead to something interesting. Indeed, if we add these two equations we find

(33) $$\sin(A + B) + \sin(A - B) = 2 \sin A \cos B,$$

and if we subtract (18) from (17) we find

(34) $$\sin(A + B) - \sin(A - B) = 2 \cos A \sin B.$$

If now we divide each of the equations (33) and (34) by 2 and then put the right side first, we have the formulas of

Theorem 7. *For all angles A and B*

(35) $$\boxed{\sin A \cos B = \tfrac{1}{2}[\sin(A + B) + \sin(A - B)],}$$

and

(36) $$\boxed{\cos A \sin B = \tfrac{1}{2}[\sin(A + B) - \sin(A - B)].}$$

The importance of this theorem is that it gives a method of replacing a product of two trigonometric functions by a sum of two trigonometric functions.

Example 14. Express $\sin 5\theta \cos 3\theta$ as a sum of trigonometric functions.
Solution. By (35)

$$\begin{aligned}\sin 5\theta \cos 3\theta &= \tfrac{1}{2}[\sin(5\theta + 3\theta) + \sin(5\theta - 3\theta)]\\ &= \tfrac{1}{2}[\sin 8\theta + \sin 2\theta].\end{aligned}$$

A similar manipulation can be performed on the addition formulas for the cosine function:

(12) $$\cos(A - B) = \cos A \cos B + \sin A \sin B,$$

and

(3) $$\cos(A + B) = \cos A \cos B - \sin A \sin B.$$

If we add these two equations we find

(37) $$\cos(A + B) + \cos(A - B) = 2 \cos A \cos B,$$

and if we subtract (3) from (12) we find

(38) $$\cos(A - B) - \cos(A + B) = 2 \sin A \sin B.$$

Again we divide each of these equations by 2 and put the right side first.

We then have

Theorem 8. *For all angles A and B*

$$\cos A \cos B = \tfrac{1}{2}[\cos (A + B) + \cos (A - B)], \tag{39}$$

and

$$\sin A \sin B = -\tfrac{1}{2}[\cos (A + B) - \cos (A - B)]. \tag{40}$$

Here again we have formulas that help us to replace a product of two trigonometric functions by a sum of two trigonometric functions.

If we want formulas that replace a sum (or difference) of two trigonometric functions by a product, it is sufficient to take (33), (34), (37), and (38). However for convenience we would like to replace the angle $A + B$ by a single angle C, and the angle $A - B$ by another single angle D. Suppose we do this, then adding the two equations

$$A + B = C,$$

and

$$A - B = D,$$

gives

$$2A = C + D$$

Subtraction gives

$$2B = C - D.$$

Hence $A = (C + D)/2$ and $B = (C - D)/2$. Making these substitutions in (33), (34), (37), and (38) gives

Theorem 9. *For all angles C and D*

$$\sin C + \sin D = 2 \sin \frac{C + D}{2} \cos \frac{C - D}{2}, \tag{41}$$

$$\sin C - \sin D = 2 \cos \frac{C + D}{2} \sin \frac{C - D}{2}, \tag{42}$$

$$\cos C + \cos D = 2 \cos \frac{C + D}{2} \cos \frac{C - D}{2}, \tag{43}$$

(44)
$$\cos C - \cos D = -2 \sin \frac{C + D}{2} \sin \frac{C - D}{2}.$$

It is obvious from an inspection of these formulas that they can be used to convert sums of two trigonometric functions into products of two trigonometric functions.

Example 15. Convert $\cos 5\alpha - \cos 3\alpha$ into a product of trigonometric functions.

Solution. By (44) with $C = 5\alpha$ and $D = 3\alpha$,

$$\cos 5\alpha - \cos 3\alpha = -2 \sin \frac{5\alpha + 3\alpha}{2} \sin \frac{5\alpha - 3\alpha}{2} = -2 \sin 4\alpha \sin \alpha.$$

Example 16. Simplify the expression $(\cos 7\beta + \cos \beta)/(\sin 7\beta + \sin \beta)$.

Solution. We apply (43) to the numerator and (41) to the denominator. This gives

$$\frac{\cos 7\beta + \cos \beta}{\sin 7\beta + \sin \beta} = \frac{2 \cos \frac{7\beta + \beta}{2} \cos \frac{7\beta - \beta}{2}}{2 \sin \frac{7\beta + \beta}{2} \cos \frac{7\beta - \beta}{2}} = \frac{\cancel{2} \cos 4\beta \cancel{\cos 3\beta}}{\cancel{2} \sin 4\beta \cancel{\cos 3\beta}} = \cot 4\beta.$$

EXERCISE 34

Convert the following products into sums of trigonometric functions.

1. $\sin 15° \cos 5°$.

2. $\cos 44° \cos 20°$.

3. $\cos A \cos 3A$.

4. $\cos 3B \sin B$.

5. $\cos 2C \cos 3C \cos 4C$.

6. $\cos 2D \sin 3D \cos 4D$.

Convert the following expressions into products of trigonometric functions.

7. $\sin \theta + \sin 3\theta$.

8. $\cos \theta + \cos 5\theta$.

9. $\cos 2\theta + \cos 6\theta$.

10. $\sin 3\theta - \sin 9\theta$.

Prove the following identities.

11. $\cos(\alpha + \beta)\cos(\alpha - \beta) = \cos^2 \alpha - \sin^2 \beta$.

12. $\dfrac{\cos 3\gamma - \cos \gamma}{\sin 3\gamma - \sin \gamma} = -\tan 2\gamma$.

13. $\dfrac{\sin 5A + \sin A}{\cos 5A + \cos A} = \tan 3A$.

14. $\dfrac{\sin 6A + \sin 4A}{\sin 4A + \sin 2A} = \cos 2A + \sin 2A \cot 3A$.

15. $\sin B + \sin 2B + \sin 3B = \sin 2B(1 + 2\cos B)$.

16. $\cos 2C + \cos 4C + \cos 6C = \cos 4C(1 + 2\cos 2C)$.

★ **17.** $\sin D - \sin 2D + \sin 3D - \sin 4D = -4 \sin \dfrac{D}{2} \cos D \cos \dfrac{5D}{2}$.

★ **18.** $\cos E - \cos 2E + \cos 3E - \cos 4E = 4 \sin \dfrac{E}{2} \cos E \sin \dfrac{5E}{2}$.

19. $\dfrac{\sin \alpha + \sin 2\alpha + \sin 3\alpha}{\cos \alpha + \cos 2\alpha + \cos 3\alpha} = \tan 2\alpha$.

20. $\dfrac{\sin \alpha - \sin 2\alpha + \sin 3\alpha}{\cos \alpha - \cos 2\alpha + \cos 3\alpha} = \tan 2\alpha$.

21. $\dfrac{\sin (A + B) \cos (A - B) + \cos (A + B) \sin (A - B)}{\cos (A + B) \cos (A - B) - \sin (A + B) \sin (A - B)} = \tan 2A$.

★ **22.** $\dfrac{\sin^2 (C + D) + \sin^2 (C - D)}{2 \cos^2 C \cos^2 D} = \tan^2 C + \tan^2 D$.

★★ **23.** If $\cos (A + B) = \frac{1}{3}$ and $\cos (A - B) = \frac{1}{2}$ find $\cos A$ and $\cos B$. Assume that $0 < A < B < 90°$.

★★ **24.** If $\cos (A + B) = \frac{1}{5}$ and $\cos (A - B) = \frac{4}{5}$ find $\cos A$ and $\cos B$. Assume that $0 < A < B < 90°$.

★★★ **25.** A generalization of the two preceding problems. Let $\cos (A + B) = x$ and $\cos (A - B) = y$, where $0 < x < y < 1$. If $0 < A < B < 90°$, find $\cos A$ and $\cos B$ in terms of x and y. Also find $\sin A$ and $\sin B$ in terms of x and y.

★★ **26.** Check the answers in Problem 25 by showing that $\sin^2 A + \cos^2 A = 1$ and $\sin^2 B + \cos^2 B = 1$ for the values obtained in Problem 25.

★★ **27.** Use the formulas of Theorem 3 of this chapter to give an alternate proof of the Duality Principle (Theorem 2 of Chapter 5).

CHAPTER 8

RADIAN MEASURE

1. Objective. Our first objective is to introduce a new unit, the radian, for measuring angles. Although the degree is completely adequate for all of trigonometry there is no scientific reason for selecting this unit as the unit for angular measurements. More than twenty-five hundred years ago the Babylonians decided to divide the circumference of a circle into 360 equal arcs and to use the central angle subtended by one of these arcs as the unit. It is possible that they chose 360 because they thought that a year consisted of 360 days, or perhaps they used 360 because it has so many integral divisors [$360 = 2^3 \times 3^2 \times 5$ and hence it has $(3 + 1)(2 + 1)(1 + 1) = 24$ different divisors]. Whatever may have been the reason for their choice, this unit, the degree, is now the popularly accepted one and for better or for worse we are stuck with it.

The radian is a "natural" unit for measuring angles, but the naturalness of this unit will not appear to the student until he studies the calculus of the trigonometric functions. However in §3 we will attempt to indicate briefly just why the radian is a "natural" unit.

The rest of this chapter is devoted to examples and exercises intended to acquaint the student with this new unit, so that he will feel comfortable when using it. Then when he meets this unit again in calculus it will be an old friend.

2. Definition of Radian Measure. Let us place an angle θ so that its vertex is at the common center of a pair of concentric circles, as shown in Fig. 1. Let r_1 and r_2 be the radii of these circles and suppose that the angle θ intercepts on the circumference of these circles arcs of lengths s_1 and s_2 respectively.

It is intuitively obvious from the picture that

(1) $$\frac{s_1}{r_1} = \frac{s_2}{r_2}$$

and in fact this is proved in plane geometry by using the properties of similar triangles. In other words the ratio

(2) $$\frac{s}{r}$$

depends only on θ, the central angle, and not on r the radius of the circle. Hence we can use this ratio as a measure of the central angle θ.

FIGURE 1

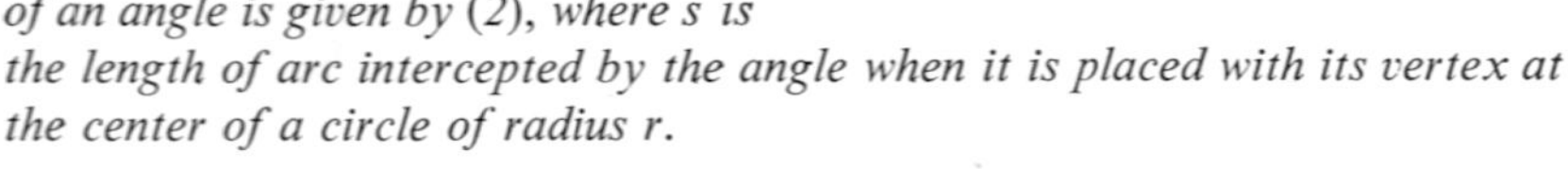

Definition 1. *The radian measure of an angle is given by* (2), *where s is the length of arc intercepted by the angle when it is placed with its vertex at the center of a circle of radius r.*

If θ denotes the measure of the angle in radians, this definition simply states that

(3) $$\boxed{\theta = \frac{s}{r}.}$$

An angle of 1 radian, shown in Fig. 2*b*, is obtained by setting $s = r$ in (3). Thus *a radian is the angle subtended at the center of the circle by an arc of the circle equal to the radius.* To obtain an angle of $\frac{1}{2}$ radian we merely bisect this arc, or what is the same thing, we bisect the angle. The result is shown in Fig. 2*a*. Similarly Fig. 2*c* shows an angle of 2

FIGURE 2

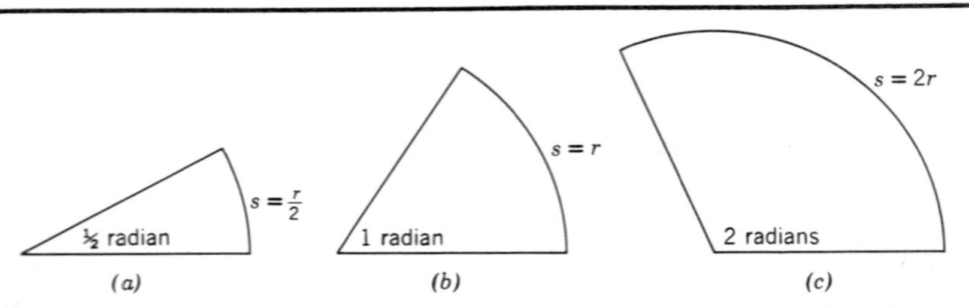

(*a*) (*b*) (*c*)

radians obtained by doubling the length of the intercepted arc, or what is the same thing, doubling the angle of Fig. 2*b*.

It is easy to find the number of radians for an angle of 360°. In this case the intercepted arc s is just the circumference of the circle, hence $s = 2\pi r$. Then (3) gives $\theta = s/r = 2\pi r/r = 2\pi$ radians. Consequently $360° = 2\pi$ radians.

If we divide both sides of this equation by 2 we have the important formula

$$180° = \pi \text{ radians.} \tag{4}$$

Equation (4) is very convenient for converting from radians to degrees or from degrees to radians. Equations (3) and (4) will be sufficient to solve all of the problems in Exercise 35.

Example 1. What is the radian measure of a 1° angle?

Solution. Divide both sides of (4) by 180. This gives

$$1° = \frac{\pi}{180} \text{ radian} = \frac{3.14159\cdots}{180} = .017453\cdots \text{ radian.}$$

Example 2. How many degrees are there in a 1-radian angle?

Solution. This time divide both sides of (4) by π. This gives

$$1 \text{ radian} = \frac{180°}{3.14159\cdots} = 57.296\cdots° = 57°\ 17.75\cdots .$$

Example 3. If $\theta = 85°$, what is the radian measure of the angle?

Solution. For 1° we divide both sides of (4) by 180. To obtain 85° we would multiply the resulting equation on both sides by 85. Thus

$$85° = 85 \times 1° = 85 \times \frac{\pi}{180} \text{ radians} = \frac{17\pi}{36} \text{ radians.}$$

Example 4. A flywheel of diameter 12.0 ft makes 500 revolutions in an hour. (*a*) How far does a point on the perimeter travel in one hour? (*b*) If a bug clinging to the flywheel travels one mile during the hour how far is the bug from the center of the wheel? Give answers with 3-figure accuracy.

Solution. (*a*) Each revolution is 2π radians so the angle through which the point rotates in one hour is $2\pi \times 500$ or 1000π radians. Then by (3) the distance traveled is

$$s = r\theta = 6 \times 1000\pi = 18{,}800 \text{ ft} = 3.57 \text{ miles.}$$

(*b*) If the bug travels one mile when $\theta = 1000\pi$ radians then by (3)

$$r = \frac{s}{\theta} = \frac{1 \text{ mi}}{1000\pi} = \frac{5280 \text{ ft}}{3140} = 1.68 \text{ ft},$$

and this is the distance of the bug from the center of the wheel.

It is sometimes convenient to write $\theta = 3^{(r)}$ instead of $\theta = 3$ radians. In this text book we will go even further and drop the superscript. The statement "$\theta = 3$" will mean that θ is an angle whose measure is 3 radians, while $\theta = 3°$ will mean an angle of 3 degrees. Similarly $\sin(\pi/2)$ will mean $\sin(\pi/2$ radians) and hence $\sin(\pi/2) = \sin 90° = 1$.

EXERCISE 35

1. The number 360 has more integral divisors than any other integer $n < 360$. Show that 360 has 24 such divisors by listing them all and counting them.

★**2.** Among the integers less than 360, the number 240 has the greatest number of integral divisors. Show that this number has 20 such divisors by listing them.

3. Convert each of the following angles to radians; (*a*) 60°, (*b*) 240°, (*c*) 720°, (*d*) −135°, (*e*) 12°, (*f*) 132°, (*g*) 36°, (*h*) −150°.

4. Convert each of the following angles to radians: (*a*) 90°, (*b*) 450°, (*c*) −1080°, (*d*) 45°, (*e*) 225°, (*f*) 3°, (*g*) 21°, (*h*) −210°.

5. Convert each of the following to degrees: (*a*) $\pi/4$, (*b*) $-9\pi/4$, (*c*) $5\pi/2$, (*d*) $11\pi/120$, (*e*) $-2\pi/9$, (*f*) $19\pi/36$, (*g*) 7π, (*h*) -8π.

6. Convert each of the following to degrees: (*a*) $\pi/12$, (*b*) 3π, (*c*) $7\pi/6$, (*d*) $-11\pi/4$, (*e*) $13\pi/45$, (*f*) $-17\pi/30$, (*g*) $5\pi/8$, (*h*) -4π.

7. Evaluate each of the following without using tables: (*a*) $\sin(\pi/6)$, (*b*) $\cos(-2\pi/3)$, (*c*) $\tan(3\pi/4)$, (*d*) $\sec 3\pi$, (*e*) $\cot(-\pi/2)$, (*f*) $\csc 0$, (*g*) $\sin(7\pi/2)$, (*h*) $\cos 7\pi$.

8. Evaluate each of the following without using tables: (*a*) $\sin(3\pi/4)$, (*b*) $\cos(\pi/6)$, (*c*) $\tan 3\pi$, (*d*) $\cot(-2\pi/3)$, (*e*) $\sec 5\pi$, (*f*) $\csc \pi$, (*g*) $\sin 0$, (*h*) $\cos 5\pi$.

In each of the following problems obtain the answer to three significant figures. For convenience take $\pi = \frac{22}{7}$.

9. A central angle of 44° is drawn in a circle of radius 9 in. What is the length of arc intercepted on the circumference of this circle?

10. How far does the tip of the big hand of a clock move in 35 min if the hand is 6 in. long?

11. A turn in a road changes the direction of the road from N 18° E to N 6° W. If the turn is circular with a radius of 810 ft, what is the length of this curve in the road?

12. A turn in the road changes the direction of the road from S 82° E to N 21° W. If the turn is circular with a radius of 720 ft, what is the length of this curve in the road?

13. If a car travels 11 ft without skidding and the radius of the wheels is 1 ft, through how many radians does each wheel turn? How many degrees?

14. If a truck travels 21 ft without skidding and the radius of the wheels is 2 ft 6 in., through how many radians does each wheel turn? How many degrees?

15. Assuming that the radius of the earth is 3960 mi find the length of arc on the earth's surface of one degree latitude on a meridian. What is the length of arc for one minute of latitude?

16. Washington, D.C. is located at 38° 52′ north latitude. How far is it from the equator?

17. Seattle, Washington is located at 47° 42′ north latitude. How far is it from the North Pole?

★ **18.** Eratosthenes (born 275 B.C., died 194 B.C.) conjectured that the earth was round, and computed the radius of the earth in the following manner. The Egyptian city of Alexandria (in which he worked as a librarian) lies directly north of Syene (his birthplace) so that the sun attains its maximum angle of elevation at the same time for both cities. On a certain day the sun was directly overhead at Syene while on the same day at Alexandria, the maximum angle of elevation for the sun was 82° 48′. Assuming that Alexandria is 498 miles north of Syene, compute the radius of the earth.

★ 3. A Brief Motivation for the Radian Measure. In deriving a number of formulas for the calculus the ratio

$$\frac{\sin \theta}{\theta} \tag{5}$$

enters in a natural way. Speaking roughly we want to know how this ratio behaves when θ is a small positive angle. Let us imagine that this ratio is computed for an infinite number of angles $\theta_1, \theta_2, \theta_3, \cdots$ each one positive and each one smaller than the preceding one. Since $\sin 0 = 0$, it is clear that in the ratio (5) the numerator and the denominator are both small. It can be proved that as the angle θ gets closer and closer to zero, the ratio (5) gets closer and closer to a fixed number which we denote by L. This is symbolized by writing the formula

$$\lim_{\theta \to 0} \frac{\sin \theta}{\theta} = L \tag{6}$$

(read, the limit of $\sin \theta/\theta$ as θ approaches 0 is L). This limit number L enters into quite a few of the formulas that are used over and over again in the calculus, and it is very convenient to try to make $L = 1$. Can we do such a thing? The answer is yes, if we select the unit for measuring angles in the proper way. As the student has already guessed, if the angle θ is measured in radians then $L = 1$ in (5). Of course we have not proved this assertion. In fact, we have not even given the precise definition of the meaning of equation (6). But the ideas are clear, and the details can easily be reserved for the calculus course.

Summarizing. The radian is called the natural unit for measuring angles, because when it is used $L = 1$ in (6) and many formulas from mathematics, engineering, and physics are thereby simplified.

★ 4. Linear and Angular Velocity. If a particle moves in a straight line with uniform motion, then the *linear velocity* v is defined to be

$$v = \frac{s}{t} \tag{7}$$

where s is the distance traveled by the particle in time t. We may equally well suppose that the particle moves uniformly on a circle. In this case (7) is still taken as the definition of the velocity of the particle, but now s represents the length of arc the particle travels in time t.

If we imagine that the particle is joined to the center of the circle by a radial line, then as the particle travels along the circle this radial line will sweep out an angle θ. The *angular velocity*, ω (omega), of the particle is defined to be

$$\boxed{\omega = \frac{\theta}{t}} \tag{8}$$

where t is the time required for the radial line to rotate through the angle θ.

Example 5. With what angular velocity does the earth spin on its axis?
Solution. Since the earth makes a full revolution in 24 hr, we have

$$\omega = \frac{360^\circ}{24 \text{ hr}} = 15^\circ/\text{hr}.$$

If we wish the answer in radians per minute we would write

$$\omega = \frac{2\pi}{24 \times 60} = \frac{\pi}{720} = .00436 \text{ radians/min.}$$

Linear velocity and angular velocity are related by the formula of

Theorem 1. *If a particle moves uniformly on a circle of radius r with an angular velocity ω then its velocity v is given by*

$$\boxed{v = r\omega} \tag{9}$$

when ω is expressed in radians per unit of time.

$$V = r\frac{\theta}{T}$$

Proof. By the definition of radian measure, equation (3),

$$s = r\theta. \tag{10}$$

If we divide both sides of (10) by t, the time required for the particle to travel the distance s, we find

$$\frac{s}{t} = r\frac{\theta}{t}.$$

But $s/t = v$ and $\theta/t = \omega$. Q.E.D.

Example 6. With what velocity does a man standing on the equator travel as a result of the earth's rotation about its axis?

Solution. In Example 5, we found $\omega = .00436$ radians/min. Using 3960 mi for the radius of the earth we have by formula (9), $v = 3960 \times .00436 = 17.3$ mi/min. Observe that the distance unit for v (miles) is the same as the distance unit for r. Note also that we have neglected the velocity that the man might have due to the earth's rotation about the sun.

EXERCISE 36

Obtain all the answers to three significant figures. For convenience take $\pi = \frac{22}{7}$.

1. Assuming that the path described by the earth about the sun is a circle with radius 92,000,000 mi, compute the velocity of the earth in miles per second.

2. Assuming that the planet Venus travels about the sun in a circular orbit with a radius of 67,200,000 mi in 225 days, compute the velocity of Venus in miles per second.

3. An automobile is traveling 50 mi/hr. If the wheels are 30 in. in diameter find the angular velocity of the wheels in revolutions per minute (rpm).

4. A truck passing the automobile of Problem 3 is traveling 60 mi/hr. If the truck's wheels are 48 in. in diameter find the revolutions per minute of these wheels.

5. An airplane propeller 6 ft from tip to tip, turns at 2200 rpm. Find the velocity of the tip in miles per hour.

6. If the tip of the propeller in Problem 5 travels at 600 mi/hr, find the revolutions per minute of the propeller.

7. A pulley 18 in. in diameter makes 1200 rpm. If the belt that drives the pulley does not slip, find the speed of this belt in feet per second.

8. A rotary lawn mower has a blade 18 in. in diameter. If the tip of the cutting edge is to travel 2000 ft/sec, at how many revolutions per minute should the motor operate?

9. The outer horse on a merry-go-round is 20 ft from the center. At how many revolutions per minute should the merry-go-round turn to give the outer horse a velocity of 10 mi/hr?

10. How fast is the outer horse of Problem 9 going if the merry-go-round turns at 12 rpm?

11. A ferris wheel has a radius of 25 ft. If the passengers are to travel 15 mi/hr, at how many revolutions per minute should the wheel operate?

12. If the ferris wheel of Problem 11 turns at 14 rpm, how fast are the passengers traveling?

13. The pedals of a bicycle are attached to a sprocket wheel, which has a diameter of 6 in. A chain connects the sprocket wheel to a cog wheel whose diameter is 3.3 in., and this wheel is fastened to the rear wheel of the bicycle so that they both make the same number of revolutions. If the diameter of the rear wheel is 20 in. and if the pedals make 1 revolution/sec. find the speed of the bicycle in miles per hour.

14. A proposed racing bicycle is to travel at 20 mi/hr when the sprocket wheel turns 1 revolution/sec. If the rear wheel has a 30-in. diameter, and the cog wheel has a 3-in. diameter, what should be the diameter of the sprocket wheel?

15. One of the earliest artificial satellites put up by the Russians was approximately 940 mi high, and traveled about 26,000 ft/sec. How many minutes did it take for this satellite to make one revolution around the world?

CHAPTER 9

GRAPHS OF THE TRIGONOMETRIC FUNCTIONS

1. Objective. In this chapter we present the graphs of the six trigonometric functions. With these curves firmly in mind it is easy for the student to visualize the behavior of the trigonometric functions. Each of these graphs has a certain periodicity, and in fact, these trigonometric functions are the first and the simplest examples of periodic functions.

FIGURE 1

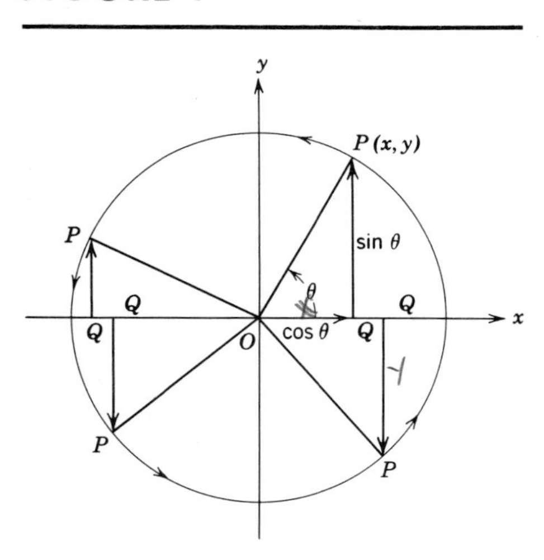

Periodic functions are of great importance in engineering, physics, and pure mathematics. In all three of these disciplines the most complicated problems involving periodic functions are ultimately reduced to problems involving combinations of the six trigonometric functions. It is a strange and fascinating fact that the lowly sine function, originally designed to assist in the solution of right triangles, turns out to be essential in the theory of light, sound, mechanics, and a myriad of other diverse fields. Using appropriate combinations of sin $n\theta$ one can give an equation for the skyline of New York City.

Of course, we cannot touch on these various applications in this short chapter. But we can begin the study of periodic functions by giving the relevant definitions and a few simple examples.

2. The Graph of $y = \sin \theta$. Let a point $P(x, y)$ describe the *unit circle* (a circle of radius 1 with center at the origin) as illustrated in Fig. 1. Since $r = 1$, we have

$$\sin \theta = \frac{y}{r} = \frac{y}{1} = y,$$

so that $\sin \theta$ is just *the directed line segment QP*. It is easy to visualize the behavior of $\sin \theta$ as θ increases from 0 to 2π, by visualizing the behavior of this directed line segment. The student should use Fig. 1 to check the entries in Table 1.

TABLE 1

As θ increases

From	To	$\sin \theta = QP$
0	$\pi/2$	Increases from 0 to 1
$\pi/2$	π	Decreases from 1 to 0
π	$3\pi/2$	Decreases from 0 to -1
$3\pi/2$	2π	Increases from -1 to 0

The graph of the function $y = \sin \theta$, shown in Fig. 2, is also very useful in studying the sine function. In this graph the angle θ is plotted along the horizontal axis and the values of the function $\sin \theta$ are plotted along the vertical axis. The values shown in Table 2 are sufficient for a rough

TABLE 2

θ	0°	30°	60°	90°	120°	150°	180°	210°	240°	270°	300°	330°	360°
	0	$\frac{\pi}{6}$	$\frac{\pi}{3}$	$\frac{\pi}{2}$	$\frac{2\pi}{3}$	$\frac{5\pi}{6}$	π	$\frac{7\pi}{6}$	$\frac{4\pi}{3}$	$\frac{3\pi}{2}$	$\frac{5\pi}{3}$	$\frac{11\pi}{6}$	2π
$\sin \theta$	0	$\frac{1}{2}$	$\frac{\sqrt{3}}{2}$	1	$\frac{\sqrt{3}}{2}$	$\frac{1}{2}$	0	$-\frac{1}{2}$	$-\frac{\sqrt{3}}{2}$	-1	$-\frac{\sqrt{3}}{2}$	$-\frac{1}{2}$	0

sketch of the curve. Further points can be plotted by using multiples of $\pi/4$ or by referring to Table B of the Appendix.

The curve of Fig. 2 shows in a different way how $\sin \theta$ behaves as θ increases from 0 to 2π. The student should verify that this curve is consistent with the entries of Table 1.

Both Figs. 1 and 2 show quite clearly that the maximum value for $\sin \theta$ is $+1$ and the minimum value is -1.

FIGURE 2

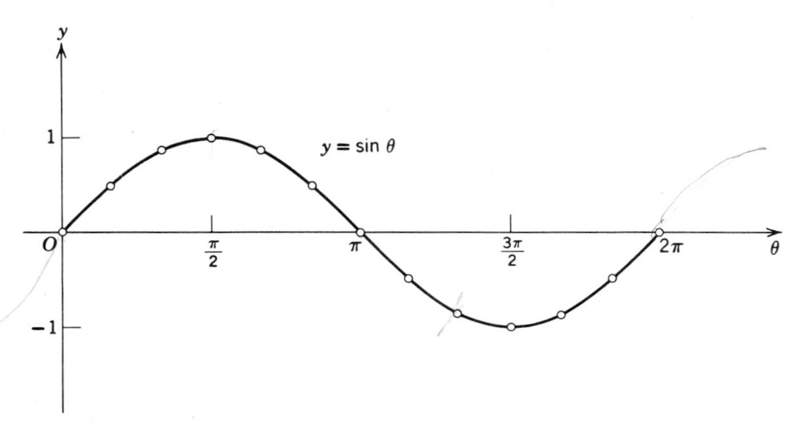

We have described the behavior of $\sin \theta$ as the line OP turns through one complete revolution. If the line OP continues to turn, this pattern is repeated. This repetition is shown in Fig. 3, where a smaller scale has been used in order to allow θ to vary over a larger interval,[1] in this case from -2π to 4π. To obtain the complete graph of $y = \sin \theta$, the x-axis would be extended indefinitely in both directions, and the pattern of Fig. 2 would be repeated infinitely often to the right as well as to the left.

FIGURE 3

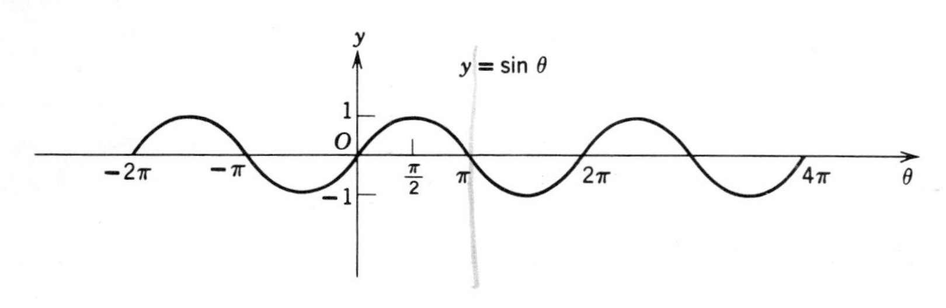

[1] An interval is the set of all numbers between two limits, for example the set of all x such that $1 \leq x \leq 5$ is called the interval from 1 to 5.

3. Periodicity. Either Fig. 1 or Fig. 3 shows immediately that

$$\sin(\theta + 2\pi) = \sin\theta \qquad (1)$$

for all values of θ. Geometrically this means that a copy of the graph in Fig. 3 could be shifted 2π units to the left (or to the right) and the copy would then fall on the original curve. Or stated differently, in sketching the curve of Fig. 3 it is necessary to sketch only the portion for θ between 0 and 2π, since the rest of the curve may be drawn by reproducing this pattern. A function with this property is called a periodic function. More precisely, we have

Definition 1. *If p is a constant (not zero) and if for every θ, the function value of θ equals the function value for $\theta + p$, then the function is said to be periodic and the number p is said to be a period of the function.*

Using function notation we could write $f(\theta + p) = f(\theta)$, if p is a period for the function $f(\theta)$. Clearly $\sin\theta$ is a periodic function and $p = 2\pi$ is a period. But notice that $\sin(\theta - 2\pi) = \sin\theta$ and $\sin(\theta + 4\pi) = \sin\theta$ for all angles θ, so -2π and 4π are also periods. This suggests

Definition 2. *The smallest positive period of a function is called* **the** *period of the function.*

Thus 2π is **the** period for $\sin\theta$. Because the curve of Fig. 3 resembles the cross-section picture of a gently moving lake, the period is frequently called the *wave length* of the function. Obviously, the period is the distance from the crest of one wave to the crest of the next wave. The greatest distance of the curve from the horizontal axis is called the *amplitude* of the function. Clearly it is just the maximum of the absolute value of the function. Thus, the curve $y = \sin\theta$ has amplitude 1, the maximum value of $|\sin\theta|$.

Example 1. Find the period and amplitude for the curve $y = 2\sin 3\theta$.

Solution. For convenience introduce a new angle $\alpha = 3\theta$. Then $y = 2\sin\alpha$. Since $|\sin\alpha|$ has maximum value 1, $|2\sin\alpha|$ will have maximum value $2 \times 1 = 2$. Hence the amplitude is 2. This maximum value is reached when $\alpha = \pi/2$. Since $3\theta = \alpha = \pi/2$, the maximum value is reached when $\theta = \pi/6$. The function $y = 2\sin\alpha$ has the period 2π. But $\alpha = 3\theta$. What change in θ will induce a change of 2π in α? Clearly if θ changes by $2\pi/3$, the change in α is three times as much, i.e., it is 2π. Therefore $2\pi/3$ is the period for $y = 2\sin 3\theta$.

If we wish to graph this function, it is very helpful to arrange the computations in tabular form as illustrated in Table 3.

The student should (*a*) check these entries, (*b*) extend the table by taking more values for θ, and (c) plot the points using the entries in the first and last rows.

TABLE 3

θ	0	$\frac{\pi}{18}$	$\frac{\pi}{12}$	$\frac{\pi}{9}$	...
3θ	0	$\frac{\pi}{6}$	$\frac{\pi}{4}$	$\frac{\pi}{3}$	...
$\sin 3\theta$	0	$\frac{1}{2}$	$\frac{\sqrt{2}}{2}$	$\frac{\sqrt{3}}{2}$	...
$y = 2 \sin 3\theta$	0	1	$\sqrt{2}$	$\sqrt{3}$	...

EXERCISE 37

In Problems 1 through 8 find the period and amplitude of each function and graph the function for θ in the indicated interval. The scale need not be the same for the horizontal and vertical axis, but should be chosen conveniently.

1. $y = 5 \sin 2\theta, 0 \leqq \theta \leqq \pi$.
2. $y = 4 \sin 3\theta, 0 \leqq \theta \leqq 2\pi/3$.
3. $y = -2 \sin 4\theta, 0 \leqq \theta \leqq \pi$.
4. $y = -3 \sin 2\theta, 0 \leqq \theta \leqq 2\pi$.
5. $y = \sin (\theta + \pi/3), -\pi \leqq \theta \leqq 3\pi$.
6. $y = \sin (\theta - \pi/3), -\pi \leqq \theta \leqq 3\pi$.
7. $y = 6 \sin (2\theta - \pi/4), 0 \leqq \theta \leqq \pi$.
8. $y = 5 \sin (3\theta + \pi/4), 0 \leqq \theta \leqq 2\pi/3$.

★**9.** Prove that the function $R \sin (K\theta + B)$ has the amplitude $|R|$ and the period $2\pi/|K|$.

★**10.** Find the period and the amplitude for the function $y = R \cos (K\theta + B)$.

4. Graphs of the Other Trigonometric Functions. The line segment QP of Fig. 1 is called the *line representation* (or *line value*) of the sine function, because the directed distance from Q to P is equal to $\sin \theta$. It is also possible to give line representations for the other five trigonometric functions, but we shall consider only those for the cosine and tangent functions.

Referring again to Fig. 1, where $r = 1$, we have $\cos \theta = x/r = x/1 = x$. But this is just the directed distance from O to Q, positive when Q is to the right of O and negative when Q is to the left of O. Therefore *the line segment OQ is the line representation of the cosine function.* It is easy to visualize the behavior of $\cos \theta$ as θ increases from 0 to 2π, by visualizing the behavior of this line segment.

A graph of the function $y = \cos\theta$ can easily be made by preparing a table of values similar to Table 2. However there is an easier way. By

FIGURE 4

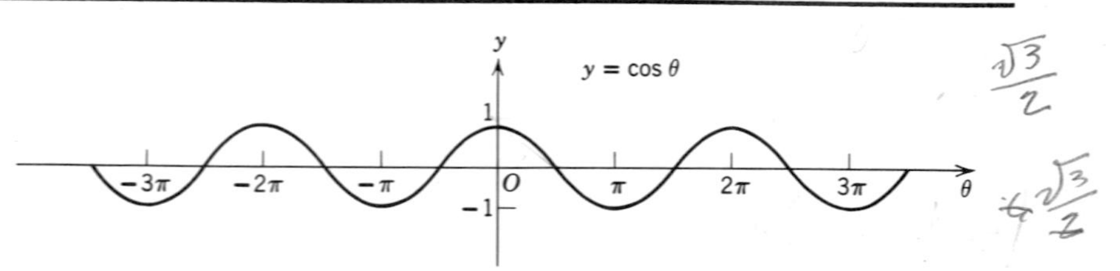

the addition formula for the cosine function, $\cos(\theta - \pi/2) = \cos\theta \cos(\pi/2) + \sin\theta \sin(\pi/2) = 0 \times \cos\theta + 1 \times \sin\theta$. Hence for all angles θ

$$\cos\left(\theta - \frac{\pi}{2}\right) = \sin\theta. \tag{2}$$

Geometrically (2) means that *the curve $y = \cos\theta$ can be obtained by translating (moving) the curve $y = \sin\theta$ (Fig. 3) to the left $\pi/2$ units, thus obtaining the curve of Fig. 4.* To prove this statement, consider the y-coordinate of the curve $y = \sin\theta$ for some fixed angle θ. Equation (2) states that this y-coordinate is the same as that obtained for the curve $y = \cos\theta$ when the angle is decreased by $\pi/2$. But this decrease in the angle is obtained by shifting the curve $\pi/2$ units to the left. Q.E.D.

Since the two curves are congruent, all of our knowledge about the sine curve—its period, its amplitude, etc.—can be applied directly to the cosine curve.

FIGURE 5

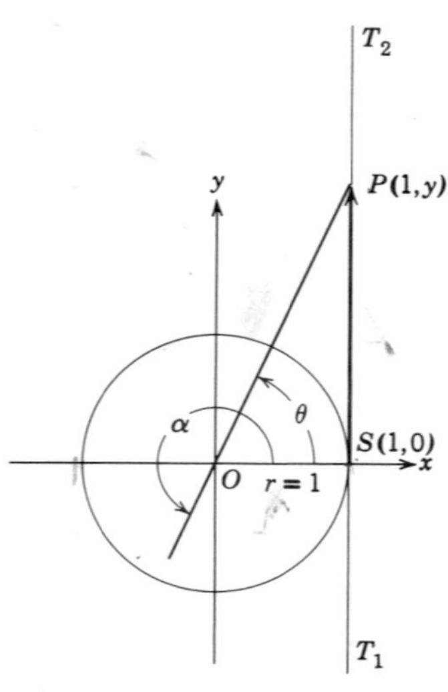

Figure 5 shows the line representation for the tangent function. A line T_1T_2 is drawn tangent to the unit circle at the point $S(1, 0)$. If OP, the terminal side of θ, meets the line T_1T_2 at P then the directed distance from S to P equals $\tan\theta$. For if θ is in Q.I as shown in the figure, then

$$\tan\theta = \frac{y}{x} = \frac{y}{1} = y$$

so $\tan\theta = SP$. Suppose next that the angle is in Q.III and let us call it α. To find the intersection of the terminal side of α with the line T_1T_2 it is necessary to extend the terminal side backwards. Notice that this extended line makes an angle $\alpha - \pi = \theta$ with the positive x-axis. Since

$$(3) \qquad \tan\theta = \tan(\alpha - \pi) = \frac{\tan\alpha - \tan\pi}{1 + \tan\alpha\tan\pi} = \frac{\tan\alpha - 0}{1 + 0} = \tan\alpha,$$

this reversal of direction does not change the tangent function, hence in this case also, $\tan\alpha = SP$.

If the angle in question is in Q.II, or in Q.IV, the intersection point of the terminal side with the line T_1T_2 will lie below the x-axis so that the directed distance SP will be negative. But this is consistent with the fact that for angles in Q.II and Q.IV, $\tan\theta$ is negative. Thus in all cases $\tan\theta = SP$.

FIGURE 6

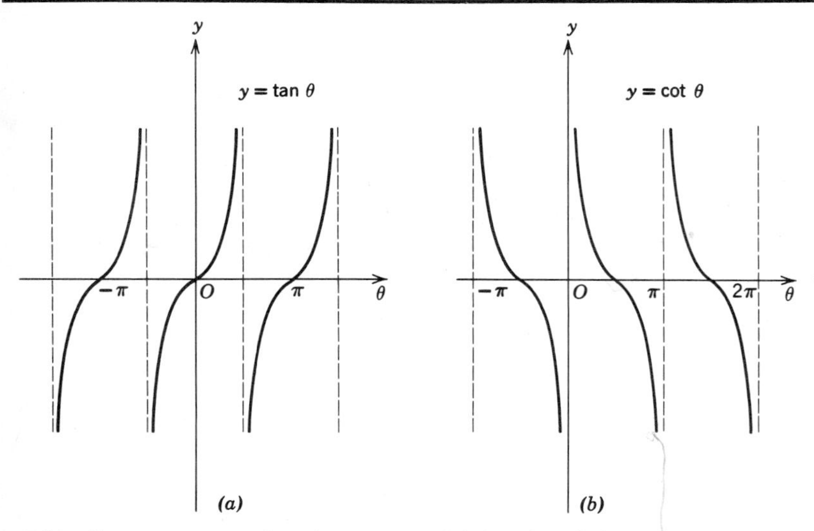

This line representation is very useful in visualizing the behavior of $\tan\theta$ as θ increases from 0 to 2π. As an example, consider what happens as θ approaches the angle $\pi/2$ through values of θ that are slightly less than $\pi/2$. The line OP turns so that it is nearly parallel to T_1T_2 and the point P recedes further and further away. Thus, the length of the line segment SP increases without bound. This is symbolized by writing

$$(4) \qquad \tan\theta \to \infty \qquad \text{as} \qquad \theta \to \frac{\pi^-}{2},$$

(read, $\tan\theta$ approaches infinity as θ approaches $\pi/2$ from the negative side) and this means that given any number M, no matter how large, there is an angle θ near $\pi/2$ *but less than* $\pi/2$, such that

$$\tan \theta > M. \tag{5}$$

It is easy to make a graph of the function $y = \tan \theta$ by preparing a table of values similar to Table 2. The resulting curve is shown in Fig. 6*a*. Notice that this curve has breaks or jumps at the points $\theta = -\pi/2, \pi/2, 3\pi/2, \cdots$. This happens whenever the line SP of Fig. 5 is parallel to T_1T_2. The graph of $y = \cot \theta$ shown in Fig. 6*b* has the same type of jump at $\theta = 0, \pm\pi, \pm 2\pi, \cdots$.

Although $\sin \theta$ and $\cos \theta$ both have the period 2π, their quotient $\tan \theta$ has period π. This is easy to visualize from the curve of Fig. 6*a*, and the

FIGURE 7

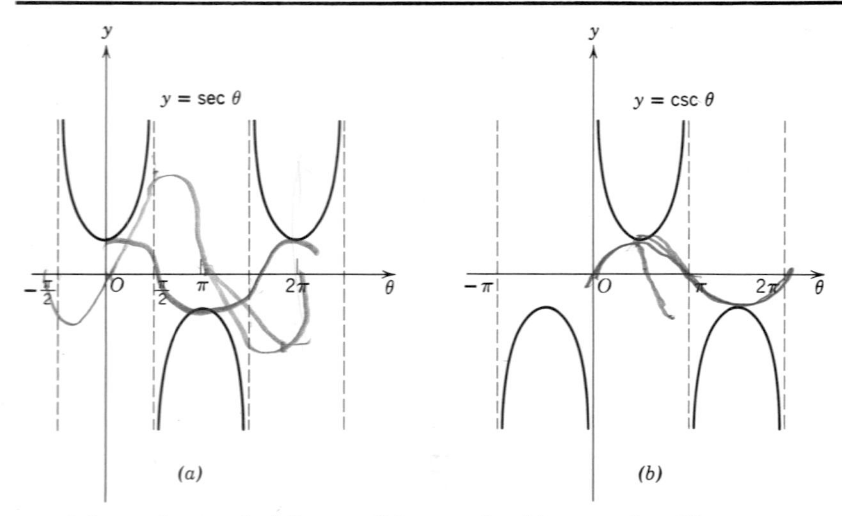

proof that π is a period for $\tan \theta$ is contained in equation (3).

The curve for $y = \csc \theta$ is shown in Fig. 7*b*. Since

$$\csc \theta = \frac{1}{\sin \theta}, \tag{6}$$

it is easy to trace the curve for $y = \csc \theta$, knowing the curve for $y = \sin \theta$, Fig. 3. Whenever $\sin \theta$ is positive its reciprocal $\csc \theta$ is also positive. Whenever $\sin \theta$ is negative its reciprocal $\csc \theta$ is negative. When $0 < \sin \theta < 1$, then by equation (6) $\csc \theta > 1$. As θ approaches zero through positive values, so also does $\sin \theta$, and (6) shows that $\csc \theta$ becomes large without bound (in symbols, $\csc \theta \to \infty$ as $\theta \to 0^+$). If θ approaches zero through negative values, then $|\csc \theta|$ becomes large without bound, but $\csc \theta$ is negative (in symbols $\csc \theta \to -\infty$ as $\theta \to 0^-$). All of these assertions should be verified visually by referring to Fig. 7*b* and comparing it with Fig. 3.

Finally, the graph of $y = \sec \theta$, shown in Fig. 7*a* is easily obtained by translating the curve of Fig. 7*b* to the left $\pi/2$ units.

These graphs give an easy way to visualize

Theorem 1. *For the zeros of the six trigonometric functions we have*

$$\sin \theta = 0 \quad \textit{if and only if} \quad \theta = n\pi, \qquad n = 0, \pm 1, \pm 2, \pm 3, \cdots.$$

$$\cos \theta = 0 \quad \textit{if and only if} \quad \theta = \frac{\pi}{2} + n\pi, \quad n = 0, \pm 1, \pm 2, \pm 3, \cdots.$$

$$\tan \theta = 0 \quad \textit{if and only if} \quad \theta = n\pi, \qquad n = 0, \pm 1, \pm 2, \pm 3, \cdots.$$

$$\cot \theta = 0 \quad \textit{if and only if} \quad \theta = \frac{\pi}{2} + n\pi, \quad n = 0, \pm 1, \pm 2, \pm 3, \cdots.$$

$\sec \theta$ and $\csc \theta$ are never zero.

Example 2. Find five values of θ for which $\sin(2\theta + \pi/6) = 0$. That is, find five roots for this equation.

Solution. By Theorem 1 the angle $2\theta + \pi/6$ must assume the values listed, that is,

$$2\theta + \frac{\pi}{6} = 0, \pi, -\pi, 2\pi, -2\pi, \cdots.$$

Hence, on subtracting $\pi/6$ from both sides of *these* equations,

$$2\theta = -\frac{\pi}{6}, \frac{5\pi}{6}, -\frac{7\pi}{6}, \frac{11\pi}{6}, -\frac{13\pi}{6}, \cdots.$$

Finally, dividing both sides of *these* equations by 2, gives

$$\theta = -\frac{\pi}{12}, \frac{5\pi}{12}, -\frac{7\pi}{12}, \frac{11\pi}{12}, -\frac{13\pi}{12}, \cdots.$$

EXERCISE 38

1. Use the line representation OQ of Fig. 1 for the cosine function to prepare a table similar to Table 1.

2. Use the line representation SP of Fig. 5 for the tangent function to prepare a table similar to Table 1.

3. Prove that $\sin(\theta + \pi/2) = \cos \theta$ for all angles θ.

4. Draw figures similar to Fig. 5, showing θ in Q.II and θ in Q.IV and prove that in each case $\tan \theta = SP$.

5. Discuss the behavior of $\tan \theta$ as θ approaches $\pi/2$ through values of θ that are slightly larger than $\pi/2$.

6. Discuss the behavior of $\sec \theta$ as θ approaches $\pi/2$ through values of θ that are slightly larger than $\pi/2$.

7. Discuss the behavior of $\csc \theta$ as θ approaches π through angles less than π.

8. Discuss the behavior of $\csc \theta$ as θ approaches π through angles larger than π.

9. Prove that $\tan \theta$ has the period π.

10. What is the period for $\cot \theta$, $\sec \theta$, $\csc \theta$?

11. Prove the identity $\sec(\theta - \pi/2) = \csc \theta$. What does this identity imply for the curves $y = \sec \theta$ and $y = \csc \theta$?

12. Correct the statement "tan 90° is very large."

Find 3 solutions for each of the following equations.

13. $\cos \theta = 0$. **14.** $\cot \theta = 0$. **15.** $\tan \theta = 0$.

16. $\sin 2\theta = 0$. **17.** $\sin(3\theta + \pi/3) = 0$. **18.** $\sin(4\theta - \pi/6) = 0$.

19. $\cos(2A - \pi/4) = 0$. **20.** $\cos(5B - \pi/3) = 0$. **21.** $\cot(2C + 5\pi/2) = 0$.

★ 5. The Graph of $y = \sin(\alpha + C)$. We first study the substitution $\theta = \alpha + C$ where for convenience we suppose that C is positive. Figure 8 shows two horizontal axes, one for the variable θ and one for the variable α. The origin for the α-axis is C units to the right of the origin for the

FIGURE 8

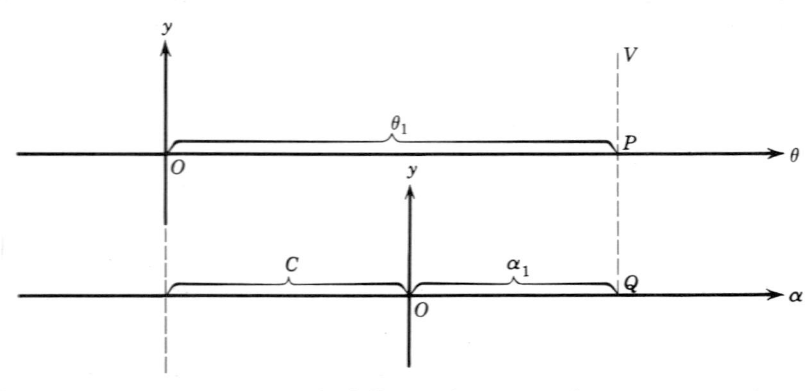

θ-axis. Suppose that a vertical line V intersects these axes at points P and Q with coordinates θ_1 and α_1 respectively. Then it is obvious from Fig. 8 that for these coordinates $\theta_1 = \alpha_1 + C$. Therefore we have

Theorem 2. *The substitution $\theta = \alpha + C$ $(C > 0)$ can be regarded as a change in the coordinate system. In this change the origin for the θ-axis*

is shifted C units to the right to give the origin for the α-axis. If C is negative the shift is to the left.

This is easy to recall by putting $\alpha = 0$ in the equation $\theta = \alpha + C$. Then $\alpha = 0$ corresponds to $\theta = C$.

Now make the substitution $\theta = \alpha + C$ in the equation $y = \sin(\alpha + C)$. This gives $y = \sin\theta$, and the graph of this equation is shown in Fig. 3.

FIGURE 9

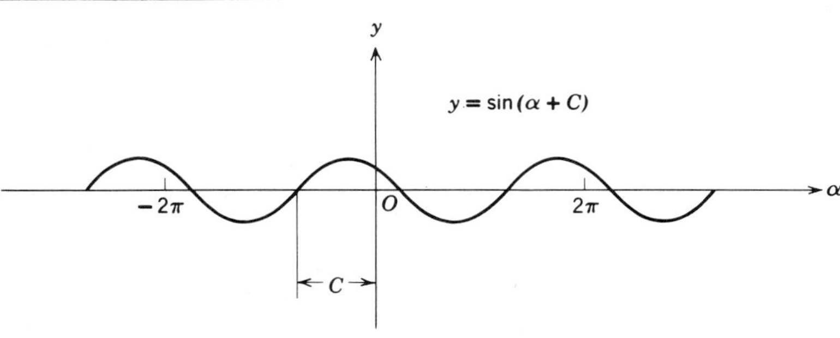

Then the graph for $y = \sin(\alpha + C)$ is easily obtained by an appropriate shift of the origin in Fig. 3. The resulting graph is shown in Fig. 9, where for convenience we have assumed $C > 0$.

FIGURE 10

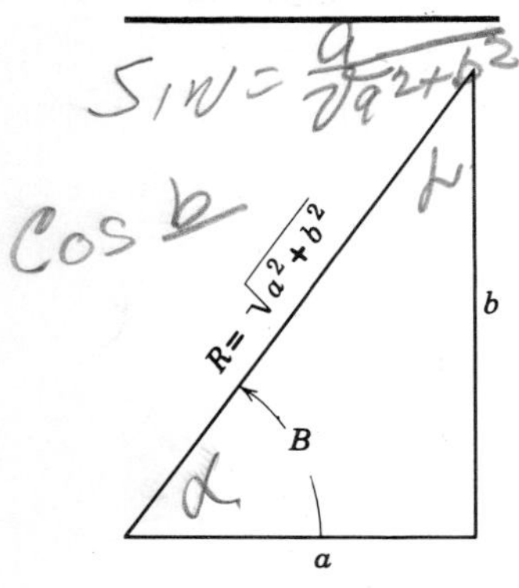

★6. The Graph of $y = a \sin\alpha + b\cos\alpha$.

We shall prove that *this graph is just a sine wave.*

$$y = \sqrt{a^2 + b^2}\sin(\alpha + B) \tag{7}$$

where B is an angle such that

$$\sin B = \frac{b}{\sqrt{a^2 + b^2}}, \quad \text{and} \quad \cos B = \frac{a}{\sqrt{a^2 + b^2}}. \tag{8}$$

The set (8) is easy to remember if one refers to Fig. 10. Using the set (8) we can write

$$\begin{aligned} y = a\sin\alpha + b\cos\alpha &= \sqrt{a^2 + b^2}\left(\frac{a}{\sqrt{a^2 + b^2}}\sin\alpha + \frac{b}{\sqrt{a^2 + b^2}}\cos\alpha\right), \\ &= \sqrt{a^2 + b^2}(\cos B \sin\alpha + \sin B\cos\alpha), \\ &= \sqrt{a^2 + b^2}\sin(\alpha + B). \end{aligned}$$

Q.E.D.

This means simply that the graph of $y = a \sin \alpha + b \cos \alpha$ is a sine wave as shown in Fig. 9 (with $C = B$) except that the amplitude $\sqrt{a^2 + b^2}$ need not be 1. Of course, the angle B may be a negative angle, for example if $a > 0$ and $b < 0$.

★7. Graphing by the Addition of y-Coordinates. In sketching the curve for a function such as

$$y = \tfrac{1}{3}\theta + \cos\theta \tag{9}$$

the labor of computing the coordinates for points on the curve may be quite tedious. However, we can obtain a sketch of the curve very quickly if we first graph the individual curves

(10) $y_1 = \tfrac{1}{3}\theta$, and (11) $y_2 = \cos\theta$.

These are shown in Fig. 11. With this notation (9) is

$$y = y_1 + y_2. \tag{12}$$

In other words, to sketch the curve of (9) we merely add the y-coordinates of the two curves for (10) and (11) for each fixed value of x. For example, as indicated in Fig. 11, we have from equation (12) that

$$AD = AB + AC,$$

where these are directed line segments. This addition can be done by compass or ruler, or merely by sight if we do not require a high degree of accuracy. The resulting curve, the curve for (9), is shown in a heavy line in Fig. 11. Thus, if we already know the curves for individual members of the right side of (9), then with little or no computation we can quickly sketch the composite curve.

FIGURE 11

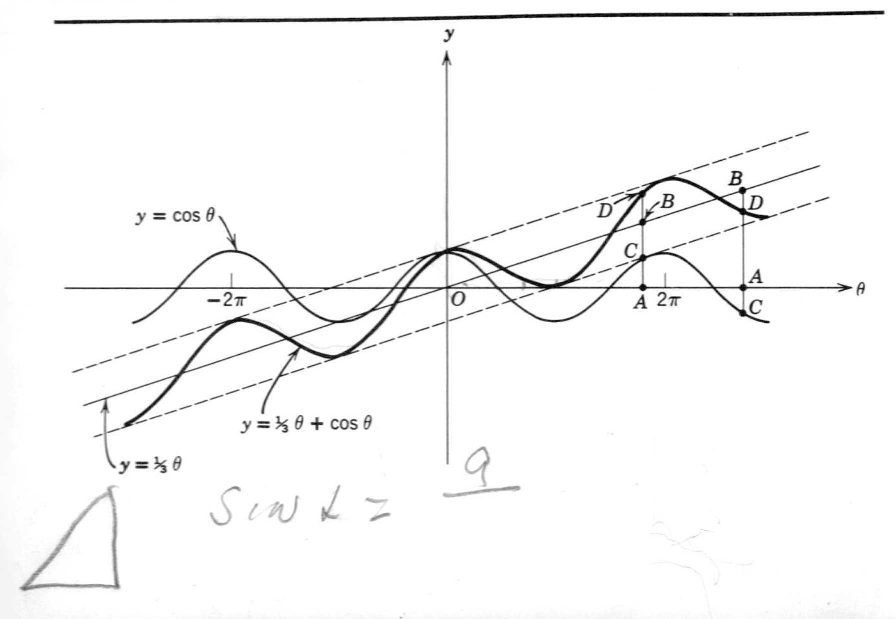

Notice that in this particular case $y_1 = \theta/3$ is the equation of a straight line through the two points (0, 0) and (3, 1), and the curve for $y_2 = \cos\theta$ is already known (Fig. 4). Further, since $|\cos\theta| \leqq 1$ we can draw the two parallel lines shown dotted in the figure, which form the boundaries of an infinite strip in which the curve must lie.

EXERCISE 39

In Problems 1 through 6, make a rough sketch of the curve for α in the interval $-\pi \leqq \alpha \leqq \pi$. For each curve find all of the values of α in this interval for which the curve cuts the horizontal axis.

1. $y = \sin(\alpha + 2\pi/3)$.

2. $y = \cos(\alpha - \pi/4)$.

3. $y = \tan(\alpha - \pi/3)$.

4. $y = \sec(\alpha + \pi/6)$.

5. $y = 3\sin\alpha + 3\cos\alpha$.

6. $y = \sin\alpha + \sqrt{3}\cos\alpha$.

7. What is the amplitude of the curves of Problems 5 and 6?

8. What is the amplitude of the curve $y = 5\cos\alpha + 12\sin\alpha$?

★**9.** Show that the curve $y = a\sin\alpha + b\cos\alpha$ can be written in the form $y = R\cos(\alpha + A)$, where $R > 0$. Find R and the equations that determine A.

In problems 10 through 17 sketch the curve over the indicated interval.

★**10.** $y = 1 + \sin\theta,\ -2\pi \leqq \theta \leqq 2\pi$.

★**11.** $y = 2 + \cos\theta,\ -\pi \leqq \theta \leqq \pi$.

★**12.** $y = \sin\theta + \cos 2\theta,\ 0 \leqq \theta \leqq 2\pi$.

★**13.** $y = \frac{1}{3}\theta + \sin\theta,\ -4\pi \leqq \theta \leqq 4\pi$.

★**14.** $y = x + \sin x,\ -4\pi \leqq x \leqq 4\pi$

★**15.** $y = |\sin x|,\ -2\pi \leqq x \leqq 2\pi$.

★**16.** $y = |\sin x| + x^2/4,\ -2\pi \leqq x \leqq 2\pi$.

★**17.** $y = \sin x + \frac{1}{8}\sin 2x,\ 0 \leqq x \leqq 2\pi$.

★**18.** What is the period for each of the following functions: (*a*) $y = \sin^2\theta$, (*b*) $y = \cos^2\theta$, (*c*) $y = \sin^3\theta$, (*d*) $y = |\sin\theta|$, (*e*) $y = \cos x + \sin 2x$, (*f*) $y = \cos 2x + \cos 3x$.

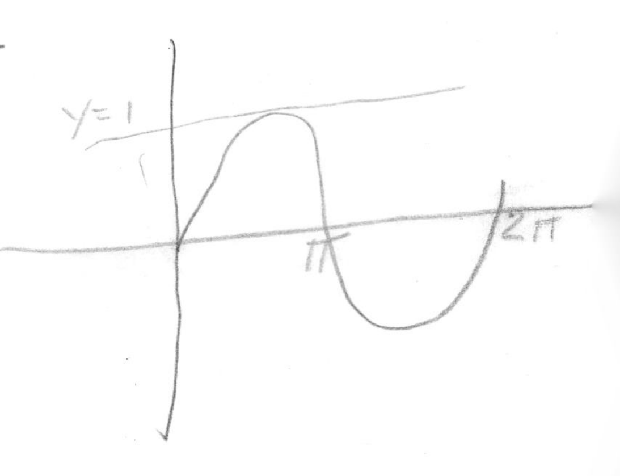

CHAPTER 10

TRIGONOMETRIC EQUATIONS

1. Objective. A trigonometric equation is an equation in which trigonometric functions of an angle occur. Such equations arise frequently in mathematics, physics, and in all types of engineering. To solve a trigonometric equation completely, means to find all values of the angle for which the equation is a true statement. Frequently there are infinitely many such values, and so in order to restrict the number of solutions we usually ask that the angle lie in some suitable interval, for example the interval $0° \leqq \theta < 360°$. In this chapter we will illustrate some of the methods that are used to solve trigonometric equations.

2. Some Simple Examples. All of the rules used in solving algebraic equations can be applied directly to trigonometric equations.

Example 1. Solve the equation

$$8 \sin \theta - 6 = 2 \sin \theta - 3, \tag{1}$$

(*a*) completely, (*b*) in the interval $0° \leqq \theta < 360°$.

Solution. (*a*) Transposition gives

$$\begin{aligned} 8 \sin \theta - 2 \sin \theta &= 6 - 3, \\ 6 \sin \theta &= 3, \\ \sin \theta &= \tfrac{1}{2}. \end{aligned}$$

Thus θ must be in Q.I or in Q.II. The related angle is 30°, so two of the solutions are $\theta = 30°$ and $\theta = 180° - 30° = 150°$. All angles coterminal with these angles are also solutions. But these are all of the solutions, and they can be listed by writing

$$\theta = 30° + n360°, \qquad \theta = 150° + n360°, \qquad n \text{ any integer.}$$

(*b*) If we ask that $0° \leqq \theta < 360°$, then only two of the infinitely many solutions for (1) will lie in this interval. These are $\theta = 30°, 150°$.

Example 2. Find all solutions of the equation

$$2\cos^2\theta - 5\cos\theta - 3 = 0, \tag{2}$$

in the interval $0° < \theta < 720°$.

Solution. We turn this into an algebraic equation by setting $x = \cos\theta$. Then (2) becomes $2x^2 - 5x - 3 = 0$. Factoring gives

$$(2x + 1)(x - 3) = 0.$$

Either	$2x + 1 = 0,$	Or	$x - 3 = 0,$
	$\cos\theta = x = -\frac{1}{2},$		$\cos\theta = x = 3,$
either	$\theta = 120° + n360°,$		No real angles.
or	$\theta = 240° + n360°.$		

To obtain the solutions in the given interval set $n = 0$ or 1. The solutions are $\theta = 120°, 240°, 480°, 600°$.

Example 3. Solve the equation

$$\tan\theta + 3\sec^2\theta = 8. \tag{3}$$

in the interval $0° < \theta < 180°$.

Solution. Using $\sec^2\theta = \tan^2\theta + 1$ in (3) gives

$$\tan\theta + 3(\tan^2\theta + 1) = 8,$$

and setting $x = \tan\theta$ yields

$$3x^2 + x - 5 = 0.$$

By the quadratic formula, $x = (-b \pm \sqrt{b^2 - 4ac})/2a$, we find

$$\tan\theta = x = \frac{-1 \pm \sqrt{1 + 60}}{6} = \frac{-1 \pm 7.810}{6} = 1.135, \text{ or } -1.468.$$

Therefore, from Table B in the Appendix, $\theta = 48°\,37'$ or $124°\,16'$.

Example 4. Solve the equation

$$\sin\theta\tan^2\theta - 3 + \tan^2\theta - 3\sin\theta = 0 \tag{4}$$

in the interval $-180° < \theta < 180°$.

Solution. In Example 3 it was possible to make a substitution so that only one trigonometric function appeared. In (4) the appropriate substitution is not obvious, but it can be solved by grouping the terms and factoring. We have

$$\sin\theta\tan^2\theta + \tan^2\theta - 3 - 3\sin\theta = 0,$$
$$\tan^2\theta(\sin\theta + 1) - 3(\sin\theta + 1) = 0,$$
$$(\tan^2\theta - 3)(\sin\theta + 1) = 0.$$

Either $\tan^2\theta - 3 = 0,$ $\tan^2\theta = 3,$ $\tan\theta = \pm\sqrt{3},$ $\theta = 60°, 120°, -60°, -120°.$

Or $\sin\theta + 1 = 0,$ $\sin\theta = -1,$ $\theta = -90°.$

Arranging the answers in increasing order, we have $\theta = -120°, -90°, -60°, 60°, 120°$.

Example 5. Solve[1]

(5) $$\sin\theta + \cos\theta = 1$$

Solution. If we substitute $\cos\theta = \pm\sqrt{1 - \sin^2\theta}$ and transpose we find

(6) $$\sin\theta - 1 = \pm\sqrt{1 - \sin^2\theta}.$$

Then on squaring both sides of this equation,

$$\sin^2\theta - 2\sin\theta + 1 = 1 - \sin^2\theta,$$
$$2\sin^2\theta - 2\sin\theta = 0,$$
$$2\sin\theta(\sin\theta - 1) = 0.$$

Either $2\sin\theta = 0,$ $\sin\theta = 0,$ $\theta = 0°, 180°.$

Or $\sin\theta - 1 = 0,$ $\sin\theta = 1,$ $\theta = 90°.$

Check. In the first four examples, each one of the steps was reversible, so that logically no check was necessary for the answers. In this example the step in which we squared both sides of (6) is not reversible. Every solution of (5) is in the list $\theta = 0°, 90°, 180°$, but it is possible that the list contains entries that are not solutions. Such entries are called *extraneous solutions*. A tabular arrangement makes checking an easy matter.

If	$\theta = 0°$	then	$\sin\theta + \cos\theta = 0 + 1 = 1,$
If	$\theta = 90°$	then	$\sin\theta + \cos\theta = 1 + 0 = 1,$
If	$\theta = 180°$	then	$\sin\theta + \cos\theta = 0 + (-1) \neq 1.$

Hence there are only *two* solutions for equation (5): $\theta = 0°, 90°$.

[1] Henceforth, whenever the interval is not specified, solve the equation for θ in the interval $0° \leqq \theta < 360°$.

Example 6. Solve

$$2\cos(3\theta + 24^\circ) = \sqrt{2}. \tag{7}$$

Solution. Obviously this equation is equivalent to $\cos(3\theta + 24^\circ) = \sqrt{2}/2$. Thus the angles in question are 45°, 315°, etc. But these are values for $3\theta + 24^\circ$. Hence we must write that:

Either $\quad 3\theta + 24^\circ = 45^\circ + n360^\circ, \qquad n = 0, \pm 1, \pm 2, \cdots.$

Or $\quad 3\theta + 24^\circ = 315^\circ + n360^\circ, \qquad n = 0, \pm 1, \pm 2, \cdots.$

Subtracting 24° from each side and dividing by 3 gives:

Either $\quad \theta = \dfrac{45^\circ - 24^\circ + n360^\circ}{3} = 7^\circ + n120^\circ,$

Or $\quad \theta = \dfrac{315^\circ - 24^\circ + n360^\circ}{3} = 97^\circ + n120^\circ.$

Taking $n = 0$, 1, and 2 successively, we find that $\theta = 7^\circ, 97^\circ, 127^\circ, 217^\circ, 247^\circ, 337^\circ$.

Example 7. Solve

$$\sin 7\theta + \sin\theta = 0. \tag{8}$$

Solution. By equation (41) of Chapter 7 this sum can be converted into the product

$$2\sin\frac{7\theta + \theta}{2}\cos\frac{7\theta - \theta}{2} = 0.$$

Either		Or	
	$\sin 4\theta = 0,$		$\cos 3\theta = 0,$
	$4\theta = n180^\circ,$		$3\theta = 90^\circ + n180^\circ,$
	$\theta = n45^\circ.$		$\theta = 30^\circ + n60^\circ.$

Using $n = 0, 1, 2, 3, 4, 5, 6, 7$ in the first solution, and $n = 0, 1, 2, 3, 4, 5$, in the second solution, gives all of the values of θ in the interval $0^\circ \leq \theta < 360^\circ$. Hence $\theta = 0^\circ, 30^\circ, 45^\circ, 90^\circ, 135^\circ, 150^\circ, 180^\circ, 210^\circ, 225^\circ, 270^\circ, 315^\circ, 330^\circ$.

★ 3. A General Principle. A fundamental theorem in algebra states that a polynomial equation of nth degree

$$a_0x^n + a_1x^{n-1} + a_2x^{n-2} + \cdots + a_{n-1}x + a_n = 0, \quad a_0 \neq 0,$$

cannot have more than n roots. For example, a quadratic equation has at most 2 roots. Is there a similar principle for trigonometric equations? There is, but it is somewhat more complicated to state.

For convenience we consider polynomials that involve only the sine and cosine functions. Naturally a term such as $\sin^3 \theta$ counts as a term of 3rd degree. But $\sin 3\theta$ will also be counted as a term of 3rd degree. To find the degree of the product of two terms, we add the degrees of each term: for example, $\sin 4\theta \cos 5\theta$ counts as a term of 9th degree. Then we have

Theorem 1. *If n is the largest degree of the terms of a polynomial equation in $\sin \theta$ and $\cos \theta$ then this equation has at most $2n$ roots in the interval* $0° \leqq \theta < 360°$.

The proof of this theorem is quite difficult and lies outside the scope of this book. However, we can observe this theorem in operation, in our examples. Equation (1) is obviously of 1st degree and there are 2 solutions in $0° \leqq \theta < 360°$. Equation (2) is of 2nd degree and so has at most 4 roots in this interval. Actually (2) has only 2 roots in $0° \leqq \theta < 360°$, but it is easy to account for the deficiency. Equations (5) and (7) are of degrees 1 and 3 respectively and both equations have the maximum number of roots possible in $0° \leqq \theta < 360°$. Finally equation (8) is of the 7th degree, so it may have 14 roots in this interval. Actually the final list contains only 12 entries, but this deficiency can be explained, if we wish, by pointing out that $\theta = 90°$ and $\theta = 270°$ are obtained from both factors, and hence each should be listed twice and counted as multiple roots.

Finally, we observe that an equation may not have any solutions. For example, the equation $\sin^2 \theta - 7 \sin \theta + 12 = 0$ is equivalent to $(\sin \theta - 3)(\sin \theta - 4) = 0$ so that either $\sin \theta = 3$ or $\sin \theta = 4$. Since neither of these possibilities can actually occur, for real angles θ, this equation has no real solutions. It is possible to give a satisfactory definition of the trigonometric functions for complex values of θ, and when this is done this equation will have complex solutions. The details of this fascinating story must be reserved for the course in complex variables.

EXERCISE 40

Solve each of the following equations for θ in the interval $0° \leqq \theta < 360°$. Give answers to the nearest 10′.

1. $\sin(\theta + 10°) = \sqrt{3}/2$.
2. $\cos(\theta - 15°) = \frac{1}{2}$.
3. $\tan(\theta - 70°) = -1$.
4. $\cot(\theta + 230°) = -\sqrt{3}$.
5. $2 \sin^2 \theta - 7 \sin \theta + 3 = 0$.
6. $2 \cos^2 \theta + 11 \cos \theta + 5 = 0$.

7. $\sin^2 \theta - \cos \theta + 1 = 0$.
8. $6(1 + \sin \theta) = \cos^2 \theta$.
9. $\sin \theta + 2 \csc \theta = 4$.
10. $5 \cos \theta + \sec \theta = 5$.
11. $\tan 2\theta = 2 \cot 2\theta$.
12. $\sin 3\theta = 2 \cos 3\theta$.
13. $\tan 2\theta = 2 \tan \theta$.
14. $\sin 2\theta = \sin \theta$.
15. $\cos 2\theta = \sin \theta$.
16. $\sin 4\theta = \cos 2\theta$.
17. $8 \tan \theta + 3 + 2 \sec^2 \theta = 0$.
18. $7 \csc^2 \theta = 6(1 + \cot \theta)$.
19. $2 \sin 5\theta \cos 3\theta - 2 \cos 5\theta \sin 3\theta = \sqrt{3}$.
20. $\cos 6\theta \cos 2\theta + \sin 6\theta \sin 2\theta = 1$
21. $\tan 4\theta - \tan 2\theta = 1 + \tan 2\theta \tan 4\theta$.
22. $1 + \tan \theta + \tan 2\theta = \tan \theta \tan 2\theta$.
23. $3 \sin \theta - \cos \theta = -3$.
24. $2 \sin \theta + \cos \theta = 2$.
★ **25.** $8 \sin \theta + \cos \theta = 4$.
★ **26.** $11 \sin \theta + 3 \cos \theta = 9$.
27. $\tan (3\theta - 10°) = \cot (2\theta + 15°)$.
28. $\sin \theta \csc (2\theta + 15°) = \cos \theta \sec (2\theta + 15°)$.
29. $\cos 5\theta + \cos 3\theta = 0$.
30. $\sin 5\theta + \sin \theta = 0$.
31. $2 \sin 2\theta - \tan 2\theta = 0$.
32. $\csc \theta + 3 \cot \theta = 0$.
33. $\sin^2 \theta + \sin \theta \cos \theta - 6 \cos^2 \theta = 0$.
34. $2 \sin^2 \theta + 7 \sin \theta \cos \theta + 3 \cos^2 \theta = 0$.
35. $1 - 2 \sin \theta = \cot \theta - 2 \cos \theta$.
36. $3 + \cos \theta = 3 \tan \theta + \sin \theta$.
37. $4 \cos^3 \theta + 3 = 4 \cos^2 \theta + 3 \cos \theta$.
38. $4 \sin^3 \theta + 8 \sin^2 \theta = 3 \sin \theta + 6$.
★ **39.** $\sin \theta + \cos \theta = \sin \theta \tan \theta + \cos \theta \cot \theta$.
★ **40.** $\sin \theta + \cos \theta = \sqrt{3} \sin \theta \cos \theta$.
★ **41.** $\sin 2\theta + \cos 3\theta = \sin 4\theta$.
★ **42.** $\cos \theta - \cos 5\theta = \sin 3\theta$.
★★ **43.** $\sin 6\theta \cos \theta = \sin 8\theta \cos 3\theta$.
★★ **44.** $\tan \theta + \tan 2\theta = \tan 3\theta$.

★ **45.** In a certain right triangle the sum of the lengths of the two sides is $\frac{7}{5}$ of the length of the hypotenuse. Find the angles of this triangle.

★ **46.** The area of a right triangle is $\frac{1}{8}$ of the square of the length of the hypotenuse. Find the angles of this triangle.

★ **47.** In an isosceles triangle the sum of the two equal altitudes is $\frac{1}{2}$ of the longer altitude. Find the base angles of this triangle.

★ **48.** The sides of a right triangle form a geometric progression. Find the smallest angle of this triangle.

★★ **49.** The sides of a right triangle form an arithmetic progression. Find the smallest angle of this triangle.

★★ **50.** Prove that for a root of the equation $a \sin \theta + b \cos \theta = c$, where a, b, and c are integers, $\sin \theta$ is rational if and only if $a^2 + b^2 - c^2$ is the square of an integer.

★ **51.** A homogeneous straight wire AB, 34.0 in. long is bent to form a right angle at a point C, 14.0 in. from the end A. The wire is then supported at C by a horizontal pin. If the wire is free to rotate about the pin at C, find the angle that the arm CB makes with the horizontal plane when the wire is in equilibrium under the forces of gravity.

★ **52.** A square is inscribed in a second square in such a way that the ratio of their areas is $\frac{8}{13}$. If θ is the smaller of the two angles that one side of the square makes with a side of the other square, find θ to the nearest 10 minutes.

Sin²θ+1−cos

Sin² = cos−1

HL on .345 on

LL S index to

6.345

Sin² =

Sin²

Sin² + 1 − cos

Sin² = ±√Sin²

Sin²θ + Sin = 0

Sinθ(Sinθ − 1) = 0;

Sinθ = 0

Sin

CHAPTER 11

INVERSE TRIGONOMETRIC FUNCTIONS

1. Objective. If we solve the equation $y = 2x + 3$ for x in terms of y, we find that $x = (y - 3)/2$. The function $x = (y - 3)/2$ is called the inverse function for the function $y = 2x + 3$. A function and its inverse relate the same pair of numbers (x, y). For example, both of these

TABLE 1

Name of the Primitive Function	Primitive Function	Inverse Function	A Pair That Satisfies Both Equations	
			x	y
Linear	$y = 3x - 7$	$x = (y + 7)/3$	6	11
Quadratic	$y = x^2$	$x = \sqrt{y}$	3	9
Cubic	$y = x^3 + 5$	$x = \sqrt[3]{y - 5}$	2	13
Exponential	$y = 10^x$	$x = \log y$	2	100
General	$y = f(x)$	$x = g(y)$	x_1	y_1

equations are satisfied by the pair $x = 1$, $y = 5$. A few other examples of functions and their inverses are listed in Table 1.

The symbol $\sqrt{y}$ was introduced to denote the function inverse to the function $y = x^2$. Similarly, the symbol $\log y$ was introduced to denote the function inverse to the function $y = 10^x$. Our objective is to introduce the appropriate symbols for the functions inverse to the trigonometric functions and to study the properties of these new functions.

★ 2. A Precise Definition.

We have given a few examples of functions and their inverses. The precise definition of an inverse function can be given very briefly if we use function notation. This is

Definition 1. *The function $x = g(y)$ is an inverse function for $y = f(x)$ if*

$$f(g(y)) = y. \tag{1}$$

We will illustrate equation (1) using the examples from Table 1. In the first example $f(x) = 3x - 7$ and $g(y) = (y + 7)/3$. The left side of equation (1) tells us to replace x by $g(y)$ wherever x occurs in $f(x)$. Doing this we find in this case

$$f(g(y)) = 3\left(\frac{y+7}{3}\right) - 7 = y + 7 - 7 = y$$

as required. The computations for the other three examples of Table 1 are:

Quadratic: $f(g(y)) = (\sqrt{y})^2 = y.$

Cubic: $f(g(y)) = (\sqrt[3]{y-5})^3 + 5 = y - 5 + 5 = y.$

Exponential: $f(g(y)) = 10^{\log y} = y.$

Inverse functions are not always unique. For example $x = -\sqrt{y}$ is also an inverse function for $y = x^2$. In such cases it is customary to call each such function *a branch of the inverse function*, and to settle on one such branch as *the principal branch of the inverse function*.

EXERCISE 41

For each of the functions listed below (*a*) find an inverse function by solving for x in terms of y, (*b*) check your answer by substituting in equation 1 as in the examples, and (*c*) find a pair of numbers (x, y) that satisfies both equations.

1. $y = -5x + 3.$ **2.** $y = -2x + 5.$ **3.** $y = \frac{1}{3}x - 7.$

4. $y = \frac{1}{2}x + 1.$ **5.** $y = \dfrac{2x+3}{x-1}.$ **6.** $y = \dfrac{x-5}{2x+7}.$

7. $y = x^2 + 2x - 15.$ **8.** $y = x^2 - 4x + 3.$

9. $y = -x^2 + 4x + 5.$ **10.** $y = -x^2 + 3x + 7.$

★**11.** Prove that if $y = (-x + 2)/(3x + 1) = f(x)$; then the inverse function is just $x = f(y)$. In other words, this function is its own inverse.

3. The Inverse Trigonometric Functions. If

(2) $$u = \sin\theta$$

then the inverse function is expressed by saying

(3) θ is an angle whose sine is u.

Just as the symbols $\theta = \sqrt{u}$ are an abbreviation for the phrase "θ is an angle whose square is u," the symbols

(4) $$\theta = \text{arc}\sin u$$

are an abbreviation for the statement (3). The other inverse trigonometric functions are abbreviated similarly:

	Symbols	Meaning
(5)	$\theta = \text{arc}\cos u$,	θ is an angle whose cosine is u,
(6)	$\theta = \text{arc}\tan u$,	θ is an angle whose tangent is u,
(7)	$\theta = \text{arc}\cot u$,	θ is an angle whose cotangent is u,
(8)	$\theta = \text{arc}\sec u$,	θ is an angle whose secant is u,
(9)	$\theta = \text{arc}\csc u$,	θ is an angle whose cosecant is u.

Some authors use the symbols $\sin^{-1} u$ instead of arc sin u, but since $\sin^{-1} u$ may easily be confused with $(\sin u)^{-1} = 1/\sin u = \csc u$, we prefer the symbols arc sin u.

Example 1. Find $\theta = \text{arc}\sin 1$.

Solution. This means find an angle θ whose sine is 1. Since $\sin 90° = 1$, we have $\theta = 90°$ as a possible answer. But any angle coterminal with 90° is also a solution. Therefore

$$\text{arc}\sin 1 = 90° + n360°, \qquad n = 0, \pm 1, \pm 2, \cdots,$$

or

$$\text{arc}\sin 1 = 90°, 450°, 810°, \cdots, -270°, -630°, \cdots.$$

As this example shows, arc sin u is not uniquely determined, indeed there are infinitely many angles θ for which $\sin\theta = 1$. We want to make the angle θ unique by agreeing on a principal branch for $\theta = \text{arc}\sin u$, but this is best done after we have examined the graph of this function.

The graph of any function such as $\theta = \text{arc}\sin u$, is merely the collection of all points whose coordinates (u, θ) satisfy the equation. It is customary to plot the independent variable (in this case u) on the horizontal axis, and the dependent variable (in this case θ) on the vertical axis. Since the equations $u = \sin\theta$, and $\theta = \text{arc}\sin u$ are satisfied by the same points (u, θ), the graph of $\theta = \text{arc sin } u$ is identical with the graph of $u = \sin \theta$, except that the two axes are interchanged. These curves are shown in Figs. 1 and 2. It is obvious that the interchange of the horizontal and vertical axes can be obtained by rotating the plane around the line L (shown in Fig. 1) which passes through the origin and makes an angle of 45° with the horizontal axis. This same rotation then carries the graph of $u = \sin \theta$ into the graph of $\theta = \text{arc sin } u$.

FIGURE 1

FIGURE 2

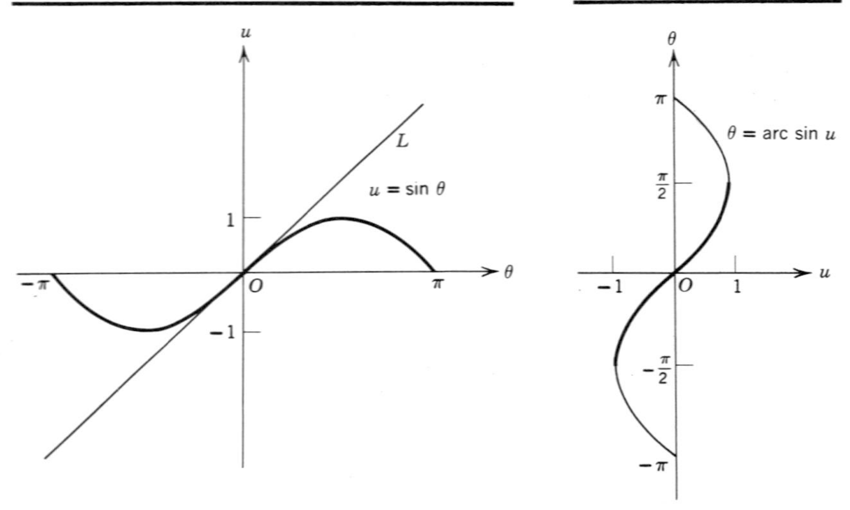

Similarly, by rotating the plane of Fig. 4 Chapter 9 we can obtain the graph of $\theta = \text{arc cos } u$ shown in Fig. 3. To obtain the graph of $\theta = \text{arc tan } u$, shown in Fig. 4, we merely rotate the plane of Fig. 6*a* Chapter 9. We leave it as an exercise for the student to use this method to sketch the curves for $\theta = \text{arc cot } u$, $\theta = \text{arc sec } u$, and $\theta = \text{arc csc } u$.

4. The Principal Branch. We have seen that arc sin 1 has many possible values. Our task is to select one of these as the principal value. This amounts to selecting a piece of the curve of Fig. 2 in such a way that for each fixed value u_0 of u there is only one point on this piece of the curve with the horizontal coordinate $u = u_0$. Stated differently: we want a piece of the curve such that each vertical line intersects the piece of the curve in at most one point. Such a piece of the curve is called a *branch of the curve*. In each of Figs. 2, 3, and 4, the principal branch of the curve is shown in heavy lines. The student should show that these drawings are consistent with

Definition 2. *The principal branches of the inverse trigonometric functions are determined by the following inequalities:*

$$-\pi/2 = -90^\circ \leqq \text{arc sin } u \leqq 90^\circ = \pi/2, \tag{10}$$

$$0 = 0^\circ \leqq \text{arc cos } u \leqq 180^\circ = \pi, \tag{11}$$

$$-\pi/2 = -90^\circ < \text{arc tan } u < 90^\circ = \pi/2, \tag{12}$$

$$-\pi/2 = -90^\circ < \text{arc cot } u \leqq 90^\circ = \pi/2, \tag{13}$$

$$0 = 0^\circ \leqq \text{arc sec } u \leqq 180^\circ = \pi, \tag{14}$$

$$-\pi/2 = -90^\circ \leqq \text{arc csc } u \leqq 90^\circ = \pi/2. \tag{15}$$

FIGURE 3 **FIGURE 4**

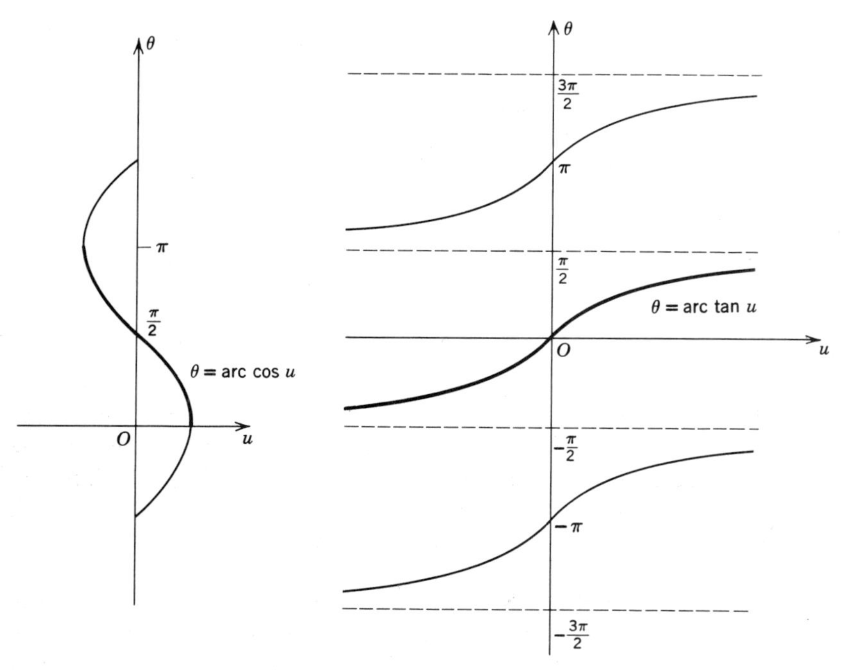

The principal value of an inverse trigonometric function is a value that satisfies the pertinent inequality from the above set.

Hereafter, unless otherwise specified, we shall mean the principal value, whenever we use an inverse function.

Example 2. Find (*a*) arc cos $\frac{1}{2}$, (*b*) arc tan -1, (*c*) arc cot $\sqrt{3}$, (*d*) arc sec $-\sqrt{2}$.

Solution. In each case we recognize from experience the angles with the required property. All that remains is to check that these angles are principal values. The answers are:

(*a*) $\text{arc cos } \frac{1}{2} = 60° = \pi/3$,

(*b*) $\text{arc tan } -1 = -45° = -\pi/4$,

(*c*) $\text{arc cot } \sqrt{3} = 30° = \pi/6$,

(*d*) $\text{arc sec } -\sqrt{2} = 135° = 3\pi/4$.

FIGURE 5

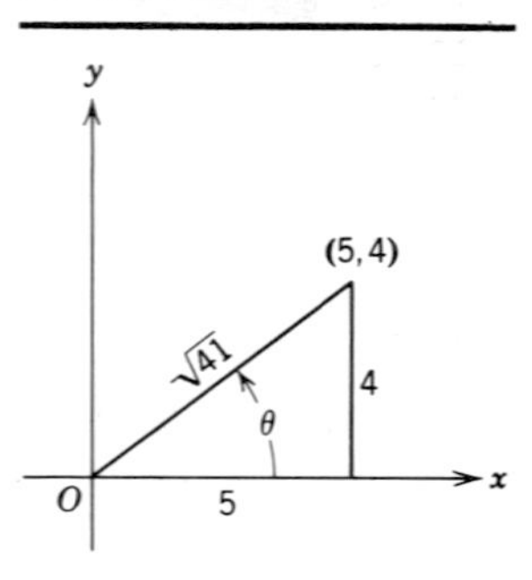

Example 3. Find sec (arc tan $\frac{4}{5}$).

Solution. It is convenient to sketch the angle in standard position as shown in Fig. 5. Then $\theta = \text{arc tan } \frac{4}{5}$. By the Pythagorean Theorem $r = \sqrt{41}$. Hence sec (arc tan $\frac{4}{5}$) $=$ $\sec \theta = \sqrt{41}/5$.

FIGURE 6

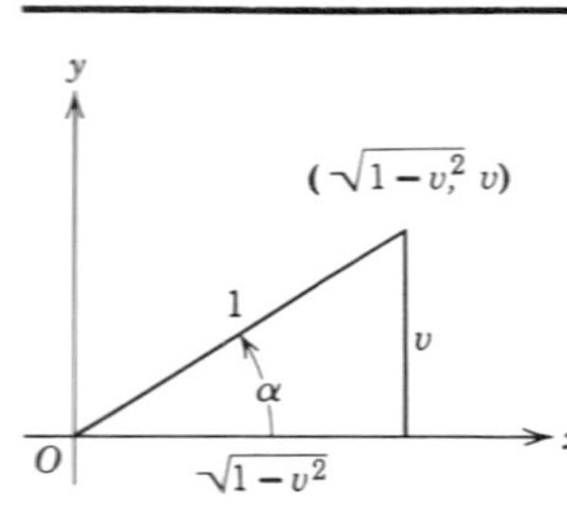

Example 4. Find cos (arc sin v).

Solution. Let $\alpha = \text{arc sin } v$. We must find $\cos \alpha$. A sketch showing the angle α in standard position is quite helpful (Fig. 6). If we select a point on the terminal side of α with $r = 1$ then by the Pythagorean Theorem the coordinates of this point will be $(\sqrt{1 - v^2}, v)$.

Hence $\cos (\text{arc sin } v) = \cos \alpha = \sqrt{1 - v^2}$. One might expect to find $\pm\sqrt{1 - v^2}$, but for the principal value of the inverse sine function, α must be either in Q.I or Q.IV. In either case $\cos \alpha \geqq 0$, and so the minus sign must be dropped from in front of the radical. Similarly $\sin (\text{arc cos } u) = \sqrt{1 - u^2}$, and hence is never negative.

EXERCISE 42

In Problems 1 through 10 find the angle in degrees to the nearest 10 minutes. In Problems 11 through 18 find the angle in radians.

1. arc cos 0.	**2.** arc tan 0.	**3.** $\text{arc sin}(-\frac{1}{2})$.
4. $\text{arc cos}(-\sqrt{2}/2)$.	**5.** $\text{arc sec}\sqrt{2}$.	**6.** arc csc 1.
7. arc tan .2401.	**8.** arc sin −.3007.	**9.** arc cos −.7642.
10. arc cot 1.220.	**11.** arc sin −1.	**12.** arc cos −1.
13. $\text{arc tan}\sqrt{3}$.	**14.** $\text{arc csc}\sqrt{2}$.	**15.** arc cot 1.
16. $\text{arc sin}\sqrt{3}/2$.	**17.** $\text{arc cos}(-\frac{1}{2})$.	**18.** arc tan 1.

In Problems 19 through 40 simplify the given expression and find a numerical value whenever possible.

19. $\cos(\text{arc tan } \frac{3}{4})$.

20. $\tan(\text{arc cos } \frac{3}{5})$.

21. $\sin(\text{arc cos } \frac{5}{13})$.

22. $\cos(\text{arc sin } \frac{7}{25})$.

23. $\tan(\text{arc sin } -.7009)$.

24. $\sin(\text{arc tan } -.4245)$.

25. $\cos(\text{arc cos } a)$.

26. $\tan(\text{arc tan } b)$.

27. $\cot(\text{arc cot } c)$.

28. $\sin(\text{arc sin } d)$.

29. $\sin(\text{arc tan } e)$.

30. $\cos(\text{arc sec } f)$.

31. $\sec(\text{arc sin } g)$.

32. $\tan(\text{arc cos } h)$.

33. $\sin(2 \text{ arc cos } u)$.

34. $\cos(2 \text{ arc sin } u)$.

35. $\cos(2 \text{ arc tan } u)$.

36. $\sin(2 \text{ arc cot } u)$.

37. $\sin(\frac{1}{2} \text{ arc sin } u)$.

38. $\cos(\frac{1}{2} \text{ arc cos } u)$.

39. $\tan(\frac{1}{2} \text{ arc cos } u)$.

40. $\sec(\frac{1}{2} \text{ arc cos } u)$.

In Problems 41 through 51 identify the statement as true or false and give reasons.

41. $2 \text{ arc sin } u = \text{arc sin } 2u$.

42. $2 \text{ arc sin } u = \text{arc cos } (1 - 2u^2)$, for $u \geqq 0$.

43. $\text{arc tan } u = \dfrac{\text{arc sin } u}{\text{arc cos } u}$.

44. $\cos\left(\dfrac{\pi}{2} - \text{arc sin } \dfrac{2}{3}\right) = \dfrac{2}{3}$.

45. $\tan(\pi - \text{arc tan } \frac{7}{8}) = -\frac{7}{8}$.

46. $\text{arc cot } v = \dfrac{1}{\text{arc tan } v}$.

47. $\text{arc cot } v = \text{arc tan } \dfrac{1}{v}$.

48. $\text{arc sec } \sqrt{v} = \text{arc cos } 1/\sqrt{v}$.

49. $\text{arc sin}(-w) = -\text{arc sin } w$.

50. $\text{arc cos}(-u) = \text{arc cos } u$.

51. $\text{arc cos}(-u) = \pi - \text{arc cos } u$.

★5. Further Examples. Problems involving the inverse trigonometric functions may be more involved than those of the preceding paragraph.

Example 5. If $C = \text{arc tan } 3 + \text{arc sin } (\frac{5}{13})$, find the quadrant for C without using tables.

Solution. Let $A = \text{arc tan } 3$, and let $B = \text{arc sin } \frac{5}{13}$. Since A and B are both in Q.I then $C = A + B$ is either in Q.I or Q.II. Hence it will suffice to determine the sign of $\cos C$. By constructing suitable triangles we find that:

$$\sin A = \frac{3}{\sqrt{10}} = \frac{3\sqrt{10}}{10}, \qquad \sin B = \frac{5}{13},$$

$$\cos A = \frac{1}{\sqrt{10}} = \frac{\sqrt{10}}{10}, \qquad \cos B = \frac{12}{13},$$

$$\cos C = \cos A \cos B - \sin A \sin B = \frac{\sqrt{10}}{10}\frac{12}{13} - \frac{3\sqrt{10}}{10}\frac{5}{13}$$

$$= \frac{(12-15)\sqrt{10}}{130} = \frac{-3\sqrt{10}}{130} < 0.$$

Therefore C is in Q.II.

Example 6. Simplify the expression $\sin(\text{arc}\sin x + \text{arc}\sin y)$.

Solution. Let $A = \text{arc}\sin x$, and $B = \text{arc}\sin y$. Then

$$\sin A = x, \quad \cos A = \sqrt{1-x^2}, \quad \sin B = y, \quad \cos B = \sqrt{1-y^2}.$$

Consequently the given expression is equal to

$$\sin(A+B) = \sin A \cos B + \cos A \sin B = x\sqrt{1-y^2} + y\sqrt{1-x^2},$$

which is manifestly much simpler than the original expression.

Example 7. Prove that $\text{arc}\cot(1/9) + \text{arc}\cot(4/5) = 3\pi/4$.

Solution. Let $A = \text{arc}\cot(1/9)$, and let $B = \text{arc}\cot(4/5)$. Then obviously $\tan A = 9$ and $\tan B = 5/4$. Therefore

$$\tan(A+B) = \frac{\tan A + \tan B}{1 - \tan A \tan B} = \frac{9 + 5/4}{1 - 9 \times 5/4}$$

$$= \frac{36+5}{4-45} = \frac{41}{-41} = -1.$$

Whence $A + B = 3\pi/4 + n\pi$, where n is an integer. But A and B are both in Q.I. Therefore n must be zero.

EXERCISE 43

In Problems 1 through 4 determine the sine and cosine of the given angle without using tables, and determine the quadrant of the angle.

1. $\text{arc}\cos \frac{3}{5} + \text{arc}\tan \frac{5}{12}$.
2. $\text{arc}\tan 2 + \text{arc}\sin \frac{3}{5}$.
3. $\text{arc}\tan 3 + \text{arc}\csc 3$.
4. $\text{arc}\cot \frac{2}{5} + \text{arc}\tan \frac{3}{7}$.
5. Find $\sin(\text{arc}\sin x + 2\,\text{arc}\tan x)$.
6. Find $\cos(2\,\text{arc}\cos y + \text{arc}\tan y)$.
7. Prove that $\text{arc}\tan 2/3 + \text{arc}\tan 1/5 = \pi/4$.

★8. Prove that $2\,\text{arc}\tan u + \text{arc}\sin 2u/(1+u^2) = \pi$ if $u > 1$.

★9. Graph the functions for the indicated intervals:

(a) $y = \text{arc}\cos x^2, \quad -1 \leqq x \leqq 1,$

(b) $y = (\text{arc}\cos x)^2, \quad -1 \leqq x \leqq 1,$

(c) $y = \text{arc}\cos(\cos x), \quad -4\pi \leqq x \leqq 4\pi.$

★ **10.** Graph the functions for the indicated intervals:

(*a*) $y = \text{arc sin } x^2, \qquad -1 \leqq x \leqq 1,$

(*b*) $y = (\text{arc sin } x)^2, \qquad -1 \leqq x \leqq 1,$

(*c*) $y = \text{arc sin } (\sin x), \qquad -4\pi \leqq x \leqq 4\pi.$

★ **11.** Among the following functions defined for the interval $-1 < x < 1$, determine which are odd functions, which are even functions, and which are neither:

(*a*) arc tan x, (*b*) (arc sin x)(arc cos x), (*c*) (arc sin x)(arc tan x), (*d*) $x^2 +$ arc cos x, (*e*) $x^3 -$ arc cos $x + \pi/2$, (*f*) x arc sin x.

★ CHAPTER 12

SPECIAL TOPICS

1. The Area of a Triangle. If two sides and the included angle are known, the area of a triangle is given by

Theorem 1. *The area K of a triangle ABC is given by*

$$K = \tfrac{1}{2}ab \sin C, \qquad K = \tfrac{1}{2}bc \sin A, \qquad K = \tfrac{1}{2}ca \sin B. \tag{1}$$

Proof. It is sufficient to prove any one of these formulas, because the other two follow from it by a cyclic permutation of the letters.

Let h be the length of the perpendicular dropped from point B to the

FIGURE 1

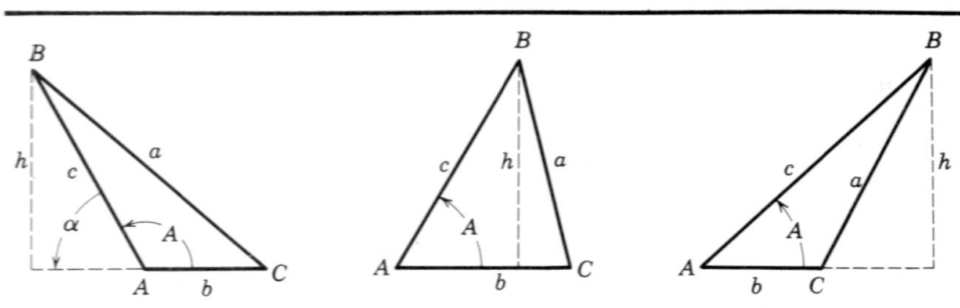

opposite side. Three cases may occur, according as the foot of the perpendicular: (1) lies to the left of the line segment b, (2) falls on this segment, or (3) lies to the right of it, and these cases are shown in Fig. 1. In any of these cases we know from geometry that

$$K = \tfrac{1}{2}bh \tag{2}$$

so our task is to compute h. In cases (2) and (3) we see that

$$\frac{h}{c} = \sin A \tag{3}$$

so that $h = c \sin A$. Substituting this expression for h in (2) gives $K = \frac{1}{2}bc \sin A$ as desired. In case (1) $h/c = \sin \alpha$. But $\alpha + A = 180°$ so that $\sin \alpha = \sin A$. This gives (3), hence $K = \frac{1}{2}bc \sin A$ just as in the other two cases. Q.E.D.

If two angles and the included side are given then the third angle is easily found. In this case we would use

Theorem 2. *The area K of a triangle ABC is given by*

$$K = \frac{a^2 \sin B \sin C}{2 \sin A} = \frac{b^2 \sin C \sin A}{2 \sin B} = \frac{c^2 \sin A \sin B}{2 \sin C}. \tag{4}$$

Proof. By the law of sines we have for any triangle

$$\frac{b}{\sin B} = \frac{a}{\sin A}, \qquad \text{or} \qquad b = \frac{a \sin B}{\sin A}.$$

Substituting this expression for b in the first equation of set (1) yields the first equation of set (4). Q.E.D.

If the three sides of a triangle are given, we would employ Heron's formula given in

Theorem 3. *The area K of a triangle ABC is given by*

$$K = \sqrt{s(s-a)(s-b)(s-c)} \tag{5}$$

where s is the semiperimeter,

$$s = \frac{a+b+c}{2}. \tag{6}$$

Proof. Square both sides of $K = \frac{1}{2}ab \sin C$. Then

$$K^2 = \frac{a^2b^2}{4} \sin^2 C = \frac{a^2b^2}{4}(1 - \cos^2 C) = \frac{ab}{2}(1 + \cos C)\frac{ab}{2}(1 - \cos C).$$

From the law of cosines, $\cos C = (a^2 + b^2 - c^2)/2ab$. So

$$\begin{aligned} K^2 &= \frac{ab}{2}\left(1 + \frac{a^2 + b^2 - c^2}{2ab}\right)\frac{ab}{2}\left(1 - \frac{a^2 + b^2 - c^2}{2ab}\right) \\ &= \left(\frac{2ab + a^2 + b^2 - c^2}{4}\right)\left(\frac{2ab - a^2 - b^2 + c^2}{4}\right) \\ &= \left(\frac{(a+b)^2 - c^2}{4}\right)\left(\frac{c^2 - (a-b)^2}{4}\right) \end{aligned}$$

$$K^2 = \frac{(a+b+c)}{2}\frac{(a+b-c)}{2}\frac{(c+a-b)}{2}\frac{(c-a+b)}{2}. \tag{7}$$

Since $(a + b + c)/2 = s$, we have

$$s - c = \frac{a + b + c}{2} - c = \frac{a + b + c}{2} - \frac{2c}{2} = \frac{a + b - c}{2}.$$

Similarly $(a - b + c)/2 = s - b$, and $(-a + b + c)/2 = s - a$. Substituting these results in (7) gives $K^2 = s(s - a)(s - b)(s - c)$ and since all of the quantities involved are positive this is equivalent to equation (5). Q.E.D.

EXERCISE 44

In Problems 1 through 4 find the area of the given triangle without using logarithms.

1. $a = 8,\ b = 5,\ C = 150°$.

2. $a = 6, c = 3\sqrt{2}, B = 135°$.

3. $a = 11, b = 13, c = 20$.

4. $a = 17, b = 25, c = 26$.

In Problems 5 through 12 use logarithms to find the area of the given triangle to four significant figures.

5. $a = 2345, b = 5678, c = 6789$.

6. $a = 1.776, b = 1.861, c = 1.941$.

7. $a = .1984, B = 19° 29', C = 45° 45'$.

8. $b = 20.20, A = 33° 33', C = 25° 25'$.

9. $c = 77.55, A = 12° 34', C = 23° 45'$.

10. $b = 4321, A = 32° 10', B = 22° 22'$.

11. $b = 444.4, c = 929.2, A = 61° 16'$.

12. $a = .1728, c = .6060, B = 42° 24'$.

13. Derive a formula for finding the included angle when two sides and the area of a triangle are given.

14. Derive a formula for finding one side of a triangle when the angles and the area are given.

15. Prove that the area of any quadrilateral equals one-half the product of its two diagonals times the sine of their included angle.

16. Use equation (5) to obtain a formula for the area of an equilateral triangle in terms of a side.

17. The angles of a triangle are in arithmetic progression and the area is 2002 sq ft. If one of the angles is 20° find the length of the side opposite this angle to four significant figures.

18. Solve Problem 17 if one of the angles is 25°, and the area is 33.33 sq ft.

19. A triangular-shaped corner lot has an area of 987 sq yds. Find the angle of intersection of the two streets if the lot measures 221 ft along one of the streets, and 123 ft along the other street.

★**20.** Let q be a positive integer. Show that the triangle with sides $a = 2q^2 + 1$, $b = 2q^2 + 2$, and $c = 4q^2 + 1$ has integer sides *and integer area.*

2. The Inscribed and Circumscribed Circles of a Triangle. Let r denote the radius of the inscribed circle of a triangle ABC, and let R denote the radius of the circumscribed circle of this triangle. These radii are given by the formulas of

Theorem 4. *In any triangle ABC,*

$$r = \sqrt{\frac{(s-a)(s-b)(s-c)}{s}}, \qquad s = \frac{a+b+c}{2} \tag{8}$$

and

$$R = \frac{a}{2\sin A} = \frac{b}{2\sin B} = \frac{c}{2\sin C}. \tag{9}$$

Proof. The center of the inscribed circle is at the common intersection point O of the three angle bisectors, as shown in Fig. 2. Since the three radii OX, OY, and OZ are perpendicular to the sides AB, BC, and CA respectively, we have the following:

FIGURE 2

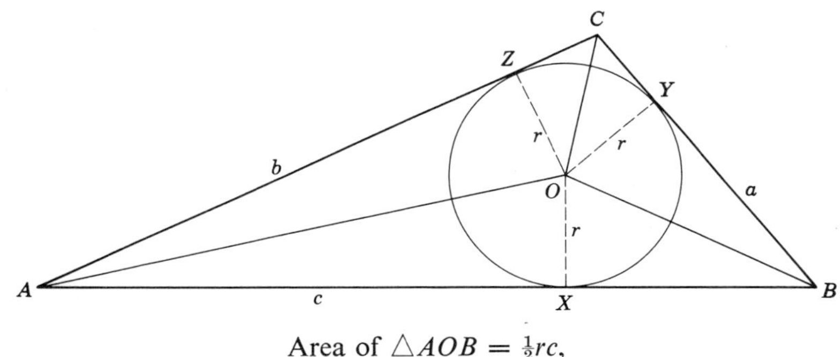

$$\text{Area of } \triangle AOB = \tfrac{1}{2}rc,$$
$$\text{area of } \triangle BOC = \tfrac{1}{2}ra,$$
$$\text{area of } \triangle COA = \tfrac{1}{2}rb.$$

The area of triangle ABC is the sum of these areas, hence

$$K = \tfrac{1}{2}r(a+b+c) = rs.$$

But by Theorem 3, $K = \sqrt{s(s-a)(s-b)(s-c)}$, hence

$$rs = \sqrt{s(s-a)(s-b)(s-c)}. \tag{10}$$

If we divide both sides of (10) by s, we obtain (8).

The circumscribed circle of a triangle ABC is shown in Fig. 3. Let us construct an auxiliary triangle $A'BC$ so that the side $A'B$ passes through the center O of the circumscribed circle, and hence has length $2R$. Since the angles at A and A' are inscribed in the same circle, and since both subtend the same arc BC they are equal. Further, the angle $A'CB$ is inscribed in a semicircle, hence it is a right angle. Therefore

FIGURE 3

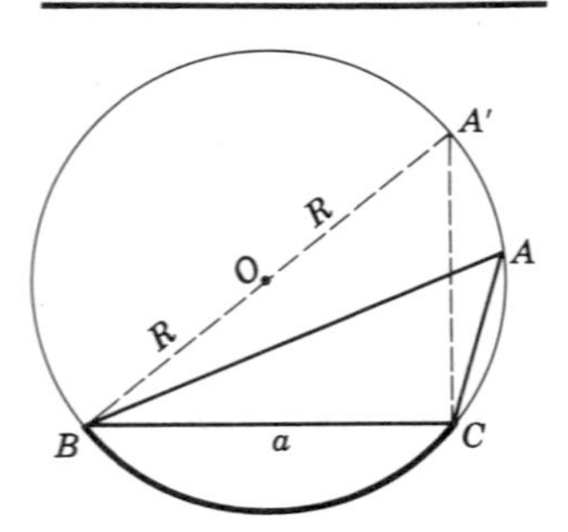

(11) $$\sin A = \sin A' = \frac{a}{2R}.$$

But (11) gives $R = a/2 \sin A$, and the remaining equations of the set (9) follow by cyclic permutation of the letters. Q.E.D.

Notice that (9) is essentially the law of sines, and that this proof of (9) provides a second proof of the law of sines.

3. The Half-Angle Formulas. If three sides of a triangle are given, the angles can be found by using the law of cosines. However, that formula is not suitable for logarithmic computations. The angles can also be computed with the half-angle formulas given in Theorem 5. Moreover logarithmic computation is quite easy with these formulas.

Theorem 5. *In any triangle ABC*

(12) $$\tan\frac{A}{2} = \sqrt{\frac{(s-b)(s-c)}{s(s-a)}},$$

(13) $$\tan\frac{B}{2} = \sqrt{\frac{(s-c)(s-a)}{s(s-b)}},$$

(14) $$\tan\frac{C}{2} = \sqrt{\frac{(s-a)(s-b)}{s(s-c)}},$$

where $s = (a + b + c)/2$ is the semiperimeter of the triangle.

Proof. It is sufficient to prove equation (12), since the others follow by a cyclic permutation of the letters. In Fig. 2 the line AO bisects the angle A. Therefore

(15) $$\tan\frac{A}{2} = \frac{r}{AX}$$

where r is the radius of the inscribed circle. Now $\triangle AXO \cong \triangle AZO$, hence $AX = AZ$. Similarly $BX = BY$ and $CY = CZ$. Since $2s$ is the perimeter of the triangle, we have

$$2s = AX + BX + BY + CY + CZ + AZ = 2AX + 2BY + 2CY$$
$$= 2(AX + a).$$

Therefore $AX = s - a$. If we use this in (15), and the value of r given in Theorem 4, we find

$$\tan\frac{A}{2} = \frac{1}{s-a}\sqrt{\frac{(s-a)(s-b)(s-c)}{s}} = \sqrt{\frac{(s-b)(s-c)}{s(s-a)}}. \quad \text{Q.E.D.}$$

Example 1. Solve the triangle ABC given $a = 24.24$, $b = 31.31$, and $c = 33.33$.

Solution.

$$\begin{aligned} a &= 24.24 & s - a &= 20.20 \\ b &= 31.31 & s - b &= 13.13 \\ c &= 33.33 & s - c &= 11.11 \\ \hline a + b + c &= 88.88 & \text{sum} &= 44.44 = s. \\ s &= 44.44 \end{aligned}$$

This is a check, because

$$(s - a) + (s - b) + (s - c) = 3s - (a + b + c) = 3s - 2s = s.$$

$$\begin{aligned} \log(s-b) &= \log 13.13 = 1.11826 & \log s &= \log 44.44 = 1.64777 \\ \log(s-c) &= \log 11.11 = 1.04571 & \log(s-a) &= \log 20.20 = 1.30535 \end{aligned}$$

$$\begin{aligned} \log \text{numerator} &= 12.16397 - 10 & \log \text{denominator} &= 2.95312 \\ \log \text{denominator} &= 2.95312 \\ \hline \log \text{radicand} &= 9.21085 - 10 \\ \tfrac{1}{2}\log \text{radicand} &= 4.60542 - 5 = \log\tan\frac{A}{2} \end{aligned}$$

$$\frac{A}{2} = 21^\circ\ 57' \qquad A = 43^\circ\ 54'$$

A similar computation gives $B = 63^\circ\ 36'$ and $C = 72^\circ\ 28'$. Since the sum of the angles of a triangle is 180°, we can check our computations. We find that $43^\circ\ 54' + 63^\circ\ 36' + 72^\circ\ 28' = 179^\circ\ 58'$. This $2'$ error is within the limits of this procedure.

EXERCISE 45

In Problems 1 through 6 find all of the angles of the triangle, and check by finding their sum. In each problem find also the radius of the inscribed circle.

1. $a = 2345$, $b = 5678$, $c = 6789$.

2. $a = 3456$, $b = 5656$, $c = 6770$.

3. $a = .04321$, $b = .05432$, $c = .06543$.

4. $a = .0003214$, $b = .0004325$, $c = .0005436$.

5. $a = 17.76$, $b = 18.61$, $c = 19.41$.

6. $a = 149.2$, $b = 162.0$, $c = 181.2$.

7. Using the angle A, find the radius of the circumscribed circle for the triangles of Problems 1 and 3.

★ **8.** Using $2 \sin^2 (A/2) = 1 - \cos A$ and the law of cosines, prove that in any triangle

$$\sin \frac{A}{2} = \sqrt{\frac{(s-b)(s-c)}{bc}}.$$

★ **9.** Use the method of Problem 8 to prove that in any triangle

$$\cos \frac{A}{2} = \sqrt{\frac{s(s-a)}{bc}}.$$

★ **10.** Use the results of the two preceding problems to derive formula (12) of Theorem 5. Notice that in this proof of Theorem 5 we do not need the radius of the inscribed circle.

★ **11.** Since for any angle θ, $\sin^2 \theta + \cos^2 \theta$, the results of Problems 8 and 9 imply that $(s-b)(s-c) + s(s-a) = bc$. Prove this identity algebraically.

Prove that in any triangle ABC:

★ **12.** $K = \dfrac{abc}{4R}$.

★ **13.** $R = \dfrac{abc}{4\sqrt{s(s-a)(s-b)(s-c)}}$.

★ **14.** $\dfrac{R}{r} = \dfrac{abc}{4(s-a)(s-b)(s-c)}$.

★ **15.** $K = Rr(\sin A + \sin B + \sin C)$.

★ **16.** $K = 2R^2 \sin A \sin B \sin C$.

★ **17.** $\dfrac{1}{2rR} = \dfrac{1}{ab} + \dfrac{1}{bc} + \dfrac{1}{ca}$.

★ **18.** $\sin A = \dfrac{2\sqrt{s(s-a)(s-b)(s-c)}}{bc}$.

★ **19.** Prove that in any triangle with integer sides, $\tan (A/2) \tan (B/2)$ is a rational number.

★ **20.** Prove that in a right triangle with the right angle at C, $r = (a + b - c)/2$.

4. The Law of Tangents. If two sides and the included angle of a triangle are given, the third side can be found using the law of cosines. However that formula is not suitable for logarithmic computation. It is much easier to use logarithms together with the law of tangents given in

Theorem 6. *In any triangle ABC*

$$\frac{a-b}{a+b} = \frac{\tan\dfrac{A-B}{2}}{\tan\dfrac{A+B}{2}}. \tag{16}$$

Other formulas can be derived from this one by a cyclic permutation of the letters. It is convenient to assume that $a > b$, so that both sides of (16) are positive. By (9) of Theorem 4, $a = 2R\sin A$, and $b = 2R\sin B$. Therefore

$$\frac{a-b}{a+b} = \frac{2R\sin A - 2R\sin B}{2R\sin A + 2R\sin B} = \frac{\sin A - \sin B}{\sin A + \sin B}. \tag{17}$$

Using the sum to product formulas, (41) and (42) of Chapter 7, the right side of (17) becomes

$$\frac{2\cos\dfrac{A+B}{2}\sin\dfrac{A-B}{2}}{2\sin\dfrac{A+B}{2}\cos\dfrac{A-B}{2}} = \frac{\tan\dfrac{A-B}{2}}{\tan\dfrac{A+B}{2}}. \qquad \text{Q.E.D.}$$

Example 2. Solve the triangle ABC given $a = 1492$, $b = 1776$, and $C = 19°\,14'$.

Solution. Since C is known we can compute the angle $(A + B)/2$, hence from (16) we can find $(A - B)/2$. This will then give A and B. In the problem at hand $b > a$, so it is convenient to rewrite (16) as

$$\frac{b-a}{b+a} = \frac{\tan\dfrac{B-A}{2}}{\tan\dfrac{B+A}{2}}, \tag{18}$$

in order to avoid negative quantities.

$$\begin{aligned} A + B &= 180° - C \\ &= 180° - 19°\,14' \\ &= 160°\,46' \end{aligned} \qquad \tan\frac{B-A}{2} = \frac{b-a}{b+a}\tan\frac{B+A}{2}.$$

$$\frac{A+B}{2} = 80^\circ\ 23' \longrightarrow \log\tan\frac{B+A}{2} = \log\tan 80^\circ\ 23' = 10.77099 - 10$$

$$\longrightarrow \log(b-a) = \log 284 = 2.45332$$

$b = 1776$

$$\text{log numerator} = 13.22431 - 10$$

$a = 1492$

$$\longrightarrow \log(b+a) = \log 3268 = 3.51428$$

$b - a = 284$

$b + a = 3268$

$$\log\tan\frac{B-A}{2} = 9.71003 - 10$$

$$\frac{B-A}{2} = 27^\circ\ 9'$$

$$\frac{B+A}{2} = 80^\circ\ 23'$$

$B = 107^\circ\ 32'$ (by adding)

$A = 53^\circ\ 14'$ (by subtracting)

The side c can then be found using either $c = a \sin C/\sin A$, or $c = b \sin C/\sin B$. Each of these formulas gives $c = 613.5$.

EXERCISE 46

Solve the triangles in Problems 1 through 4.

1. $a = 9876$, $b = 7654$, $C = 23^\circ\ 54'$.

2. $b = 5454$, $c = 3232$, $A = 111^\circ\ 22'$.

3. $c = 42.08$, $a = 53.19$, $B = 123^\circ\ 44'$.

4. $a = 32.10$, $b = 54.32$, $C = 42^\circ\ 24'$.

★ CHAPTER 13

VECTORS

1. Objective. Many quantities that occur in nature have both direction and magnitude. A force is such a quantity. It is customary to represent a force by an arrow which points in the direction of the force and whose length gives the magnitude of the force. Thus in Fig. 1, the two arrows shown could represent forces of 5 and 10 lbs respectively, the first force acting vertically and the second one horizontally.

FIGURE 1

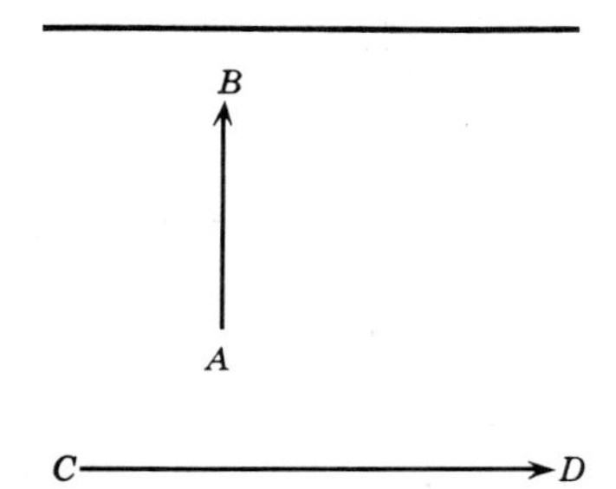

The very same pair of arrows might also represent velocities, the first being a velocity of 30 mph northward, and the second being a velocity of 60 mph eastward.

Such arrows are called vectors, and there is an extensive mathematical theory of vectors constructed so as to be useful in solving physical problems involving forces, velocities, and other quantities that have direction as well as magnitude. Our objective is to touch on the first elements of this theory and to show how it is used to solve some simple problems.

2. The Addition and Decomposition of Vectors. A vector is a directed line segment. An arrow is attached to one end of the segment to indicate the direction. The magnitude of the vector is proportional to the length of the line segment. The vector may be described by naming the beginning and the end point of the line segment, and an arrow is placed over the letters to emphasize that it is a vector. For example the vectors of Fig. 1 would be denoted by $\overrightarrow{AB}$ and $\overrightarrow{CD}$. The unadorned symbol AB denotes the length or magnitude of the vector $\overrightarrow{AB}$.

Definition 1. *Two vectors are said to be equal if and only if the two line segments are parallel, equal in length, and have the same direction.*

Definition 2. *To add the vectors $\overrightarrow{AB}$ and $\overrightarrow{CD}$, place $\overrightarrow{CD}$ so that its beginning point C falls on B, the end point of $\overrightarrow{AB}$. Then the sum $\overrightarrow{AB} + \overrightarrow{CD}$ is the vector $\overrightarrow{AD}$.*

This definition is illustrated in Fig. 2. Observe that the vectors need not be perpendicular in order to form a sum. The sum vector is also called the *resultant*, and the individual vectors in the sum are called *components* of the resultant.

FIGURE 2

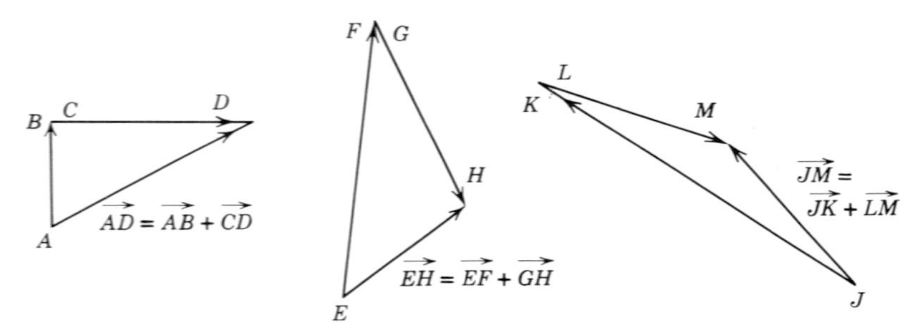

An alternate definition for the sum of two vectors is illustrated in Fig. 3. In this construction, the two vectors to be added are placed so that their beginning points coincide. The sum or resultant is then the diagonal of the parallelogram shown in the figure.

FIGURE 3

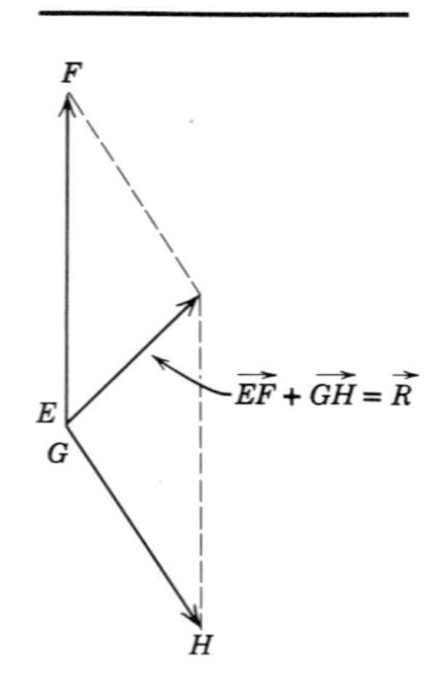

Theorem 1. *Given any vector $\overrightarrow{AC}$ and two nonparallel lines L_1 and L_2, the vector $\overrightarrow{AC}$ can be written as a sum $\overrightarrow{AC} = \overrightarrow{AB} + \overrightarrow{BC}$, where $\overrightarrow{AB}$ is parallel to L_1 and $\overrightarrow{BC}$ is parallel to L_2.*

Proof. As illustrated in Fig. 4, draw a line through point A parallel to L_1 and a line through C parallel to L_2. If B is the point of intersection of these two lines, then obviously

$$\overrightarrow{AC} = \overrightarrow{AB} + \overrightarrow{BC} \tag{1}$$

Q.E.D.

This process is called the *resolution* of the vector $\overrightarrow{AC}$ into its components in the directions of L_1 and L_2, and the vectors $\overrightarrow{AB}$ and $\overrightarrow{BC}$ are called the *components* in these directions.

FIGURE 4

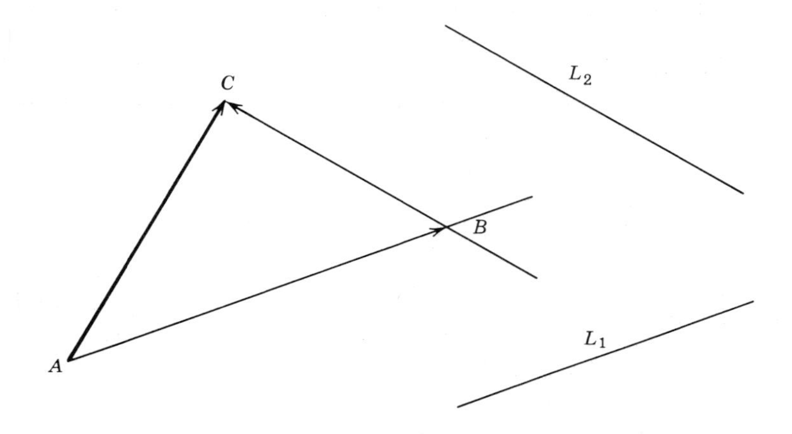

3. Forces. It is an *experimental fact* that forces behave like vectors. This means that if a number of forces act on a particle, that particle will move as though it were acted on by a single force equal to the vector sum of the forces. If the particle does not move, then the vector sum of all of the forces acting on the particle is zero.

FIGURE 5

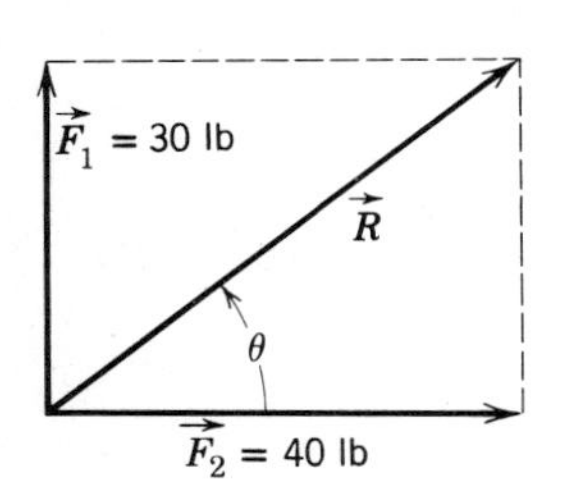

Example 1. Find the resultant of two forces, one a 30-lb force acting northward, the other a 40-lb force acting eastward.

Solution. The resultant is just the diagonal of the rectangle shown in Fig. 5. The magnitude of the resultant is

$$R = \sqrt{30^2 + 40^2} = 50 \text{ lb},$$

and $\tan \theta = \frac{3}{4}$ so that $\theta = 37°$. Hence $\overrightarrow{R}$ is a force of 50 lb acting in the direction N 53° E.

Example 2. A car weighing 4540 lb is held on an inclined plane by a tow rope which runs parallel to the plane. If the plane makes an angle of 15° 40′ with the horizontal and if friction is neglected, find the tension in the tow rope.

Solution. As indicated in Fig. 6, we regard the weight as concentrated at the center of gravity of the car. The force $\overrightarrow{W}$ exerted by gravity is then resolved into two components, one $\overrightarrow{A}$ parallel to the inclined plane, and the other $\overrightarrow{B}$ perpendicular to it. Then $\theta = 15^\circ\, 40'$. (Why?) Since

FIGURE 6

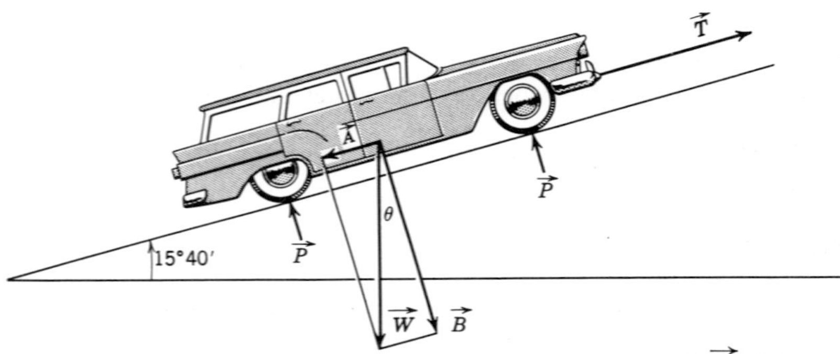

the car does not move, the force A is balanced by the pull $\overrightarrow{T}$ of the tow rope. Therefore

$$T = W \sin\theta = 4540 \sin 15^\circ\, 40' = 1230 \text{ lb}.$$

The force $\overrightarrow{B}$ is balanced by the force exerted by the ramp on the wheels of the car and this force is

$$W \cos\theta = 4540 \cos 15^\circ\, 40' = 4370 \text{ lb}$$

distributed over the four wheels of the car.

FIGURE 7

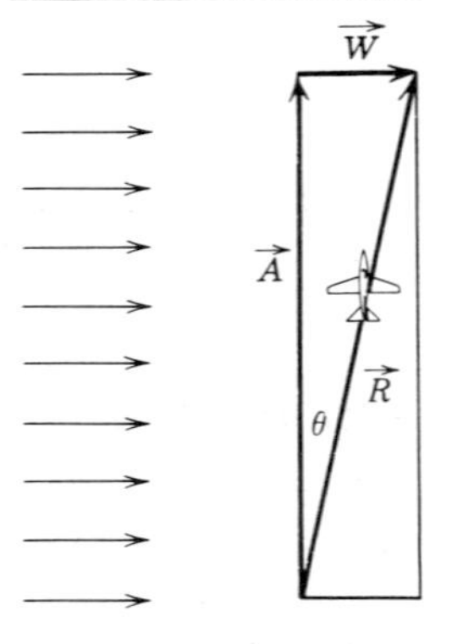

4. Velocity. Suppose that an airplane headed due north travels with an *airspeed* (speed in still air) of 225 mph. If a wind is blowing from the west at 45.5 mph, the airplane will be blown off its course. In order to determine its *ground velocity* $\overrightarrow{R}$ (its velocity with respect to the ground) we might argue thus. In one hour the airplane would travel 225 mi due north if there were no wind. But during this hour the entire mass of air in which the airplane is moving, has moved 45.5 mi to the east carrying the plane with it. We would expect that after one hour the plane would be at a point 225 mi north and 45.5 mi east of its starting point. Then the ground velocity $\overrightarrow{R}$ of the airplane would be the vector sum as indicated in Fig. 7. It is an experimental fact that in such a case the resultant velocity is just the vector sum as indicated in the figure. Therefore

$$\overrightarrow{R} = \overrightarrow{A} + \overrightarrow{W}, \tag{2}$$

hence for the ground speed R we have

$$R = \sqrt{225^2 + 45.5^2} = \sqrt{52{,}695} = 230 \text{ mph},$$

and $\tan \theta = 45.5/225 = .2022$. The vector $\overrightarrow{R}$ has the bearing N 11° 30′ E.

The same type of argument applies to boats traveling in water, and in general to any object traveling in a medium (air or water) that is also moving. Experimental evidence substantiates the following

Principle. *If an object travels with the velocity* $\overrightarrow{A}$ *in a medium which is moving with the velocity* $\overrightarrow{W}$ *with respect to the earth, then* $\overrightarrow{R}$*, the velocity of the object with respect to the earth, is the vector sum of* $\overrightarrow{A}$ *and* $\overrightarrow{W}$.

FIG. 8

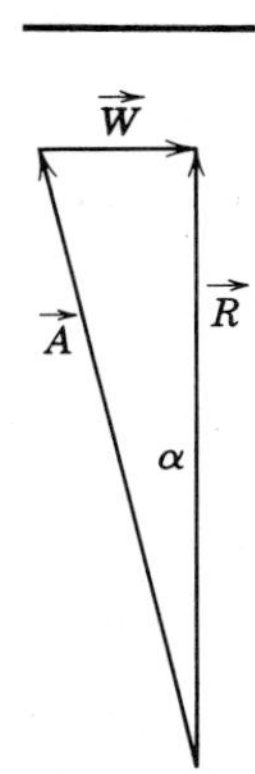

Example 2. Suppose that the aviator in the preceding discussion wishes to travel due north. In what direction must he point his plane? What will be his *ground speed* (the magnitude of his ground velocity)?

Solution. We again use equation (2) but this time $\overrightarrow{R}$ is a vector due north and the direction of $\overrightarrow{A}$ is unknown. The vector diagram is shown in Fig. 8. We find

$$\sin \alpha = \frac{45.5}{225} = .2022,$$

$$\alpha = 11° \, 40'.$$

$$R = \sqrt{225^2 - 45.5^2} = \sqrt{48{,}555} = 220 \text{ mph}.$$

Observe that the angle α is not equal to the angle θ of Fig. 7. Also notice that in this example the ground speed is less than the air speed, although in the preceding example the ground speed is greater than the air speed.

EXERCISE 47

1. Find the resultant of two forces, one of 25 lb acting due south and one of 32 lb acting due west.

2. Find the resultant if both of the forces in Problem 1 are doubled.

3. A force of 66 lb acts in the direction N 66° W. Find its north and east components.

4. Find the north and east components of a 77-lb force acting in the direction S 22° W.

5. Find the resultant of the following forces acting simultaneously at a point: (*a*) 22 lb in the direction N 33° E, (*b*) 33 lb in the direction N 22° W, (*c*) 44 lb in the direction S 80° W, (*d*) 60 lb in the direction S 25° E.

Hint: Resolve each force into north and east components, find the total component in each direction, and then the resultant of these two forces.

6. A barrel full of water is held on an inclined plane by a man who pushes on it parallel to the plane. If the angle of inclination of the plane is 10° 10′ and the barrel together with its contents weighs 555 lb what force does the man exert? With what force does the barrel press on the supporting plane?

7. Solve Problem 6 if the barrel is empty so that the weight is only 55.5 lb, and the angle of inclination of the plane is increased to 22° 20′.

8. If a young boy can push on the barrel with a force of at most 76 lb, find the weight of the heaviest barrel he can just hold on the inclined plane of Problem 7.

9. A tightrope walker weighing 165 lb is balanced on a wire *ABC* at point *B* midway between the support points *A* and *C*. If these supports are at the same height and if each of the lines *AB* and *BC* makes an angle of 24° 20′ with the horizontal, find the tension in the wire.

10. The wire in Problem 9 is tightened so that under the artist's weight the tension is now 1500 lb. Find the angle that *AB* and *BC* make with the horizontal.

11. A man can row a boat in still water at the rate of 4 mph. If he points his boat directly northward in rowing across a river that flows due east with a speed of 3 mph, in what direction will he actually travel and with what speed? If the river is one mile wide, how many minutes will the trip across require?

12. If, in Problem 11, the man wishes to travel due north, in what direction should he point his boat? Find to the nearest minute the time it will take to cross the river.

13. An airplane can fly at 140 mph in still air. Find its speed in a wind of 35 mph, if it is headed (*a*) with the wind, (*b*) against the wind, and (*c*) in such a direction that its ground velocity is at right angles to the wind.

14. A pilot headed north with an airspeed of 155 mph finds after two hours that he has drifted 45.6 mi eastward off his course. If the drift is due to a west wind, find his ground velocity.

15. In what direction should the pilot of Problem 14 fly in order to be due north of his starting place after flying an additional hour? Assume that the wind velocity is constant for the three-hour period.

★ CHAPTER 14

COMPLEX NUMBERS AND DE MOIVRE'S THEOREM

1. Objective. Every quadratic equation

$$(1) \qquad Ax^2 + Bx + C = 0, \qquad A \neq 0,$$

has two roots:

$$(2) \quad x_1 = \frac{-B + \sqrt{B^2 - 4AC}}{2A}, \qquad \text{and} \qquad x_2 = \frac{-B - \sqrt{B^2 - 4AC}}{2A}.$$

For example the roots of $x^2 - 3x + 5 = 0$ are

$$x_1 = \frac{3 + \sqrt{-11}}{2}, \qquad \text{and} \qquad x_2 = \frac{3 - \sqrt{-11}}{2}.$$

In this case $B^2 - 4AC = 9 - 20 = -11$, and so the square root cannot be found among the real numbers. There is a natural feeling that solutions involving the square root of a negative number ought to be rejected. On the other hand, our desire for beauty in mathematics leads us to demand that every second-degree equation have two roots. If we introduce a new symbol i for $\sqrt{-1}$ and make certain definitions about the behavior of this symbol, then the real-number system can be enlarged in such a way that every second-degree equation has the two roots given by (2), and these two roots are the only ones. Our objective is to study the elementary algebra of this enlarged number system, obtained by adjoining $i = \sqrt{-1}$ to the real-number system.

Although i is called an imaginary number, it is no more a creation of the imagination than any other number used in mathematics. Moreover it turns out that the use of i in mathematics has very important, very real, and very practical applications.

2. Complex Numbers. We assume that the reader already knows what a real number is, since up to this point we have used only real numbers. We now make

Definition 1. *A number of the form* $a + bi$, *where* a *and* b *are real and* $i = \sqrt{-1}$, *is called a complex number.*

It is convenient to use a single letter such as z or w to denote a complex number.

Definition 2. *If* $z = a + bi$ *is a complex number, then* a *is called the real part of* z, *and* b *is called the imaginary part of* z. *If* $a = 0$, z *is called a pure imaginary number, and if* $b = 0$, z *is called a real number.*

Definition 3. *Two complex numbers are said to be equal if and only if their real parts are equal, and their imaginary parts are equal.*

Thus, if we set

$$z_1 = a + bi \quad \text{and} \quad z_2 = c + di,$$

then

$$z_1 = z_2$$

if and only if

$$a = c \quad \text{and} \quad b = d.$$

Definition 4. *Set* $z = a + bi$. *Then* $z = 0$ *if and only if* $a = 0$ *and* $b = 0$.

Definition 5. *If* $z_1 = a + bi$ *and* $z_2 = c + di$, *then the sum* $z_1 + z_2$ *is defined by the equation*

$$z_1 + z_2 = (a + c) + (b + d)i. \tag{3}$$

For example, by the definition

$$(3 + 5i) + (7 - 2i) = (3 + 7) + (5 - 2)i = 10 + 3i.$$

In order to multiply two complex numbers together we assume that the ordinary laws of multiplication hold and that in addition $i \times i = i^2 = -1$. Thus

$$\begin{aligned}(3 + 5i)(7 - 2i) &= 3 \times 7 + 5i \times 7 + 3 \times (-2i) + 5i \times (-2i) \\ &= 21 + 35i - 6i - 10i^2 = 21 + 35i - 6i + 10 = 31 + 29i.\end{aligned}$$

This example suggests

Definition 6. *If* $z_1 = a + bi$ *and* $z_2 = c + di$, *then the product* $z_1 z_2$ *is defined by the equation*

$$z_1 z_2 = (a + bi)(c + di) = ac - bd + (bc + ad)i. \tag{4}$$

We see from the example that it is not necessary to memorize this formula. Just multiply the quantities together in the usual way and remember that $i^2 = -1$.

Two complex numbers $a + bi$ and $a - bi$ which differ only in the signs of their imaginary parts are said to be *conjugate complex numbers*. Either one is said to be the *conjugate* of the other. This concept of a conjugate is very useful in division. In the first place notice that by (4)

$$(a + bi)(a - bi) = a^2 - b(-b) + [a(-b) + ba]i$$

$$= a^2 + b^2 + (-ab + ba)i = a^2 + b^2,$$

so that the product of any complex number and its conjugate is real. Furthermore $a^2 + b^2 > 0$ unless $a = b = 0$. Hence the product of z and its conjugate is positive unless $z = 0$.

In finding the quotient of two complex numbers, we start by multiplying the numerator and the denominator by the conjugate of the denominator. For example, to find $z_3 = z_1/z_2$ when $z_1 = 7 - 2i$ and $z_2 = 3 + 5i$, we write

$$z_3 = \frac{z_1}{z_2} = \frac{7 - 2i}{3 + 5i} \cdot \frac{3 - 5i}{3 - 5i} = \frac{21 - 10 + (-35 - 6)i}{9 + 25}$$

$$= \frac{11 - 41i}{34} = \frac{11}{34} - \frac{41}{34}i.$$

We can check this result for z_3 by computing the product $z_2 z_3$. Indeed we find that

$$z_2 z_3 = (3 + 5i)\left(\frac{11}{34} - \frac{41}{34}i\right) = \frac{33}{34} + \frac{205}{34} + \left(\frac{55}{34} - \frac{123}{34}\right)i$$

$$= \frac{238}{34} - \frac{68}{34}i = 7 - 2i = z_1,$$

as required. This example suggests

Definition 7. *If $z_1 = a + bi$ and $z_2 = c + di \neq 0$, then the quotient $z_1/z_2 = z_3$ is defined by the equation*

$$z_3 = \frac{z_1}{z_2} = \frac{a + bi}{c + di} = \frac{ac + bd + (-ad + bc)i}{c^2 + d^2}. \tag{5}$$

Again we see from the example that it is not necessary to memorize this formula.

EXERCISE 48

In Problems 1 through 10 compute $z_1 + z_2$, $z_1 z_2$, and z_1/z_2.

1. $z_1 = 4 + 3i$, $z_2 = 5 + 12i$.
2. $z_1 = 4 + i$, $z_2 = 1 - 2i$.
3. $z_1 = 5 - 12i$, $z_2 = 3 - 4i$.
4. $z_1 = -1 + i$, $z_2 = 1 - i$.
5. $z_1 = -2 + 3i$, $z_2 = 2 + 3i$.
6. $z_1 = 5 + 5i$, $z_2 = 2 - 2i$.
7. $z_1 = 4 + 3i$, $z_2 = 2i$.
8. $z_1 = -2 - 4i$, $z_2 = -4 + 2i$.
9. $z_1 = -3 + 4i$, $z_2 = -5i$.
10. $z_1 = -7 + i$, $z_2 = -1 + 7i$.

11. Compute the powers i^3, i^4, i^8, $(1 + i)^4$, and $(1 + i)^6$.

12. Prove that if $z_3 = z_1/z_2$ is defined as in equation (5), then $z_2 z_3 = a + bi = z_1$.

13. Frame a definition for subtraction $z_1 - z_2$, in such a way that if $z_3 = z_1 - z_2$ then $z_3 + z_2 = z_1$. Using this definition compute $z_1 - z_2$ for the complex numbers in Problems 1 through 4.

★ **14.** The conjugate of z is frequently denoted by $\bar{z}$. Prove that $z + \bar{z}$ is always a real number and $z - \bar{z}$ is always a pure imaginary number.

15. Simplify $(a - bi)/(b + ai)$ and $(a + bi)(b + ai)$.

16. Show that the roots of $x^2 + 2x + 4 = 0$ are $-1 + \sqrt{3}i$ and $-1 - \sqrt{3}i$. Then check these answers by substituting each one in the given equation.

17. Solve the equation $x^2 - 4ix + 2 = 0$ by the quadratic formula, equation (2). Check the solutions by substituting in the given equation.

★ **18.** Prove that the quadratic formula, equation (2) gives solutions x_1 and x_2 for equation (1), by substituting these expressions for x_1 and x_2 into equation (1).

★ **19.** If n is a positive integer find i^{4n}, i^{4n+1}, i^{4n+2}, and i^{4n+3}.

FIGURE 1

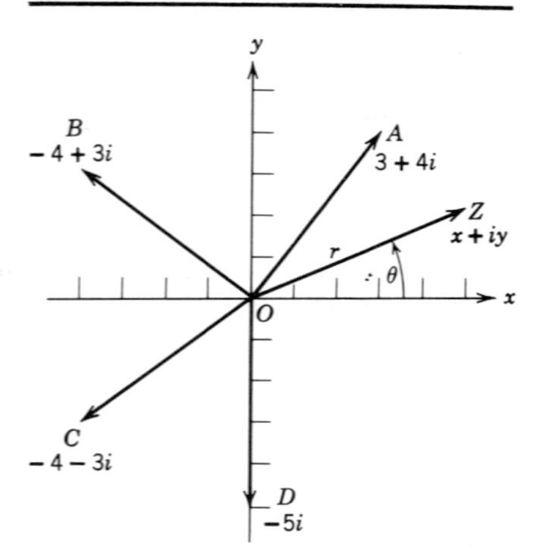

3. Graphical Representation of Complex Numbers. If we write the complex number z in the form $z = x + iy$, where x and y are real numbers, it is quite natural to represent the complex number z by the point with coordinates (x, y). Thus in Fig. 1 the points A, B, C, and D represent the complex numbers $3 + 4i$, $-4 + 3i$, $-4 - 3i$, and $-5i$ respectively. When complex numbers are represented in this way by points on a plane with a rectangular coordinate system, the plane is called the *complex plane.* The horizontal or x-axis is called the *real axis*, because the real part of z is plotted along this axis. Similarly, the vertical or y-axis is called the *imaginary axis.* Obviously we have

Theorem I. *There is a one-to-one correspondence between the complex numbers $x + iy$ and the points of the complex plane. This means that to each complex number there corresponds precisely one point of the complex plane and to each point of the plane there corresponds precisely one complex number.*

We can also associate with each complex number a vector from the origin to the point that represents the complex number. For example in Fig. 1, the vector $\overrightarrow{OA}$ represents the complex number $3 + 4i$, the vector $\overrightarrow{OB}$ represents $-4 + 3i$, $\overrightarrow{OC}$ represents $-4 - 3i$, and $\overrightarrow{OD}$ represents $-5i$. In general the vector $\overrightarrow{OZ}$ from the origin to the point (x, y) represents the complex number $x + iy$. The length of this vector is called the *modulus* or the *absolute value* or the *length* of the complex number $x + iy$. The symbol $|z| = |x + iy|$ is used for this concept, and obviously we have for the modulus of z

$$|z| = r = \sqrt{x^2 + y^2}. \tag{6}$$

The least positive angle θ that the vector $\overrightarrow{OZ}$ makes with the positive real axis is called *the argument* or *the amplitude* or *the angle* of $x + iy$. The symbol $\arg z = \arg (x + iy)$ or $\operatorname{amp} z = \operatorname{amp} (x + iy)$ is used for this concept. From Fig. 1 it is clear that the argument θ is determined by the conditions

$$\cos \theta = \frac{x}{r}, \qquad \sin \theta = \frac{y}{r}, \qquad 0^\circ \leqq \theta < 360^\circ \tag{7}$$

Conversely, if we know θ, the argument of z, and r, the modulus of z, then we can compute $x + iy$.

For from the equation set (7) we have

$$x = r \cos \theta, \qquad \text{and} \qquad y = r \sin \theta, \tag{8}$$

hence

$$z = r \cos \theta + ir \sin \theta, \tag{9}$$

$$z = r(\cos \theta + i \sin \theta). \tag{10}$$

Equation (10) is called the *polar form* of the complex number, in contrast to $z = x + iy$ which is the *rectangular form* of the complex number. It is obvious that in the polar form, θ could be any angle coterminal with the angle of z, for if θ is replaced by $\theta + n360^\circ$ where n is any integer, then the complex number z, given by (10), is unaltered. Thus if θ is *the* argument of z, then $\theta + n360^\circ$ can also be considered as *an* argument of z.

Example 1. Find the modulus and argument for $z = 1 + \sqrt{3}i$, and write z in polar form.

Solution. We have $r = \sqrt{1 + 3} = 2$, and $\theta = 60^\circ$, whence

$$z = 1 + \sqrt{3}i = 2(\cos 60^\circ + i \sin 60^\circ).$$

EXERCISE 49

1. For Problems 1 through 5 of Exercise 48 plot the complex numbers as points on the complex plane and draw the corresponding vectors.

2. Find $|z_1|$ and $\arg z_1$ for the complex numbers z_1 in Problems 1 through 5 of Exercise 48.

3. Find $|z_1|$ and $\arg z_1$ for the complex numbers z_1 in Problems 6 through 10 of Exercise 48.

In Problems 4 through 12 express the given complex number in polar form.

4. $6\sqrt{3} - 6i$ **5.** $3 - 3i$. **6.** $1 + 2i$.

7. -5. **8.** $-4\sqrt{3} + 4i$. **9.** $2i$.

10. $-3i$. **11.** $5 + 12i$. **12.** $-5 + 5i$.

In Problems 13 through 21 the modulus r and an argument θ are given. Put the complex number in rectangular form.

13. $8, 90^\circ$. **14.** $15, 180^\circ$. **15.** $\sqrt{3}, 120^\circ$.

16. $5\sqrt{2}, -135^\circ$. **17.** $8, 510^\circ$. **18.** $1, 270^\circ$.

19. $0, 1000^\circ$. **20.** $100, 25^\circ$. **21.** $\sqrt{10}, -45^\circ$.

22. Prove that if two complex numbers have equal moduli and equal arguments, then they are equal.

23. Prove that if two complex numbers are equal, then they have equal moduli and their arguments differ by an integral multiple of 360°.

4. Graphical Interpretation of Addition. In Fig. 2 we have plotted the numbers $6 + i$, $3 + 4i$, and their sum $9 + 5i$ in the complex plane as points A, B, and C respectively. If the lines OA, AC, CB, and BO are drawn, the resulting quadrilateral appears to be a parallelogram, and OC is one of the diagonals. If the figure is a parallelogram, then by the definition of a vector sum (see Chapter 13) $\overrightarrow{OC} = \overrightarrow{OA} + \overrightarrow{OB}$. Hence it appears as though the addition of two complex numbers can be accomplished merely by adding the appropriate vectors. This is the content of

FIGURE 2

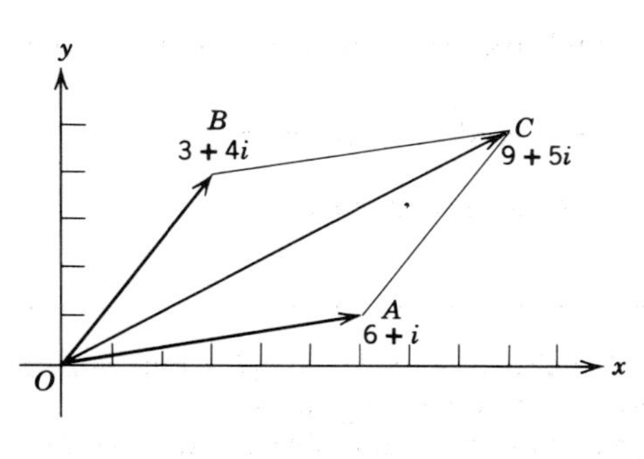

Theorem 2. *If $\overrightarrow{OA}$ is the vector that represents z_1 and $\overrightarrow{OB}$ is the vector that represents z_2, then the vector sum, $\overrightarrow{OC} = \overrightarrow{OA} + \overrightarrow{OB}$ represents the sum $z_1 + z_2$.*

Proof. Let $z_1 = x_1 + iy_1$ and $z_2 = x_2 + iy_2$. Then for the sum we have $z_3 = (x_1 + x_2) + i(y_1 + y_2)$. The corresponding points A, B, and C are shown in Fig. 3. To prove that $\overrightarrow{OC} = \overrightarrow{OA} + \overrightarrow{OB}$ we must prove that $OACB$ is a parallelogram. We can easily compute the lengths of the sides of the quadrilateral $OACB$, using the distance formula (1) of Chapter 6. Indeed we find

FIGURE 3

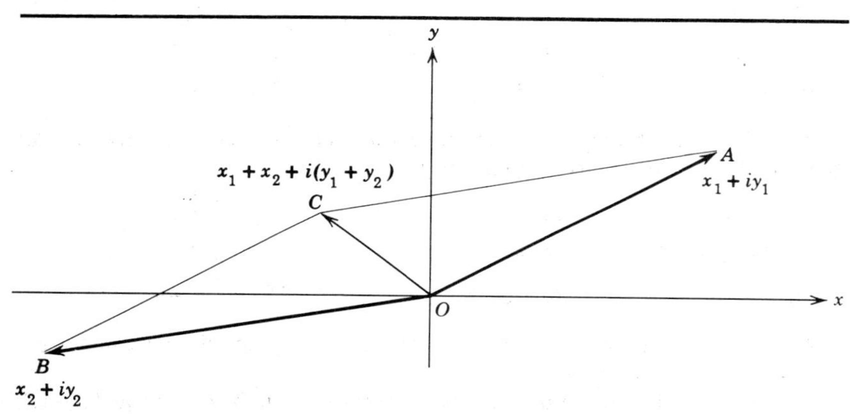

(11) $AC = \sqrt{(x_1 + x_2 - x_1)^2 + (y_1 + y_2 - y_1)^2} = \sqrt{x_2^2 + y_2^2} = OB,$

and

(12) $BC = \sqrt{(x_1 + x_2 - x_2)^2 + (y_1 + y_2 - y_2)^2} = \sqrt{x_1^2 + y_1^2} = OA$

Since the pairs of opposite sides of the quadrilateral are equal, the figure $OACB$ is a parallelogram. Q.E.D.

5. Graphical Interpretation of Multiplication. Let us compute the moduli and the arguments for the complex numbers z_1 and z_2 of Fig. 2, and also for their product $z_3 = z_1 z_2$.

We find that (to the nearest minute)

$$z_1 = 6 + i = \sqrt{37}(\cos 9^\circ 28' + i \sin 9^\circ 28'),$$

$$z_2 = 3 + 4i = 5(\cos 53^\circ 8' + i \sin 53^\circ 8'),$$

and

$$z_3 = (6 + i)(3 + 4i) = (18 - 4) + i(24 + 3) = 14 + 27i$$
$$= \sqrt{925}(\cos 62^\circ 36' + i \sin 62^\circ 36').$$

We notice that

$$r_1 r_2 = 5\sqrt{37} = \sqrt{25 \times 37} = \sqrt{925} = r_3,$$

and that

$$\theta_1 + \theta_2 = 9^\circ 28' + 53^\circ 8' = 62^\circ 36' = \theta_3.$$

It appears as though to multiply two complex numbers, we may multiply their moduli and add their arguments. This is the content of

Theorem 3. *If* $z_1 = r_1(\cos \theta_1 + i \sin \theta_1)$ *and* $z_2 = r_2(\cos \theta_2 + i \sin \theta_2)$ *then*

(13) $$z_1 z_2 = r_1 r_2 [\cos (\theta_1 + \theta_2) + i \sin (\theta_1 + \theta_2)].$$

Proof. By direct multiplication we find that

$$\begin{aligned} z_1 z_2 &= (r_1 \cos \theta_1 + i r_1 \sin \theta_1)(r_2 \cos \theta_2 + i r_2 \sin \theta_2) \\ &= (r_1 r_2 \cos \theta_1 \cos \theta_2 - r_1 r_2 \sin \theta_1 \sin \theta_2) + i(r_1 r_2 \sin \theta_1 \cos \theta_2 \\ &\quad + r_1 r_2 \cos \theta_1 \sin \theta_2) \\ &= r_1 r_2[(\cos \theta_1 \cos \theta_2 - \sin \theta_1 \sin \theta_2) + i(\sin \theta_1 \cos \theta_2 + \cos \theta_1 \sin \theta_2)] \\ &= r_1 r_2[\cos (\theta_1 + \theta_2) + i \sin (\theta_1 + \theta_2)], \end{aligned}$$

by the addition formulas (3) and (17) of Chapter 7. Q.E.D.

Notice that $\theta_1 + \theta_2$ may turn out to be larger than 360°, so it may be necessary to subtract some multiple of 360° in order to find *the* argument of the product.

Since the quotient z_1/z_2 is a number z_3 such that $z_2 z_3 = z_1$, we have immediately

Theorem 4. *If* $z_1 = r_1(\cos \theta_1 + i \sin \theta_1)$ *and* $z_2 = r_2(\cos \theta_2 + i \sin \theta_2)$ *then*

(14) $$\frac{z_1}{z_2} = \frac{r_1}{r_2} [\cos (\theta_1 - \theta_2) + i \sin (\theta_1 - \theta_2)].$$

EXERCISE 50

1. Prove that if $\overrightarrow{OA}$ represents z then the vector that represents $-z$ has the same length as $\overrightarrow{OA}$ but is in the opposite direction.

2. Use the result of Problem 1 to obtain a vector representation for $z_3 = z_1 - z_2$.

3. Prove that if z_1/z_2 is defined by equation (14) then the product of z_1/z_2 and z_2 is z_1.

In Problems 4 through 13 express z_1 and z_2 in polar form and compute z_1z_2 and z_1/z_2. Compute the angle to the nearest 10 minutes. Wherever possible without the use of tables express the answer in rectangular form.

4. $z_1 = i$, $z_2 = 6\sqrt{3} + 6i$.

5. $z_1 = -4\sqrt{3} + 4i$, $z_2 = -i$.

6. $z_1 = -\sqrt{2} + \sqrt{2}i$, $z_2 = 5 + 5i$.

7. $z_1 = -10 + 10i$, $z_2 = \sqrt{2} + \sqrt{2}i$.

8. $z_1 = 1 + 2i$, $z_2 = 5i$.

9. $z_1 = -3i$, $z_2 = 4 - 2i$.

10. $z_1 = 3 + 7i$, $z_2 = 7 + 3i$.

11. $z_1 = 2 + 5i$, $z_2 = 2 - 5i$.

12. $z_1 = 2 + 3i$, $z_2 = 4 + 6i$.

13. $z_1 = 3 - 2i$, $z_2 = -4 + 6i$.

In Problems 14 through 17 perform the indicated operations and express the answer in rectangular form without using tables.

14. $2(\cos 18° + i \sin 18°) \cdot 3(\cos 27° + i \sin 27°)$.

15. $6(\cos 42° + i \sin 42°) \cdot 3(\cos 78° + i \sin 78°)$.

16. $5(\cos 1000° + i \sin 1000°) \div 4(\cos 790° + i \sin 790°)$.

17. $12(\cos 2000° + i \sin 2000°) \div 3\sqrt{2}(\cos 1055° + i \sin 1055°)$.

6. De Moivre's Theorem. It is easy to extend Theorem 3 to the product of n complex numbers. If $z_1 = r_1(\cos \theta_1 + i \sin \theta_1)$, $z_2 = r_2(\cos \theta_2 + i \sin \theta_2)$, $\cdots$, and $z_n = r_n(\cos \theta_n + i \sin \theta_n)$ then obviously

$$z_1z_2 \cdots z_n = r_1r_2 \cdots r_n[\cos (\theta_1 + \theta_2 + \cdots + \theta_n) + i \sin (\theta_1 + \theta_2 + \cdots + \theta_n)]. \tag{15}$$

In words: The modulus of the product of n complex numbers is the product of their moduli, and the argument of their product is the sum of the arguments of the numbers, or differs from it by some integer multiple of 360°.

If now we take the special case in which the n complex numbers are all equal, (15) gives a very simple formula for z^n, known as

De Moivre's Theorem. *If $z = r(\cos \theta + i \sin \theta)$ then for any positive integer n*

$$z^n = r^n(\cos n\theta + i \sin n\theta). \tag{16}$$

The proof that we have just given is valid only for positive integer n, but it can be shown that (16) holds for any real number n.

Example 2. Compute $(2 + 2i)^{10}$.

Solution. Since $2 + 2i = 2\sqrt{2}(\cos 45^\circ + i \sin 45^\circ)$,

$$\begin{aligned}(2 + 2i)^{10} &= (2\sqrt{2})^{10}(\cos 450^\circ + i \sin 450^\circ)\\ &= 2^{10}2^5(\cos 90^\circ + i \sin 90^\circ) = (32)^2 32i = 32{,}768i.\end{aligned}$$

De Moivre's theorem can be used to compute roots as well as powers. Indeed we can prove

Theorem 5. *If $z = r(\cos\theta + i\sin\theta) \neq 0$, then there are precisely n, nth roots of z. These are given by the formula*

$$z^{1/n} = r^{1/n}\left(\cos\frac{\theta + k360^\circ}{n} + i\sin\frac{\theta + k360^\circ}{n}\right), \qquad k = 0, 1, 2, \cdots, n - 1. \tag{17}$$

The corresponding points in the complex plane all lie on a circle of radius $r^{1/n}$ with center at the origin, and form the vertices of a regular polygon of n sides inscribed in this circle.

Proof. Let $w = \rho(\cos\alpha + i\sin\alpha)$ be an nth root of z, then by De Moivre's theorem

$$w^n = \rho^n(\cos n\alpha + i\sin n\alpha) = r(\cos\theta + i\sin\theta).$$

Therefore $\rho^n = r$ or $\rho = r^{1/n}$. The angles $n\alpha$ and θ need not be equal, but they must differ at most by an integer multiple of 360°, that is

$$n\alpha = \theta + k360^\circ.$$

But then

$$\alpha = \frac{\theta + k360^\circ}{n}.$$

Setting $k = 0, 1, 2, \cdots, n - 1$ will give n distinct values in (17), but other integers k will yield no new values in this equation. Q.E.D.

Example 3. Find the four fourth roots of $z = -16$.

Solution. Here $z = 16(\cos 180^\circ + i \sin 180^\circ)$. By equation (17) the roots are

$$w = 2\left(\cos\frac{180^\circ + k360^\circ}{4} + i\sin\frac{180^\circ + k360^\circ}{4}\right), \quad k = 0, 1, 2, 3.$$

Using successively these values for k, we find

$$\begin{aligned}w_1 &= 2(\cos 45^\circ + i \sin 45^\circ) = \sqrt{2} + i\sqrt{2}\\ w_2 &= 2(\cos 135^\circ + i \sin 135^\circ) = -\sqrt{2} + i\sqrt{2}\\ w_3 &= 2(\cos 225^\circ + i \sin 225^\circ) = -\sqrt{2} - i\sqrt{2}\\ w_4 &= 2(\cos 315^\circ + i \sin 315^\circ) = +\sqrt{2} - i\sqrt{2}.\end{aligned}$$

The corresponding points are shown in Fig. 4, together with the regular polygon of four sides, known as a square.

FIGURE 4

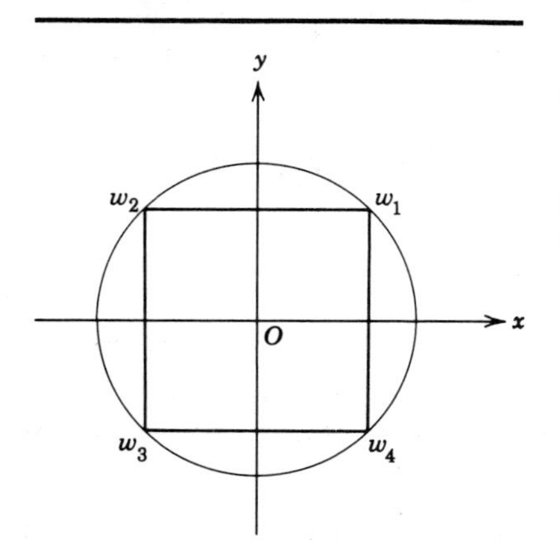

EXERCISE 51

1. Check the solution $w_2 = -\sqrt{2} + \sqrt{2}i$ in Example 3 by raising it to the fourth power.

In Problems 2 through 11 use De Moivre's theorem to compute the indicated power in rectangular form.

2. $(1 + \sqrt{3}i)^7$. **3.** $(1 - i)^{13}$.
4. $(1 + i)^5$. **5.** $(\sqrt{3} - i)^6$.
6. $(1 + 3i)^8$. **7.** $(-2 + i)^{10}$.
8. $(\cos 27° + i \sin 27°)^{10}$.
9. $(\cos 9° + i \sin 9°)^{20}$.
10. $(\cos 4° + i \sin 4°)^8$.
11. $(\cos 8° + i \sin 8°)^4$.

In Problems 12 through 23 find the indicated roots in rectangular form.

12. The fifth roots of 1. **13.** The sixth roots of -1.
14. The square roots of $8i$. **15.** The fifth roots of $16\sqrt{2} - 16\sqrt{2}i$.
16. The cube roots of -1. **17.** The square roots of $-2 + 2\sqrt{3}i$.
18. The cube roots of $-4\sqrt{3} + 4i$. **19.** The sixth roots of -64.
20. The eighth root of $256(\cos 48° + i \sin 48°)$ with the largest real part.
21. The fourth root of $81(\cos 20° + i \sin 20°)$ with the largest imaginary part.
22. The cube root of $27(\cos 30° + i \sin 30°)$ with the smallest imaginary part.
23. The fourth root of $16(\cos 164° + i \sin 164°)$ with the smallest imaginary part.

24. Solve the equation $x^4 + 1 = 0$. **25.** Solve the equation $x^6 - 1 = 0$.
★**26.** If we expand $(\cos \theta + i \sin \theta)^n = (\cos n\theta + i \sin n\theta)$ we can then equate real and imaginary parts. This will give expressions for $\cos n\theta$ and $\sin n\theta$ in terms of $\cos \theta$ and $\sin \theta$. Use this method to prove that

$$(a)\ \cos 3\theta = \cos^3 \theta - 3 \cos \theta \sin^2 \theta, \text{ and } (b)\ \sin 3\theta = 3 \cos^2 \theta \sin \theta - \sin^3 \theta.$$

★**27.** Use the method of Problem 26 to obtain $\cos 4\theta$ and $\sin 4\theta$ in terms of $\sin \theta$ and $\cos \theta$.
★**28.** Use the method of Problem 26 for $\cos 5\theta$ and $\sin 5\theta$.
★**29.** Solve the equation $x^3 + x^2 + x + 1 = 0$. *Hint*: multiply by $x - 1$, solve the new equation, and reject the root $x = 1$.

ANSWERS TO SELECTED PROBLEMS

EXERCISE 1 (Page 9)

1. 5. **3.** 13. **5.** 3. **7.** 16. **9.** $\sqrt{11}$. **11.** $6\sqrt{2}$. **13.** $\sqrt{41}$. **15.** $3\sqrt{5}$. **17.** $8\sqrt{5}$. **21.** (*a*) $s = 2, t = 1$, (*b*) $s = 3, t = 2$, (*c*) $s = 5, t = 4$.

22. It is impossible to find such integers. This was first stated by Fermat in 1637, and the first published proof was given by Euler in 1770. The general problem of finding positive integers for which $x^n + y^n = z^n$ $(n > 2)$ is still unsolved. Fermat asserted that no such integers exist, and this is called Fermat's last theorem, although it is not a theorem, because it has not yet been proved.

23. ACD/B, AD/BC, AC/BD, A/BCD.

EXERCISE 2 (Page 16)

Problem	Angle	sin	cos	tan	cot	sec	csc
1	P	p/r	q/r	p/q	q/p	r/q	r/p
	Q	q/r	p/r	q/p	p/q	r/p	r/q
3	W	w/v	u/v	w/u	u/w	v/u	v/w
	U	u/v	w/v	u/w	w/u	v/w	v/u

5. .2278. **7.** 3.526. **9.** .4094. **11.** 1.767. **13.** .6988. **15.** 1.428. **17.** 0° 10′. **19.** 8° 0′. **21.** 13° 30′. **23.** 23° 30′. **25.** 23° 30′. **27.** 36° 30′. **29.** See Chapter 1, §13.

EXERCISE 3 (Page 18)

3. 1.303. **5.** .6472. **7.** 4.989. **9.** .4067. **11.** 5.769. **13.** .2278. **15.** 79° 30′. **17.** 72° 0′. **19.** 56° 10′. **21.** 78° 30′. **23.** 51° 0′. **25.** 71° 0′.

EXERCISE 4 (Page 22)

1. $B = 59° 20'$, $a = 906$, $b = 1527$. **3.** $A = 77° 10'$, $a = 1934$, $b = 441$. **5.** $A = 41° 50'$, $B = 48° 10'$, $b = 2235$. **7.** $B = 50° 20'$, $b = 2309$, $c = 3000$. **9.** $A = 43° 30'$, $B = 46° 30'$, $c = 2757$.

EXERCISE 5 (Page 26)

1. (*a*) 2.7182818285, (*b*) 2.718283, (*c*) 2.71828, (*d*) 2.718. **2.** (*a*) 3.45×10, (*b*) 3.45×10^4, (*c*) 3.45×10^{11}, (*d*) 3.45×10^{-1}, (*e*) 3.45×10^{-3}, (*f*) 3.45×10^{-10}. **3.** (*a*) 711., (*b*) 711,000., (*c*) 700,000,000., (*d*) .07711, (*e*) .00777111, (*f*) .0000771. **4.** (*a*) 3.000, (*b*) 3.000, (*c*) 2.998, (*d*) 10.00.

EXERCISE 6 (Page 31)

1. 9° 19′. **3.** 61° 7′. **5.** 79° 4′. **7.** 79° 4′. **9.** 63° 37′. **11.** 81° 28′. **13.** 24° 14′. **15.** 62° 43′. **17.** .3368. **19.** .9442. **21.** .4752. **23.** .0995. **25.** .7296. **27.** 4.309. **29.** .1415. **31.** .7468.

EXERCISE 7 (Page 35)

1. 273 ft. **3.** 17.63, 12.14. **5.** 31°. **7.** 6.7 ft, no. **9.** 270 mph, 15 mi. **11.** S 53° W. **13.** 13.85, 19.60. **15.** 4980 ft.

EXERCISE 9 (Page 42)

1. 1. **3.** 4. **5.** −2. **7.** 5. **9.** 4. **11.** $\frac{1}{3}$. **13.** $\frac{5}{3}$. **15.** −4. **17.** $-\frac{1}{2}$. **19.** −2. **21.** 2. **23.** 3. **25.** $\frac{5}{2}$. **27.** 6. **29.** 81. **31.** 81. **33.** $\frac{1}{64}$. **35.** 8. **37.** 1. **39.** 256.

EXERCISE 10 (Page 45)

1. .602. **3.** .778. **5.** .954. **7.** 1.908. **9.** −.301. **11.** .211. **13.** 1.845. **15.** .669. **17.** −.669. **19.** 1.738. **21.** F. **23.** F. **25.** T. **27.** F.

EXERCISE 11 (Page 47)

1. .53857. **3.** .75420. **5.** .37014. **7.** .73480. **9.** 2.155. **11.** 7.741. **13.** 3.166. **15.** 1.018.

EXERCISE 12 (Page 49)

1. 2.53857. **3.** 6.75420. **5.** 4.37014. **7.** 7.97002. **9.** 3.73480. **11.** 2155. **13.** 77.41. **15.** 3,166,000. **17.** 1.018. **19.** 2.000.

EXERCISE 13 (Page 50)

1. 7.17377 − 10. **3.** 9.87685 − 10. **5.** 8.52362 − 10. **7.** .1914. **9.** .00052. **11.** .007945.

EXERCISE 14 (Page 51)

1. 4.73497. **3.** 9.94277 − 10. **5.** 1.37025. **7.** 6.47716 − 10. **9.** 2.89085. **11.** 7.81958 − 10. **13.** .87550. **15.** 8.06442 − 10. **17.** 270,460. **19.** 17.162. **21.** .00036783. **23.** .50132. **25.** 8.1113. **27.** .0010797. **29.** .000013288. **31.** 7.3228.

EXERCISE 15 (Page 53)

1. 3.505. **3.** 1,505,000. **5.** .000000003670. **7.** .2888. **9.** 8483. **11.** .0000000008939. **13.** 37,030. **15.** 2.132. **17.** .5719. **19.** .6091. **21.** .24702. **23.** .00019190. **25.** 17.626. **27.** 62,604,000. **29.** .51199. **31.** 103.28. **33.** 3,997,300,000,000. **35.** 11.971. **37.** 286,870. **39.** .75518. **41.** .75518. **43.** .074220. **45.** .83834. **47.** 635,030,000,000.

EXERCISE 16 (Page 56)

1. 9.63504 — 10. **3.** 9.17890 — 10. **5.** 10.36655 — 10. **7.** 11.04940 — 10. **9.** 9.95978 — 10. **11.** 9.96153 — 10. **13.** 9.82169 — 10. **15.** 9.35890 — 10. **17.** 29° 0′. **19.** 8° 59′. **21.** 57° 57′. **23.** 9° 44.4′. **25.** 21° 3.7′. **27.** 55° 30.2′. **29.** 82° 58.3′. **31.** 44° 55.6′.

EXERCISE 17 (Page 58)

1. $A = 39° 14'$, $c = 2{,}561$. **3.** $a = 6.779$, $b = 7.182$. **5.** $c = .049409$, $a = .023553$. **7.** $A = 33° 22.8'$, $b = 20.609$.

EXERCISE 18 (Page 62)

3. 5, 3, $7\sqrt{2}$, 3, 5. **5.** $y = -12$. **7.** $x = -4$. **9.** $y = -3$. **11.** $x = 2$. **13.** (*a*) Q.I and Q.II, (*b*) Q.IV and Q.II, (*c*) Q.I and Q.IV. **15.** (*a*) A straight line through the origin bisecting Q.I. and Q.III, (*b*) A straight line through the origin bisecting Q.II. and Q.IV, (*c*) A circle of radius 4 with center at the origin, (*d*) The two straight lines of parts (*a*) and (*b*).

EXERCISE 19 (Page 67)

1. 390°, 750°, 1110°, −330°, −690°, · · · . **3.** See Table 1 of §5, Chapter 4.

5.

θ	sin	cos	tan	cot	sec	csc
120°	$\frac{\sqrt{3}}{2}$	$-\frac{1}{2}$	$-\sqrt{3}$	$-\frac{\sqrt{3}}{3}$	-2	$\frac{2\sqrt{3}}{3}$
−45°	$-\frac{\sqrt{2}}{2}$	$\frac{\sqrt{2}}{2}$	-1	-1	$\sqrt{2}$	$-\sqrt{2}$
210°	$-\frac{1}{2}$	$-\frac{\sqrt{3}}{2}$	$\frac{\sqrt{3}}{3}$	$\sqrt{3}$	$-\frac{2\sqrt{3}}{3}$	-2
720°	0	1	0	∞	1	∞
−270°	1	0	∞	0	∞	1

7. (*a*) $\frac{5}{13}$, $\frac{12}{13}$; (*b*) $\frac{3}{5}$, $-\frac{4}{5}$; (*c*) $-5\sqrt{41}/41$, $-4\sqrt{41}/41$; (*d*) $-2\sqrt{5}/5$, $\sqrt{5}/5$.

EXERCISE 20 (Page 69)

1. Q.IV, 20°. **3.** Q.I, 60°. **5.** Q.II, 10°. **7.** Q.III, 80°.

Problem	sin	cos	tan
9	.1736	−.9848	−.1763
11	−.5736	−.8192	.7002
13	−.3420	.9397	−.3640

15. 303° 41′. **17.** 221° 25′. **19.** 138° 11′.

EXERCISE 21 (Page 71)

2. (*a*) x^5, (*b*) $x + x^3$ are odd functions; (*c*) x^6, (*d*) $1 + x^2$ are even functions.
3. (*a*) $x + x^2$, (*b*) $1 + x^3$.

EXERCISE 22 (Page 76)

15. $\frac{1}{2}(2x + 36) - x = 18$.

16. If a person has fun proving trigonometric identities, then he has a normal, healthy, inquisitive mind.

EXERCISE 25 (Page 86)

1. (*a*)
$$\sin\theta = \pm\sqrt{1-\cos^2\theta},$$
$$\tan\theta = \frac{\pm\sqrt{1-\cos^2\theta}}{\cos\theta},$$
$$\cot\theta = \frac{\pm\cos\theta}{\sqrt{1-\cos^2\theta}},$$
$$\sec\theta = \frac{1}{\cos\theta},$$
$$\csc\theta = \frac{\pm 1}{\sqrt{1-\cos^2\theta}}.$$

(*c*)
$$\sin\theta = \frac{\pm 1}{\sqrt{1+\cot^2\theta}},$$
$$\cos\theta = \frac{\pm\cot\theta}{\sqrt{1+\cot^2\theta}},$$
$$\tan\theta = \frac{1}{\cot\theta},$$
$$\sec\theta = \frac{\pm\sqrt{1+\cot^2\theta}}{\cot\theta},$$
$$\csc\theta = \pm\sqrt{1+\cot^2\theta}\cdot$$

(*e*)
$$\sin\theta = \frac{\pm\sqrt{\sec^2\theta - 1}}{\sec\theta},$$
$$\cos\theta = \frac{1}{\sec\theta},$$
$$\tan\theta = \pm\sqrt{\sec^2\theta - 1},$$

(*e*)
$$\cot\theta = \frac{\pm 1}{\sqrt{\sec^2\theta - 1}},$$
$$\csc\theta = \frac{\pm\sec\theta}{\sqrt{\sec^2\theta - 1}}.$$

EXERCISE 26 (Page 88)

4. (4), (45), (49), (50).

EXERCISE 27 (Page 91)

1. 13. **3.** 5. **5.** 10. **7.** 6. **9.** $\sqrt{74}$. **11.** $\sqrt{146}$. **13.** $\sqrt{2}$. **15.** Yes. The formula is $d = \sqrt{(x_1 - x_2)^2 + (y_1 - y_2)^2}$. **16.** No. Consider the points (1, 2) and (2, 1). **17.** $d = \sqrt{x_2^2 + y_2^2}$.

EXERCISE 28 (Page 94)

1. $c = a + b$. **2.** $c = |a - b|$. **3.** 13. **5.** 13. **7.** .013. **9.** $A = 19° 40'$, $B = 28° 10'$, $C = 132° 10'$. **11.** (16, 49, 55), (16, 26, 30), (16, 16, 16), (16, 14, 6), (16, 19, 21), (16, 14, 10). **13.** 3800 ft. **15.** 27 miles.

EXERCISE 29 (Page 97)

1. $b = 90$, $c = 73$. **3.** $a = 140$, $c = 170$. **5.** $a = .024008$, $c = .031837$. **7.** $a = 17.499$, $b = 20.763$. **9.** 192 ft. **11.** 1680 ft. **13.** 220 ft.

EXERCISE 30 (Page 102)

1. No triangle. **3.** 14° 29′. **5.** $B = 61° 3'$ or $118° 57'$. **7.** No triangle. **9.** 59° 43′. **11.** $C = 73° 59.0'$, $A = 72° 27.7'$, $a = 8{,}015.5$; or $C = 106° 1.0'$, $A = 40° 25.7'$, $a = 5{,}453.2$. **13.** No triangle. **15.** 12° 10′. **17.** 3.2×10^7 miles or 13×10^7 miles. **19.** 24.1 in.

EXERCISE 31 (Page 109)

1. cos 10°. **3.** $\frac{1}{2}$. **5.** $-\sqrt{3}/2$. **7.** cos $5A$. **9.** $-(\sqrt{6} + \sqrt{2})/4$. **11.** $-(\sqrt{6} - \sqrt{2})/4$. **25.** No. Theorem 1 of Chapter 1 was proved only for acute angles. **29.** $(\sqrt{35} - 6)/12$, Q.II. **31.** $\sqrt{13}/65$, Q.I.

EXERCISE 32 (Page 112)

1. $\frac{1}{2}$. **3.** 0. **5.** 1. **7.** tan $2C$. **9.** $(\sqrt{6} + \sqrt{2})/4$, $-(2 + \sqrt{3})$. **11.** $(\sqrt{6} + \sqrt{2})/4$, $2 + \sqrt{3}$. **13.** $\frac{49}{37}$, $-\frac{7}{61}$. **15.** $49/\sqrt{3770}$, $-7/\sqrt{3770}$. **17.** .034899, .999391.

EXERCISE 33 (Page 116)

1. tan 40°. **3.** sin 28°. **5.** cos 80 . **7.** tan $2A/2$. **9.** $(\sqrt{6} - \sqrt{2})/4$, $(\sqrt{6} + \sqrt{2})/4$. **11.** $\sqrt{10}/10$, $3\sqrt{10}/10$. **13.** $\frac{24}{25}$, $\frac{7}{25}$. **15.** $3\sqrt{10}/10$, $-\sqrt{10}/10$. **17.** $(n - 1)/\sqrt{2(1 + n^2)}$, $(n + 1)/\sqrt{2(1 + n^2)}$. **21.** $\cos 3C = 4 \cos^3 C - 3 \cos C$.

EXERCISE 34 (Page 120)

1. (sin 20° + sin 10°)/2. **3.** (cos $4A$ + cos $2A$)/2. **5.** (cos C + cos $3C$ + cos $5C$ + cos $9C$)/4. **7.** $2 \sin 2\theta \cos \theta$. **9.** $2 \cos 4\theta \cos 2\theta$. **23.** $(3\sqrt{2} + \sqrt{3})/6$, $(3\sqrt{2} - \sqrt{3})/6$.

25. $\cos A = (\sqrt{(1+x)(1+y)} + \sqrt{(1-x)(1-y)})/2$

$\cos B = (\sqrt{(1+x)(1+y)} - \sqrt{(1-x)(1-y)})/2$

$\sin A = (\sqrt{(1-x)(1+y)} - \sqrt{(1+x)(1-y)})/2$

$\sin B = (\sqrt{(1-x)(1+y)} + \sqrt{(1+x)(1-y)})/2.$

EXERCISE 35 (Page 125)

1. 1, 2, 3, 4, 5, 6, 8, 9, 10, 12, 15, 18, 20, 24, 30, 36, 40, 45, 60, 72, 90, 120, 180, 360. **3.** $\pi/3, 4\pi/3, 4\pi, -3\pi/4, \pi/15, 11\pi/15, \pi/15, -5\pi/6$. **5.** 45°, −405°, 450°, 16° 30′, −40°, 95°, 1260°, −1440°. **7.** $\frac{1}{2}, -\frac{1}{2}, -1, -1, 0, \infty, -1, -1$. **9.** 6.91 in. **11.** 339 ft. **13.** 11 radians, 630°. **15.** 69.1 mi, 1.15 mi. **17.** 2920 mi.

EXERCISE 36 (Page 128)

1. 18.3 mi/sec. **3.** 560 rpm. **5.** 471 mi/hr. **7.** 94.3 ft/sec. **9.** 7.00 rpm. **11.** 8.40 rpm. **13.** 6.49 mi/hr. **15.** 104 minutes.

EXERCISE 37 (Page 134)

1. $5, \pi$. **3.** $2, \pi/2$. **5.** $1, 2\pi$. **7.** $6, \pi$.

EXERCISE 38 (Page 138)

1. As θ increases

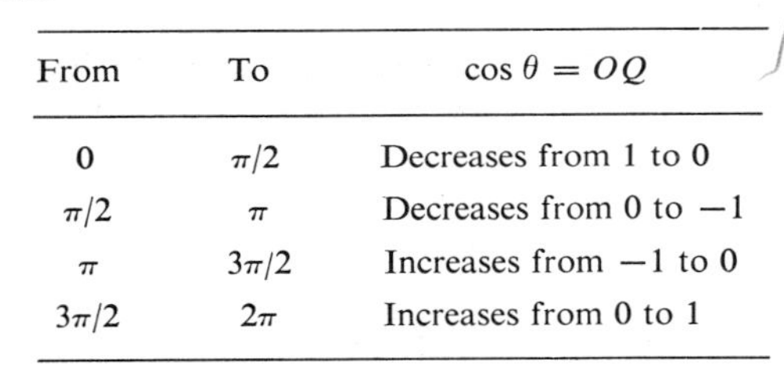

From	To	$\cos\theta = OQ$
0	$\pi/2$	Decreases from 1 to 0
$\pi/2$	π	Decreases from 0 to −1
π	$3\pi/2$	Increases from −1 to 0
$3\pi/2$	2π	Increases from 0 to 1

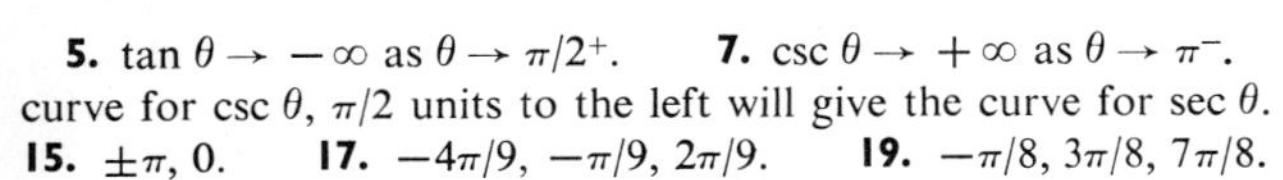

5. $\tan\theta \to -\infty$ as $\theta \to \pi/2^+$. **7.** $\csc\theta \to +\infty$ as $\theta \to \pi^-$. **11.** A shift of the curve for $\csc\theta$, $\pi/2$ units to the left will give the curve for $\sec\theta$. **13.** $\pm\pi/2, 3\pi/2$. **15.** $\pm\pi, 0$. **17.** $-4\pi/9, -\pi/9, 2\pi/9$. **19.** $-\pi/8, 3\pi/8, 7\pi/8$. **21.** $0, \pm\pi$.

EXERCISE 39 (Page 142)

1. $-2\pi/3, \pi/3$. **3.** $-2\pi/3, \pi/3$. **5.** $-\pi/4, 3\pi/4$. **7.** $3\sqrt{2}, 2$. **9.** $R = \sqrt{a^2+b^2}$, $\sin A = -a/R$, $\cos A = b/R$. **18.** $\pi, \pi, 2\pi, \pi, \pi, 2\pi$.

EXERCISE 40 (Page 147)

1. 50°, 110°. **3.** 25°, 205°. **5.** 30°, 150°. **7.** 0°. **9.** 35° 50′, 144° 10′. **11.** 27° 20′ + n90°, 62° 40′ + n90°, n = 0, 1, 2, 3. **13.** 0°, 180°. **15.** 30°, 150°, 270°.

17. 107° 10′, 142° 10′, 287° 10′, 322° 10′. **19.** 30°, 60°, 210°, 240°. **21.** 22° 30′, 112° 30′, 202° 30′, 292° 30′. **23.** 270°, 306° 50′. **25.** 22° 40′, 143° 10′. **27.** 17° + n36°, (n = 0, 1, 2, · · ·, 9). **29.** 90°, 270°, 22° 30′ + n45° (n = 0, 1, · · ·, 7). **31.** 0°, 30°, 90°, 150°, 180°, 210°, 270°, 330°. **33.** 63° 30′, 108° 30′, 243° 30′, 288° 30′. **35.** 30°, 45°, 150°, 225°. **37.** 0°, 30°, 150°, 210°, 330°. **39.** 45°, 135°, 225°, 315°. **41.** 30°, 90°, 150°, 210°, 270°, 330°. **43.** 0°, 180°, 10° + n20°, (n = 0, 1, 2, · · ·, 17). **45.** 36° 50′, 53° 10′. **47.** 82° 50′. **49.** 36° 50′. **51.** 63° 50′.

EXERCISE 41 (Page 151)

1. $x = (3 - y)/5$, $(1, -2)$. **3.** $x = 3y + 21$, $(3, -6)$. **5.** $x = (y + 3)/(y - 2)$, $(2, 7)$. **7.** $x = -1 + \sqrt{y + 16}$, $(3, 0)$. **9.** $y = 2 + \sqrt{9 - y}$, $(4, 5)$.

EXERCISE 42 (Page 155)

1. 90°. **3.** −30°. **5.** 45°. **7.** 13° 30′. **9.** 139° 50′. **11.** $-\pi/2$. **13.** $\pi/3$. **15.** $\pi/4$. **17.** $2\pi/3$. **19.** $\frac{4}{5}$. **21.** $\frac{12}{13}$. **23.** −.9827. **25.** (a). **27.** (c). **29.** $e/\sqrt{1 + e^2}$. **31.** $1/\sqrt{1 - g^2}$. **33.** $2u\sqrt{1 - u^2}$. **35.** $(1 - u^2)/(1 + u^2)$. **37.** $\pm\sqrt{(1 - \sqrt{1 - n^2})/2}$. **39.** $\sqrt{1 - u^2}/(1 + u)$. **41.** False. **43.** False. **45.** True. **47.** True. **49.** True. **51.** True.

EXERCISE 43 (Page 157)

1. $\frac{63}{65}$, $\frac{16}{65}$, Q.I. **3.** $(12\sqrt{5} + \sqrt{10})/30$, $(4\sqrt{5} - 3\sqrt{10})/30$, Q.II.
5. $x(1 - x^2 + 2\sqrt{1 - x^2})/(1 + x^2)$.

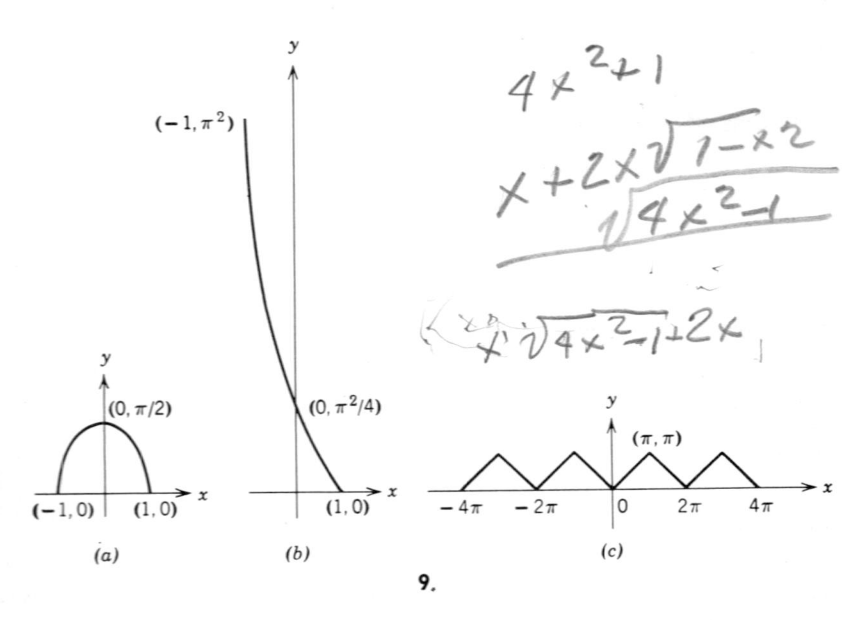

9.

11. (a) odd, (b) neither, (c) even, (d) neither, (e) odd, (f) even.

EXERCISE 44 (Page 161)

1. 10. **3.** 66. **5.** 6,322,000. **7.** .005178. **9.** 962.1. **11.** 181,000. **17.** 40.07 ft. **19.** $40° 50'$.

EXERCISE 45 (Page 165)

1. $19° 8'$, $52° 34'$, $108° 16'$, 853.6. **3.** $41° 0'$, $55° 34'$, $83° 26'$, .01429. **5.** $55° 38'$, $59° 54'$, $64° 28'$, 5.346. **7.** 3577, .03293.

EXERCISE 46 (Page 167)

1. $c = 4231$, $A = 108° 58'$, $B = 47° 8'$. **3.** $b = 84.18$, $A = 31° 42'$, $C = 24° 34'$.

EXERCISE 47 (Page 172)

1. 41 lb, S 52° W. **3.** 27 lb, −60 lb. **5.** 22 lb, S 54° W. **7.** 21.1 lb, 51.3 lb. **9.** 200 lb. **11.** N 36° 50′ E, 5.00 mph, 15.0 min. **13.** 175 mph, 105 mph, 136 mph. **15.** N 26° 10′ W.

EXERCISE 48 (Page 177)

1. $9 + 15i$, $-16 + 63i$, $(56 - 33i)/169$. **3.** $8 - 16i$, $-33 - 56i$, $(63 - 16i)/25$. **5.** $6i$, -13, $(5 + 12i)/13$. **7.** $4 + 5i$, $-6 + 8i$, $(3 - 4i)/2$. **9.** $-3 - i$, $5(4 + 3i)$, $(-4 - 3i)/5$. **11.** $-i$, 1, 1, -4, $-8i$. **13.** $-1 - 9i$, $3 + 3i$, $2 - 8i$, $-2 + 2i$. **15.** $-i$, $i(a^2 + b^2)$. **17.** $(2 \pm \sqrt{6})i$. **19.** 1, i, -1, $-i$.

EXERCISE 49 (Page 179)

3. $5\sqrt{2}$, $45°$; 5, $36° 50'$; $2\sqrt{5}$, $243° 30'$; 5, $126° 50'$; $5\sqrt{2}$, $171° 50'$. **5.** $3\sqrt{2}(\cos 315° + i \sin 315°)$. **7.** $5(\cos 180° + i \sin 180°)$. **9.** $2(\cos 90° + i \sin 90°)$. **11.** $13(\cos 67° 20' + i \sin 67° 20')$. **13.** $8i$. **15.** $(-\sqrt{3} + 3i)/2$. **17.** $-4\sqrt{3} + 4i$. **19.** 0. **21.** $\sqrt{5}(1 - i)$.

EXERCISE 50 (Page 181)

5. $4(1 + \sqrt{3}i)$, $-4(1 + \sqrt{3}i)$. **7.** $-20\sqrt{2}$, $5\sqrt{2}i$. **9.** $6\sqrt{5}(\cos 243° 30' + i \sin 243° 30')$, $(\cos 296° 30' + i \sin 296° 30')3\sqrt{5}/10$. **11.** 29, $\cos 136° 20' + i \sin 136° 20'$. **13.** $26i$, $(\cos 202° 40' + i \sin 202° 40')/2$. **15.** $9(-1 + \sqrt{3}i)$. **17.** $-2(1 + i)$.

EXERCISE 51 (Page 184)

3. $64(-1 + i)$. **5.** -64. **7.** $-236.2 + 3116i$. **9.** -1. **11.** $.8480 + .5299i$. **13.** $\pm i$, $(\pm \sqrt{3} \pm i)/2$. **15.** $.9080 + 1.782i$, $\sqrt{2}(-1 + i)$, $-1.782 - .9080i$, $.3128 - 1.9754i$, $1.9754 - .3128i$. **17.** $\pm(1 + \sqrt{3}i)$. **19.** $\pm 2i$, $\pm \sqrt{3} \pm i$. **21.** $-.2616 + 2.9886i$. **23.** $1.3122 - 1.5094i$. **25.** $(\pm 1 \pm \sqrt{3}i)/2$. **27.** $\cos 4\theta = \cos^4 \theta - 6 \cos^2 \theta \sin^2 \theta + \sin^4 \theta$, $\sin 4\theta = 4(\cos^3 \theta \sin \theta - \cos \theta \sin^3 \theta)$. **29.** -1, $\pm i$.

INDEX

APPENDIX

TABLES

Table A. Squares and square roots: 1–200

Table B. Values of the trigonometric functions to four places

Table C. Mantissas of common logarithms of numbers to five decimal places

Table D. Logarithms of the trigonometric functions to five decimal places

Table A. Squares and Square Roots: 1–200[1]

N	N^2	$\sqrt{N}$	N	N^2	$\sqrt{N}$	N	N^2	$\sqrt{N}$	N	N^2	$\sqrt{N}$
1	1	1.000	**51**	2,601	7.141	**101**	10,201	10.050	**151**	22,801	12.288
2	4	1.414	**52**	2,704	7.211	**102**	10,404	10.100	**152**	23,104	12.329
3	9	1.732	**53**	2,809	7.280	**103**	10,609	10.149	**153**	23,409	12.369
4	16	2.000	**54**	2,916	7.348	**104**	10,816	10.198	**154**	23,716	12.410
5	25	2.236	**55**	3,025	7.416	**105**	11,025	10.247	**155**	24,025	12.450
6	36	2.449	**56**	3,136	7.483	**106**	11,236	10.296	**156**	24,336	12.490
7	49	2.646	**57**	3,249	7.550	**107**	11,449	10.344	**157**	24,649	12.530
8	64	2.828	**58**	3,364	7.616	**108**	11,664	10.392	**158**	24,964	12.570
9	81	3.000	**59**	3,481	7.681	**109**	11,881	10.440	**159**	25,281	12.610
10	100	3.162	**60**	3,600	7.746	**110**	12,100	10.488	**160**	25,600	12.649
11	121	3.317	**61**	3,721	7.810	**111**	12,321	10.536	**161**	25,921	12.689
12	144	3.464	**62**	3,844	7.874	**112**	12,544	10.583	**162**	26,244	12.728
13	169	3.606	**63**	3,969	7.937	**113**	12,769	10.630	**163**	26,569	12.767
14	196	3.742	**64**	4,096	8.000	**114**	12,996	10.677	**164**	26,896	12.806
15	225	3.873	**65**	4,225	8.062	**115**	13,225	10.724	**165**	27,225	12.845
16	256	4.000	**66**	4,356	8.124	**116**	13,456	10.770	**166**	27,556	12.884
17	289	4.123	**67**	4,489	8.185	**117**	13,689	10.817	**167**	27,889	12.923
18	324	4.243	**68**	4,624	8.246	**118**	13,924	10.863	**168**	28,224	12.962
19	361	4.359	**69**	4,761	8.307	**119**	14,161	10.909	**169**	28,561	13.000
20	400	4.472	**70**	4,900	8.367	**120**	14,400	10.954	**170**	28,900	13.038
21	441	4.583	**71**	5,041	8.426	**121**	14,641	11.000	**171**	29,241	13.077
22	484	4.690	**72**	5,184	8.485	**122**	14,884	11.045	**172**	29,584	13.115
23	529	4.796	**73**	5,329	8.544	**123**	15,129	11.091	**173**	29,929	13.153
24	576	4.899	**74**	5,476	8.602	**124**	15,376	11.136	**174**	30,276	13.191
25	625	5.000	**75**	5,625	8.660	**125**	15,625	11.180	**175**	30,625	13.229
26	676	5.099	**76**	5,776	8.718	**126**	15,876	11.225	**176**	30,976	13.266
27	729	5.196	**77**	5,929	8.775	**127**	16,129	11.269	**177**	31,329	13.304
28	784	5.292	**78**	6,084	8.832	**128**	16,384	11.314	**178**	31,684	13.342
29	841	5.385	**79**	6,241	8.888	**129**	16,641	11.358	**179**	32,041	13.379
30	900	5.477	**80**	6,400	8.944	**130**	16,900	11.402	**180**	32,400	13.416
31	961	5.568	**81**	6,561	9.000	**131**	17,161	11.446	**181**	32,761	13.454
32	1,024	5.657	**82**	6,724	9.055	**132**	17,424	11.489	**182**	33,124	13.491
33	1,089	5.745	**83**	6,889	9.110	**133**	17,689	11.533	**183**	33,489	13.528
34	1,156	5.831	**84**	7,056	9.165	**134**	17,956	11.576	**184**	33,856	13.565
35	1,225	5.916	**85**	7,225	9.220	**135**	18,225	11.619	**185**	34,225	13.601
36	1,296	6.000	**86**	7,396	9.274	**136**	18,496	11.662	**186**	34,596	13.638
37	1,369	6.083	**87**	7,569	9.327	**137**	18,769	11.705	**187**	34,969	13.675
38	1,444	6.164	**88**	7,744	9.381	**138**	19,044	11.747	**188**	35,344	13.711
39	1,521	6.245	**89**	7,921	9.434	**139**	19,321	11.790	**189**	35,721	13.748
40	1,600	6.325	**90**	8,100	9.487	**140**	19,600	11.832	**190**	36,100	13.784
41	1,681	6.403	**91**	8,281	9.539	**141**	19,881	11.874	**191**	36,481	13.820
42	1,764	6.481	**92**	8,464	9.592	**142**	20,164	11.916	**192**	36,864	13.856
43	1,849	6.557	**93**	8,649	9.644	**143**	20,449	11.958	**193**	37,249	13.892
44	1,936	6.633	**94**	8,836	9.695	**144**	20,736	12.000	**194**	37,636	13.928
45	2,025	6.708	**95**	9,025	9.747	**145**	21,025	12.042	**195**	38,025	13.964
46	2,116	6.782	**96**	9,216	9.798	**146**	21,316	12.083	**196**	38,416	14.000
47	2,209	6.856	**97**	9,409	9.849	**147**	21,609	12.124	**197**	38,809	14.036
48	2,304	6.928	**98**	9,604	9.899	**148**	21,904	12.166	**198**	39,204	14.071
49	2,401	7.000	**99**	9,801	9.950	**149**	22,201	12.207	**199**	39,601	14.107
50	2,500	7.071	**100**	10,000	10.000	**150**	22,500	12.247	**200**	40,000	14.142
N	N^2	$\sqrt{N}$	N	N^2	$\sqrt{N}$	N	N^2	$\sqrt{N}$	N	N^2	$\sqrt{N}$

[1] From William Hart, *Plane Trigonometry*, 1942, reprinted by permission of D. C. Heath and Co., Boston.

Table B. Values of the Trigonometric Functions to Four Places[1]

Radians	Degrees	Sin	Tan	Cot	Cos		
.0000	**0° 00′**	.0000	.0000	——	1.0000	**90° 00′**	1.5708
029	10	029	029	343.8	000	89° 50′	679
058	20	058	058	171.9	000	40	650
.0087	30	.0087	.0087	114.6	1.0000	30	1.5621
116	40	116	116	85.94	.9999	20	592
145	50	145	145	68.75	999	10	563
.0175	**1° 00′**	.0175	.0175	57.29	.9998	**89° 00′**	1.5533
204	10	204	204	49.10	998	88° 50′	504
233	20	233	233	42.96	997	40	475
.0262	30	.0262	.0262	38.19	.9997	30	1.5446
291	40	291	291	34.37	996	20	417
320	50	320	320	31.24	995	10	388
.0349	**2° 00′**	.0349	.0349	28.64	.9994	**88° 00′**	1.5359
378	10	378	378	26.43	993	87° 50′	330
407	20	407	407	24.54	992	40	301
.0436	30	.0436	.0437	22.90	.9990	30	1.5272
465	40	465	466	21.47	989	20	243
495	50	494	495	20.21	988	10	213
.0524	**3° 00′**	.0523	.0524	19.08	.9986	**87° 00′**	1.5184
553	10	552	553	18.07	985	86° 50′	155
582	20	581	582	17.17	983	40	126
.0611	30	.0610	.0612	16.35	.9981	30	1.5097
640	40	640	641	15.60	980	20	068
669	50	669	670	14.92	978	10	039
.0698	**4° 00′**	.0698	.0699	14.30	.9976	**86° 00′**	1.5010
727	10	727	729	13.73	974	85° 50′	981
756	20	756	758	13.20	971	40	952
.0785	30	.0785	.0787	12.71	.9969	30	1.4923
814	40	814	816	12.25	967	20	893
844	50	843	846	11.83	964	10	864
.0873	**5° 00′**	.0872	.0875	11.43	.9962	**85° 00′**	1.4835
902	10	901	904	11.06	959	84° 50′	806
931	20	929	934	10.71	957	40	777
.0960	30	.0958	.0963	10.39	.9954	30	1.4748
989	40	987	992	10.08	951	20	719
.1018	50	.1016	.1022	9.788	948	10	690
.1047	**6° 00′**	.1045	.1051	9.514	.9945	**84° 00′**	1.4661
076	10	074	080	9.255	942	83° 50′	632
105	20	103	110	9.010	939	40	603
.1134	30	.1132	.1139	8.777	.9936	30	1.4573
164	40	161	169	8.556	932	20	544
193	50	190	198	8.345	929	10	515
.1222	**7° 00′**	.1219	.1228	8.144	.9925	**83° 00′**	1.4486
251	10	248	257	7.953	922	82° 50′	457
280	20	276	287	7.770	918	40	428
.1309	30	.1305	.1317	7.596	.9914	30	1.4399
338	40	334	346	7.429	911	20	370
367	50	363	376	7.269	907	10	341
.1396	**8° 00′**	.1392	.1405	7.115	.9903	**82° 00′**	1.4312
425	10	421	435	6.968	899	81° 50′	283
454	20	449	465	6.827	894	40	254
.1484	30	.1478	.1495	6.691	.9890	30	1.4224
513	40	507	524	6.561	886	20	195
542	50	536	554	6.435	881	10	166
.1571	**9° 00′**	.1564	.1584	6.314	.9877	**81° 00′**	1.4137
		Cos	Cot	Tan	Sin	Degrees	Radians

[1] Reprinted by permission from *The McGraw-Hill Five-Place Logarithmic and Trigonometric Tables*, edited by R. D. Beetle, copyright 1933 by McGraw-Hill.

Table B. Trigonometric Functions (Continued)

Radians	Degrees	Sin	Tan	Cot	Cos		
.1571	**9° 00′**	.1564	.1584	6.314	.9877	**81° 00**	1.4137
600	10	593	614	197	872	80° 50	108
629	20	622	644	084	868	40	079
.1658	30	.1650	.1673	5.976	.9863	30	1.4050
687	40	679	703	871	858	20	1.4021
716	50	708	733	769	853	10	992
.1745	**10° 00′**	.1736	.1763	5.671	.9848	**80° 00′**	1.3963
774	10	765	793	576	843	79° 50′	934
804	20	794	823	485	838	40	904
.1833	30	.1822	.1853	5.396	.9833	30	1.3875
862	40	851	883	309	827	20	846
891	50	880	914	226	822	10	817
.1920	**11° 00′**	.1908	.1944	5.145	.9816	**79° 00′**	1.3788
949	10	937	974	066	811	78° 50′	759
978	20	965	.2004	4.989	805	40	730
.2007	30	.1994	.2035	4.915	.9799	30	1.3701
036	40	.2022	065	843	793	20	672
065	50	051	095	773	787	10	643
.2094	**12° 00′**	.2079	.2126	4.705	.9781	**78° 00′**	1.3614
123	10	108	156	638	775	77° 50′	584
153	20	136	186	574	769	40	555
.2182	30	.2164	.2217	4.511	.9763	30	1.3526
211	40	193	247	449	757	20	497
240	50	221	278	390	750	10	468
.2269	**13° 00′**	.2250	.2309	4.331	.9744	**77° 00′**	1.3439
298	10	278	339	275	737	76° 50′	410
327	20	306	370	219	730	40	381
.2356	30	.2334	.2401	4.165	.9724	30	1.3352
385	40	363	432	113	717	20	323
414	50	391	462	061	710	10	294
.2443	**14° 00′**	.2419	.2493	4.011	.9703	**76° 00′**	1.3265
473	10	447	524	3.962	696	75° 50′	235
502	20	476	555	914	689	40	206
.2531	30	.2504	.2586	3.867	.9681	30	1.3177
560	40	532	617	821	674	20	148
589	50	560	648	776	667	10	119
.2618	**15° 00′**	.2588	.2679	3.732	.9659	**75° 00′**	1.3090
647	10	616	711	689	652	74° 50′	061
676	20	644	742	647	644	40	032
.2705	30	.2672	.2773	3.606	.9636	30	1.3003
734	40	700	805	566	628	20	974
763	50	728	836	526	621	10	945
.2793	**16° 00′**	.2756	.2867	3.487	.9613	**74° 00′**	1.2915
822	10	784	899	450	605	73° 50′	886
851	20	812	931	412	596	40	857
.2880	30	.2840	.2962	3.376	.9588	30	1.2828
909	40	868	994	340	580	20	799
938	50	896	.3026	305	572	10	770
.2967	**17° 00′**	.2924	.3057	3.271	.9563	**73° 00′**	1.2741
996	10	952	089	237	555	72° 50′	712
.3025	20	979	121	204	546	40	683
.3054	30	.3007	.3153	3.172	.9537	30	1.2654
083	40	035	185	140	528	20	625
113	50	062	217	108	520	10	595
.3142	**18° 00′**	.3090	.3249	3.078	.9511	**72° 00′**	1.2566
		Cos	Cot	Tan	Sin	Degrees	Radians

Table B. Trigonometric Functions (Continued)

Radians	Degrees	Sin	Tan	Cot	Cos		
.3142	**18° 00′**	.3090	.3249	3.078	.9511	**72° 00′**	1.2566
171	10	118	281	047	502	71° 50′	537
200	20	145	314	018	492	40	508
.3229	30	.3173	.3346	2.989	.9483	30	1.2479
258	40	201	378	960	474	20	450
287	50	228	411	932	465	10	421
.3316	**19° 00′**	.3256	.3443	2.904	.9455	**71° 00′**	1.2392
345	10	283	476	877	446	70° 50′	363
374	20	311	508	850	436	40	334
.3403	30	.3338	.3541	2.824	.9426	30	1.2305
432	40	365	574	798	417	20	275
462	50	393	607	773	407	10	246
.3491	**20° 00′**	.3420	.3640	2.747	.9397	**70° 00′**	1.2217
520	10	448	673	723	387	69° 50′	188
549	20	475	706	699	377	40	159
.3578	30	.3502	.3739	2.675	.9367	30	1.2130
607	40	529	772	651	356	20	101
636	50	557	805	628	346	10	072
.3665	**21° 00′**	.3584	.3839	2.605	.9336	**69° 00′**	1.2043
694	10	611	872	583	325	68° 50′	1.2014
723	20	638	906	560	315	40	985
.3752	30	.3665	.3939	2.539	.9304	30	1.1956
782	40	692	973	517	293	20	926
811	50	719	.4006	496	283	10	897
.3840	**22° 00′**	.3746	.4040	2.475	.9272	**68° 00′**	1.1868
869	10	773	074	455	261	67° 50′	839
898	20	800	108	434	250	40	810
.3927	30	.3827	.4142	2.414	.9239	30	1.1781
956	40	854	176	394	228	20	752
985	50	881	210	375	216	10	723
.4014	**23° 00′**	.3907	.4245	2.356	.9205	**67° 00′**	1.1694
043	10	934	279	337	194	66° 50′	665
072	20	961	314	318	182	40	636
.4102	30	.3987	.4348	2.300	.9171	30	1.1606
131	40	.4014	383	282	159	20	577
160	50	041	417	264	147	10	548
.4189	**24° 00′**	.4067	.4452	2.246	.9135	**66° 00′**	1.1519
218	10	094	487	229	124	65° 50′	490
247	20	120	522	211	112	40	461
.4276	30	.4147	.4557	2.194	.9100	30	1.1432
305	40	173	592	177	088	20	403
334	50	200	628	161	075	10	374
.4363	**25° 00′**	.4226	.4663	2.145	.9063	**65° 00′**	1.1345
392	10	253	699	128	051	64° 50′	316
422	20	279	734	112	038	40	286
.4451	30	.4305	.4770	2.097	.9026	30	1.1257
480	40	331	806	081	013	20	228
509	50	358	841	066	001	10	199
.4538	**26° 00′**	.4384	.4877	2.050	.8988	**64° 00′**	1.1170
567	10	410	913	035	975	63° 50′	141
596	20	436	950	020	962	40	112
.4625	30	.4462	.4986	2.006	.8949	30	1.1083
654	40	488	.5022	1.991	936	20	054
683	50	514	059	977	923	10	1.1025
.4712	**27° 00′**	.4540	.5095	1.963	.8910	**63° 00′**	1.0996
		Cos	Cot	Tan	Sin	Degrees	Radians

Table B. Trigonometric Functions (Continued)

Radians	Degrees	Sin	Tan	Cot	Cos		
.4712	**27° 00′**	.4540	.5095	1.963	.8910	**63° 00′**	1.0996
741	10	566	132	949	897	62° 50′	966
771	20	592	169	935	884	40	937
.4800	30	.4617	.5206	1.921	.8870	30	1.0908
829	40	643	243	907	857	20	879
858	50	669	280	894	843	10	850
.4887	**28° 00′**	.4695	.5317	1.881	.8829	**62° 00′**	1.0821
916	10	720	354	868	816	61° 50′	792
945	20	746	392	855	802	40	763
.4974	30	.4772	.5430	1.842	.8788	30	1.0734
.5003	40	797	467	829	774	20	705
032	50	823	505	816	760	10	676
.5061	**29° 00′**	.4848	.5543	1.804	.8746	**61° 00′**	1.0647
091	10	874	581	792	732	60° 50′	617
120	20	899	619	780	718	40	588
.5149	30	.4924	.5658	1.767	.8704	30	1.0559
178	40	950	696	756	689	20	530
207	50	975	735	744	675	10	501
.5236	**30° 00′**	.5000	.5774	1.732	.8660	**60° 00′**	1.0472
265	10	025	812	720	646	59° 50′	443
294	20	050	851	709	631	40	414
.5323	30	.5075	.5890	1.698	.8616	30	1.0385
352	40	100	930	686	601	20	356
381	50	125	969	675	587	10	327
.5411	**31° 00′**	.5150	.6009	1.664	.8572	**59° 00′**	1.0297
440	10	175	048	653	557	58° 50′	268
469	20	200	088	643	542	40	239
.5498	30	.5225	.6128	1.632	.8526	30	1.0210
527	40	250	168	621	511	20	181
556	50	275	208	611	496	10	152
.5585	**32° 00′**	.5299	.6249	1.600	.8480	**58° 00′**	1.0123
614	10	324	289	590	465	57° 50′	094
643	20	348	330	580	450	40	065
.5672	30	.5373	.6371	1.570	.8434	30	1.0036
701	40	398	412	560	418	20	1.0007
730	50	422	453	550	403	10	977
.5760	**33° 00′**	.5446	.6494	1.540	.8387	**57° 00′**	.9948
789	10	471	536	530	371	56° 50′	919
818	20	495	577	520	355	40	890
.5847	30	.5519	.6619	1.511	.8339	30	.9861
876	40	544	661	501	323	20	832
905	50	568	703	1.492	307	10	803
.5934	**34° 00′**	.5592	.6745	1.483	.8290	**56° 00′**	.9774
963	10	616	787	473	274	55° 50′	745
992	20	640	830	464	258	40	716
.6021	30	.5664	.6873	1.455	.8241	30	.9687
050	40	688	916	446	225	20	657
080	50	712	959	437	208	10	628
.6109	**35° 00′**	.5736	.7002	1.428	.8192	**55° 00′**	.9599
138	10	760	046	419	175	54° 50′	570
167	20	783	089	411	158	40	541
.6196	30	.5807	.7133	1.402	.8141	30	.9512
225	40	831	177	393	124	20	483
254	50	854	221	385	107	10	454
.6283	**36° 00′**	.5878	.7265	1.376	.8090	**54° 00′**	.9425
		Cos	Cot	Tan	Sin	Degrees	Radians

Table B. Trigonometric Functions (Continued)

Radians	Degrees	Sin	Tan	Cot	Cos		
.6283	**36° 00′**	.5878	.7265	1.376	.8090	**54° 00′**	.9425
312	10	901	310	368	073	53° 50′	396
341	20	925	355	360	056	40	367
.6370	30	.5948	.7400	1.351	.8039	30	.9338
400	40	972	445	343	021	20	308
429	50	995	490	335	004	10	279
.6458	**37° 00′**	.6018	.7536	1.327	.7986	**53° 00′**	.9250
487	10	041	581	319	969	52° 50′	221
516	20	065	627	311	951	40	192
.6545	30	.6088	.7673	1.303	.7934	30	.9163
574	40	111	720	295	916	20	134
603	50	134	766	288	898	10	105
.6632	**38° 00′**	.6157	.7813	1.280	.7880	**52° 00′**	.9076
661	10	180	860	272	862	51° 50′	047
690	20	202	907	265	844	40	.9018
.6720	30	.6225	.7954	1.257	.7826	30	.8988
749	40	248	.8002	250	808	20	959
778	50	271	050	242	790	10	930
.6807	**39° 00′**	.6293	.8098	1.235	.7771	**51° 00′**	.8901
836	10	316	146	228	753	50° 50′	872
865	20	338	195	220	735	40	843
.6894	30	.6361	.8243	1.213	.7716	30	.8814
923	40	383	292	206	698	20	785
952	50	406	342	199	679	10	756
.6981	**40° 00′**	.6428	.8391	1.192	.7660	**50° 00′**	.8727
.7010	10	450	441	185	642	49° 50′	698
039	20	472	491	178	623	40	668
.7069	30	.6494	.8541	1.171	.7604	30	.8639
098	40	517	591	164	585	20	610
127	50	539	642	157	566	10	581
.7156	**41° 00′**	.6561	.8693	1.150	.7547	**49° 00′**	.8552
185	10	583	744	144	528	48° 50′	523
214	20	604	796	137	509	40	494
.7243	30	.6626	.8847	1.130	.7490	30	.8465
272	40	648	899	124	470	20	436
301	50	670	952	117	451	10	407
.7330	**42° 00′**	.6691	.9004	1.111	.7431	**48° 00′**	.8378
359	10	713	057	104	412	47° 50′	348
389	20	734	110	098	392	40	319
.7418	30	.6756	.9163	1.091	.7373	30	.8290
447	40	777	217	085	353	20	261
476	50	799	271	079	333	10	232
.7505	**43° 00′**	.6820	.9325	1.072	.7314	**47° 00′**	.8203
534	10	841	380	066	294	46° 50′	174
563	20	862	435	060	274	40	145
.7592	30	.6884	.9490	1.054	.7254	30	.8116
621	40	905	545	048	234	20	087
650	50	926	601	042	214	10	058
.7679	**44° 00′**	.6947	.9657	1.036	.7193	**46° 00′**	.8029
709	10	967	713	030	173	45° 50′	999
738	20	988	770	024	153	40	970
.7767	30	.7009	.9827	1.018	.7133	30	.7941
796	40	030	884	012	112	20	912
825	50	050	942	006	092	10	883
.7854	**45° 00′**	.7071	1.000	1.000	.7071	**45° 00′**	.7854
		Cos	Cot	Tan	Sin	Degrees	Radians

Table C. Mantissas of Common Logarithms of Numbers to Five Decimal Places[1]

100–150

N	0	1	2	3	4	5	6	7	8	9
100	00 000	043	087	130	173	217	260	303	346	389
01	432	475	518	561	604	647	689	732	775	817
02	00 860	903	945	988	*030	*072	*115	*157	*199	*242
03	01 284	326	368	410	452	494	536	578	620	662
04	01 703	745	787	828	870	912	953	995	*036	*078
05	02 119	160	202	243	284	325	366	407	449	490
06	531	572	612	653	694	735	776	816	857	898
07	02 938	979	*019	*060	*100	*141	*181	*222	*262	*302
08	03 342	383	423	463	503	543	583	623	663	703
09	03 743	782	822	862	902	941	981	*021	*060	*100
110	04 139	179	218	258	297	336	376	415	454	493
11	532	571	610	650	689	727	766	805	844	883
12	04 922	961	999	*038	*077	*115	*154	*192	*231	*269
13	05 308	346	385	423	461	500	538	576	614	652
14	05 690	729	767	805	843	881	918	956	994	*032
15	06 070	108	145	183	221	258	296	333	371	408
16	446	483	521	558	595	633	670	707	744	781
17	06 819	856	893	930	967	*004	*041	*078	*115	*151
18	07 188	225	262	298	335	372	408	445	482	518
19	555	591	628	664	700	737	773	809	846	882
120	07 918	954	990	*027	*063	*099	*135	*171	*207	*243
21	08 279	314	350	386	422	458	493	529	565	600
22	636	672	707	743	778	814	849	884	920	955
23	08 991	*026	*061	*096	*132	*167	*202	*237	*272	*307
24	09 342	377	412	447	482	517	552	587	621	656
25	09 691	726	760	795	830	864	899	934	968	*003
26	10 037	072	106	140	175	209	243	278	312	346
27	380	415	449	483	517	551	585	619	653	687
28	10 721	755	789	823	857	890	924	958	992	*025
29	11 059	093	126	160	193	227	261	294	327	361
130	394	428	461	494	528	561	594	628	661	694
31	11 727	760	793	826	860	893	926	959	992	*024
32	12 057	090	123	156	189	222	254	287	320	352
33	385	418	450	483	516	548	581	613	646	678
34	12 710	743	775	808	840	872	905	937	969	*001
35	13 033	066	098	130	162	194	226	258	290	322
36	354	386	418	450	481	513	545	577	609	640
37	672	704	735	767	799	830	862	893	925	956
38	13 988	*019	*051	*082	*114	*145	*176	*208	*239	*270
39	14 301	333	364	395	426	457	489	520	551	582
140	613	644	675	706	737	768	799	829	860	891
41	14 922	953	983	*014	*045	*076	*106	*137	*168	*198
42	15 229	259	290	320	351	381	412	442	473	503
43	534	564	594	625	655	685	715	746	776	806
44	15 836	866	897	927	957	987	*017	*047	*077	*107
45	16 137	167	197	227	256	286	316	346	376	406
46	435	465	495	524	554	584	613	643	673	702
47	16 732	761	791	820	850	879	909	938	967	997
48	17 026	056	085	114	143	173	202	231	260	289
49	319	348	377	406	435	464	493	522	551	580
150	17 609	638	667	696	725	754	782	811	840	869
N	0	1	2	3	4	5	6	7	8	9

Prop. Parts

	44	43	42
1	4.4	4.3	4.2
2	8.8	8.6	8.4
3	13.2	12.9	12.6
4	17.6	17.2	16.8
5	22.0	21.5	21.0
6	26.4	25.8	25.2
7	30.8	30.1	29.4
8	35.2	34.4	33.6
9	39.6	38.7	37.8

	41	40	39
1	4.1	4	3.9
2	8.2	8	7.8
3	12.3	12	11.7
4	16.4	16	15.6
5	20.5	20	19.5
6	24.6	24	23.4
7	28.7	28	27.3
8	32.8	32	31.2
9	36.9	36	35.1

	38	37	36
1	3.8	3.7	3.6
2	7.6	7.4	7.2
3	11.4	11.1	10.8
4	15.2	14.8	14.4
5	19.0	18.5	18.0
6	22.8	22.2	21.6
7	26.6	25.9	25.2
8	30.4	29.6	28.8
9	34.2	33.3	32.4

	35	34	33
1	3.5	3.4	3.3
2	7.0	6.8	6.6
3	10.5	10.2	9.9
4	14.0	13.6	13.2
5	17.5	17.0	16.5
6	21.0	20.4	19.8
7	24.5	23.8	23.1
8	28.0	27.2	26.4
9	31.5	30.6	29.7

	32	31	30
1	3.2	3.1	3
2	6.4	6.2	6
3	9.6	9.3	9
4	12.8	12.4	12
5	16.0	15.5	15
6	19.2	18.6	18
7	22.4	21.7	21
8	25.6	24.8	24
9	28.8	27.9	27

Prop. Parts

[1] From William L. Hart, *Plane Trigonometry*, 1942, reprinted by permission of D. C. Heath and Co., Boston.

Table C. Five-Place Logarithms: 150–200

N	0	1	2	3	4	5	6	7	8	9
150	17 609	638	667	696	725	754	782	811	840	869
51	17 898	926	955	984	*013	*041	*070	*099	*127	*156
52	18 184	213	241	270	298	327	355	384	412	441
53	469	498	526	554	583	611	639	667	696	724
54	18 752	780	808	837	865	893	921	949	977	*005
55	19 033	061	089	117	145	173	201	229	257	285
56	312	340	368	396	424	451	479	507	535	562
57	590	618	645	673	700	728	756	783	811	838
58	19 866	893	921	948	976	*003	*030	*058	*085	*112
59	20 140	167	194	222	249	276	303	330	358	385
160	412	439	466	493	520	548	575	602	629	656
61	683	710	737	763	790	817	844	871	898	925
62	20 952	978	*005	*032	*059	*085	*112	*139	*165	*192
63	21 219	245	272	299	325	352	378	405	431	458
64	484	511	537	564	590	617	643	669	696	722
65	21 748	775	801	827	854	880	906	932	958	985
66	22 011	037	063	089	115	141	167	194	220	246
67	272	298	324	350	376	401	427	453	479	505
68	531	557	583	608	634	660	686	712	737	763
69	22 789	814	840	866	891	917	943	968	994	*019
170	23 045	070	096	121	147	172	198	223	249	274
71	300	325	350	376	401	426	452	477	502	528
72	553	578	603	629	654	679	704	729	754	779
73	23 805	830	855	880	905	930	955	980	*005	*030
74	24 055	080	105	130	155	180	204	229	254	279
75	304	329	353	378	403	428	452	477	502	527
76	551	576	601	625	650	674	699	724	748	773
77	24 797	822	846	871	895	920	944	969	993	*018
78	25 042	066	091	115	139	164	188	212	237	261
79	285	310	334	358	382	406	431	455	479	503
180	527	551	575	600	624	648	672	696	720	744
81	25 768	792	816	840	864	888	912	935	959	983
82	26 007	031	055	079	102	126	150	174	198	221
83	245	269	293	316	340	364	387	411	435	458
84	482	505	529	553	576	600	623	647	670	694
85	717	741	764	788	811	834	858	881	905	928
86	26 951	975	998	*021	*045	*068	*091	*114	*138	*161
87	27 184	207	231	254	277	300	323	346	370	393
88	416	439	462	485	508	531	554	577	600	623
89	646	669	692	715	738	761	784	807	830	852
190	27 875	898	921	944	967	989	*012	*035	*058	*081
91	28 103	126	149	171	194	217	240	262	285	307
92	330	353	375	398	421	443	466	488	511	533
93	556	578	601	623	646	668	691	713	735	758
94	28 780	803	825	847	870	892	914	937	959	981
95	29 003	026	048	070	092	115	137	159	181	203
96	226	248	270	292	314	336	358	380	403	425
97	447	469	491	513	535	557	579	601	623	645
98	667	688	710	732	754	776	798	820	842	863
99	29 885	907	929	951	973	994	*016	*038	*060	*081
200	30 103	125	146	168	190	211	233	255	276	298
N	**0**	**1**	**2**	**3**	**4**	**5**	**6**	**7**	**8**	**9**

Prop. Parts

	29	28	27	26	25	24	23	22	21
1	2.9	2.8	2.7	2.6	2.5	2.4	2.3	2.2	2.1
2	5.8	5.6	5.4	5.2	5.0	4.8	4.6	4.4	4.2
3	8.7	8.4	8.1	7.8	7.5	7.2	6.9	6.6	6.3
4	11.6	11.2	10.8	10.4	10.0	9.6	9.2	8.8	8.4
5	14.5	14.0	13.5	13.0	12.5	12.0	11.5	11.0	10.5
6	17.4	16.8	16.2	15.6	15.0	14.4	13.8	13.2	12.6
7	20.3	19.6	18.9	18.2	17.5	16.8	16.1	15.4	14.7
8	23.2	22.4	21.6	20.8	20.0	19.2	18.4	17.6	16.8
9	26.1	25.2	24.3	23.4	22.5	21.6	20.7	19.8	18.9

Table C. Five-Place Logarithms: 200–250

N	0	1	2	3	4	5	6	7	8	9
200	30 103	125	146	168	190	211	233	255	276	298
01	320	341	363	384	406	428	449	471	492	514
02	535	557	578	600	621	643	664	685	707	728
03	750	771	792	814	835	856	878	899	920	942
04	30 963	984	*006	*027	*048	*069	*091	*112	*133	*154
05	31 175	197	218	239	260	281	302	323	345	366
06	387	408	429	450	471	492	513	534	555	576
07	597	618	639	660	681	702	723	744	765	785
08	31 806	827	848	869	890	911	931	952	973	994
09	32 015	035	056	077	098	118	139	160	181	201
210	222	243	263	284	305	325	346	366	387	408
11	428	449	469	490	510	531	552	572	593	613
12	634	654	675	695	715	736	756	777	797	818
13	32 838	858	879	899	919	940	960	980	*001	*021
14	33 041	062	082	102	122	143	163	183	203	224
15	244	264	284	304	325	345	365	385	405	425
16	445	465	486	506	526	546	566	586	606	626
17	646	666	686	706	726	746	766	786	806	826
18	33 846	866	885	905	925	945	965	985	*005	*025
19	34 044	064	084	104	124	143	163	183	203	223
220	242	262	282	301	321	341	361	380	400	420
21	439	459	479	498	518	537	557	577	596	616
22	635	655	674	694	713	733	753	772	792	811
23	34 830	850	869	889	908	928	947	967	986	*005
24	35 025	044	064	083	102	122	141	160	180	199
25	218	238	257	276	295	315	334	353	372	392
26	411	430	449	468	488	507	526	545	564	583
27	603	622	641	660	679	698	717	736	755	774
28	793	813	832	851	870	889	908	927	946	965
29	35 984	*003	*021	*040	*059	*078	*097	*116	*135	*154
230	36 173	192	211	229	248	267	286	305	324	342
31	361	380	399	418	436	455	474	493	511	530
32	549	568	586	605	624	642	661	680	698	717
33	736	754	773	791	810	829	847	866	884	903
34	36 922	940	959	977	996	*014	*033	*051	*070	*088
35	37 107	125	144	162	181	199	218	236	254	273
36	291	310	328	346	365	383	401	420	438	457
37	475	493	511	530	548	566	585	603	621	639
38	658	676	694	712	731	749	767	785	803	822
39	37 840	858	876	894	912	931	949	967	985	*003
240	38 021	039	057	075	093	112	130	148	166	184
41	202	220	238	256	274	292	310	328	346	364
42	382	399	417	435	453	471	489	507	525	543
43	561	578	596	614	632	650	668	686	703	721
44	739	757	775	792	810	828	846	863	881	899
45	38 917	934	952	970	987	*005	*023	*041	*058	*076
46	39 094	111	129	146	164	182	199	217	235	252
47	270	287	305	322	340	358	375	393	410	428
48	445	463	480	498	515	533	550	568	585	602
49	620	637	655	672	690	707	724	742	759	777
250	39 794	811	829	846	863	881	898	915	933	950
N	**0**	**1**	**2**	**3**	**4**	**5**	**6**	**7**	**8**	**9**

Prop. Parts

	22	21
1	2.2	2.1
2	4.4	4.2
3	6.6	6.3
4	8.8	8.4
5	11.0	10.5
6	13.2	12.6
7	15.4	14.7
8	17.6	16.8
9	19.8	18.9

	20
1	2
2	4
3	6
4	8
5	10
6	12
7	14
8	16
9	18

	19
1	1.9
2	3.8
3	5.7
4	7.6
5	9.5
6	11.4
7	13.3
8	15.2
9	17.1

	18
1	1.8
2	3.6
3	5.4
4	7.2
5	9.0
6	10.8
7	12.6
8	14.4
9	16.2

	17
1	1.7
2	3.4
3	5.1
4	6.8
5	8.5
6	10.2
7	11.9
8	13.6
9	15.3

Prop. Parts

Table C. Five-Place Logarithms: 250–300

N	0	1	2	3	4	5	6	7	8	9
250	39 794	811	829	846	863	881	898	915	933	950
51	39 967	985	*002	*019	*037	*054	*071	*088	*106	*123
52	40 140	157	175	192	209	226	243	261	278	295
53	312	329	346	364	381	398	415	432	449	466
54	483	500	518	535	552	569	586	603	620	637
55	654	671	688	705	722	739	756	773	790	807
56	824	841	858	875	892	909	926	943	960	976
57	40 993	*010	*027	*044	*061	*078	*095	*111	*128	*145
58	41 162	179	196	212	229	246	263	280	296	313
59	330	347	363	380	397	414	430	447	464	481
260	497	514	531	547	564	581	597	614	631	647
61	664	681	697	714	731	747	764	780	797	814
62	830	847	863	880	896	913	929	946	963	979
63	41 996	*012	*029	*045	*062	*078	*095	*111	*127	*144
64	42 160	177	193	210	226	243	259	275	292	308
65	325	341	357	374	390	406	423	439	455	472
66	488	504	521	537	553	570	586	602	619	635
67	651	667	684	700	716	732	749	765	781	797
68	813	830	846	862	878	894	911	927	943	959
69	42 975	991	*008	*024	*040	*056	*072	*088	*104	*120
270	43 136	152	169	185	201	217	233	249	265	281
71	297	313	329	345	361	377	393	409	425	441
72	457	473	489	505	521	537	553	569	584	600
73	616	632	648	664	680	696	712	727	743	759
74	775	791	807	823	838	854	870	886	902	917
75	43 933	949	965	981	996	*012	*028	*044	*059	*075
76	44 091	107	122	138	154	170	185	201	217	232
77	248	264	279	295	311	326	342	358	373	389
78	404	420	436	451	467	483	498	514	529	545
79	560	576	592	607	623	638	654	669	685	700
280	716	731	747	762	778	793	809	824	840	855
81	44 871	886	902	917	932	948	963	979	994	*010
82	45 025	040	056	071	086	102	117	133	148	163
83	179	194	209	225	240	255	271	286	301	317
84	332	347	362	378	393	408	423	439	454	469
85	484	500	515	530	545	561	576	591	606	621
86	637	652	667	682	697	712	728	743	758	773
87	788	803	818	834	849	864	879	894	909	924
88	45 939	954	969	984	*000	*015	*030	*045	*060	*075
89	46 090	105	120	135	150	165	180	195	210	225
290	240	255	270	285	300	315	330	345	359	374
91	389	404	419	434	449	464	479	494	509	523
92	538	553	568	583	598	613	627	642	657	672
93	687	702	716	731	746	761	776	790	805	820
94	835	850	864	879	894	909	923	938	953	967
95	46 982	997	*012	*026	*041	*056	*070	*085	*100	*114
96	47 129	144	159	173	188	202	217	232	246	261
97	276	290	305	319	334	349	363	378	392	407
98	422	436	451	465	480	494	509	524	538	553
99	567	582	596	611	625	640	654	669	683	698
300	47 712	727	741	756	770	784	799	813	828	842
N	0	1	2	3	4	5	6	7	8	9

Prop. Parts

	18	**17**	**16**	**15**	**14**
1	1.8	1.7	1.6	1.5	1.4
2	3.6	3.4	3.2	3.0	2.8
3	5.4	5.1	4.8	4.5	4.2
4	7.2	6.8	6.4	6.0	5.6
5	9.0	8.5	8.0	7.5	7.0
6	10.8	10.2	9.6	9.0	8.4
7	12.6	11.9	11.2	10.5	9.8
8	14.4	13.6	12.8	12.0	11.2
9	16.2	15.3	14.4	13.5	12.6

Prop. Parts

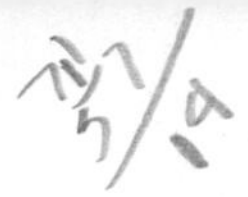

Table C. Five-Place Logarithms: 300–350

N	0	1	2	3	4	5	6	7	8	9
300	47 712	727	741	756	770	784	799	813	828	842
01	47 857	871	885	900	914	929	943	958	972	986
02	48 001	015	029	044	058	073	087	101	116	130
03	144	159	173	187	202	216	230	244	259	273
04	287	302	316	330	344	359	373	387	401	416
05	430	444	458	473	487	501	515	530	544	558
06	572	586	601	615	629	643	657	671	686	700
07	714	728	742	756	770	785	799	813	827	841
08	855	869	883	897	911	926	940	954	968	982
09	48 996	*010	*024	*038	*052	*066	*080	*094	*108	*122
310	49 136	150	164	178	192	206	220	234	248	262
11	276	290	304	318	332	346	360	374	388	402
12	415	429	443	457	471	485	499	513	527	541
13	554	568	582	596	610	624	638	651	665	679
14	693	707	721	734	748	762	776	790	803	817
15	831	845	859	872	886	900	914	927	941	955
16	49 969	982	996	*010	*024	*037	*051	*065	*079	*092
17	50 106	120	133	147	161	174	188	202	215	229
18	243	256	270	284	297	311	325	338	352	365
19	379	393	406	420	433	447	461	474	488	501
320	515	529	542	556	569	583	596	610	623	637
21	651	664	678	691	705	718	732	745	759	772
22	786	799	813	826	840	853	866	880	893	907
23	50 920	934	947	961	974	987	*001	*014	*028	*041
24	51 055	068	081	095	108	121	135	148	162	175
25	188	202	215	228	242	255	268	282	295	308
26	322	335	348	362	375	388	402	415	428	441
27	455	468	481	495	508	521	534	548	561	574
28	587	601	614	627	640	654	667	680	693	706
29	720	733	746	759	772	786	799	812	825	838
330	851	865	878	891	904	917	930	943	957	970
31	51 983	996	*009	*022	*035	*048	*061	*075	*088	*101
32	52 114	127	140	153	166	179	192	205	218	231
33	244	257	270	284	297	310	323	336	349	362
34	375	388	401	414	427	440	453	466	479	492
35	504	517	530	543	556	569	582	595	608	621
36	634	647	660	673	686	699	711	724	737	750
37	763	776	789	802	815	827	840	853	866	879
38	52 892	905	917	930	943	956	969	982	994	*007
39	53 020	033	046	058	071	084	097	110	122	135
340	148	161	173	186	199	212	224	237	250	263
41	275	288	301	314	326	339	352	364	377	390
42	403	415	428	441	453	466	479	491	504	517
43	529	542	555	567	580	593	605	618	631	643
44	656	668	681	694	706	719	732	744	757	769
45	782	794	807	820	832	845	857	870	882	895
46	53 908	920	933	945	958	970	983	995	*008	*020
47	54 033	045	058	070	083	095	108	120	133	145
48	158	170	183	195	208	220	233	245	258	270
49	283	295	307	320	332	345	357	370	382	394
350	54 407	419	432	444	456	469	481	494	506	518
N	**0**	**1**	**2**	**3**	**4**	**5**	**6**	**7**	**8**	**9**

Prop. Parts

	15	14	13	12
1	1.5	1.4	1.3	1.2
2	3.0	2.8	2.6	2.4
3	4.5	4.2	3.9	3.6
4	6.0	5.6	5.2	4.8
5	7.5	7.0	6.5	6.0
6	9.0	8.4	7.8	7.2
7	10.5	9.8	9.1	8.4
8	12.0	11.2	10.4	9.6
9	13.5	12.6	11.7	10.8

Table C. Five-Place Logarithms: 350–400

N	0	1	2	3	4	5	6	7	8	9
350	54 407	419	432	444	456	469	481	494	506	518
51	531	543	555	568	580	593	605	617	630	642
52	654	667	679	691	704	716	728	741	753	765
53	777	790	802	814	827	839	851	864	876	888
54	54 900	913	925	937	949	962	974	986	998	*011
55	55 023	035	047	060	072	084	096	108	121	133
56	145	157	169	182	194	206	218	230	242	255
57	267	279	291	303	315	328	340	352	364	376
58	388	400	413	425	437	449	461	473	485	497
59	509	522	534	546	558	570	582	594	606	618
360	630	642	654	666	678	691	703	715	727	739
61	751	763	775	787	799	811	823	835	847	859
62	871	883	895	907	919	931	943	955	967	979
63	55 991	*003	*015	*027	*038	*050	*062	*074	*086	*098
64	56 110	122	134	146	158	170	182	194	205	217
65	229	241	253	265	277	289	301	312	324	336
66	348	360	372	384	396	407	419	431	443	455
67	467	478	490	502	514	526	538	549	561	573
68	585	597	608	620	632	644	656	667	679	691
69	703	714	726	738	750	761	773	785	797	808
370	820	832	844	855	867	879	891	902	914	926
71	56 937	949	961	972	984	996	*008	*019	*031	*043
72	57 054	066	078	089	101	113	124	136	148	159
73	171	183	194	206	217	229	241	252	264	276
74	287	299	310	322	334	345	357	368	380	392
75	403	415	426	438	449	461	473	484	496	507
76	519	530	542	553	565	576	588	600	611	623
77	634	646	657	669	680	692	703	715	726	738
78	749	761	772	784	795	807	818	830	841	852
79	864	875	887	898	910	921	933	944	955	967
380	57 978	990	*001	*013	*024	*035	*047	*058	*070	*081
81	58 092	104	115	127	138	149	161	172	184	195
82	206	218	229	240	252	263	274	286	297	309
83	320	331	343	354	365	377	388	399	410	422
84	433	444	456	467	478	490	501	512	524	535
85	546	557	569	580	591	602	614	625	636	647
86	659	670	681	692	704	715	726	737	749	760
87	771	782	794	805	816	827	838	850	861	872
88	883	894	906	917	928	939	950	961	973	984
89	58 995	*006	*017	*028	*040	*051	*062	*073	*084	*095
390	59 106	118	129	140	151	162	173	184	195	207
91	218	229	240	251	262	273	284	295	306	318
92	329	340	351	362	373	384	395	406	417	428
93	439	450	461	472	483	494	506	517	528	539
94	550	561	572	583	594	605	616	627	638	649
95	660	671	682	693	704	715	726	737	748	759
96	770	780	791	802	813	824	835	846	857	868
97	879	890	901	912	923	934	945	956	966	977
98	59 988	999	*010	*021	*032	*043	*054	*065	*076	*086
99	60 097	108	119	130	141	152	163	173	184	195
400	60 206	217	228	239	249	260	271	282	293	304
N	**0**	**1**	**2**	**3**	**4**	**5**	**6**	**7**	**8**	**9**

Prop. Parts

	13	12	11	10
1	1.3	1.2	1.1	1.0
2	2.6	2.4	2.2	2.0
3	3.9	3.6	3.3	3.0
4	5.2	4.8	4.4	4.0
5	6.5	6.0	5.5	5.0
6	7.8	7.2	6.6	6.0
7	9.1	8.4	7.7	7.0
8	10.4	9.6	8.8	8.0
9	11.7	10.8	9.9	9.0

Prop. Parts

Table C. Five-Place Logarithms. 400–450

N	0	1	2	3	4	5	6	7	8	9
400	60 206	217	228	239	249	260	271	282	293	304
01	314	325	336	347	358	369	379	390	401	412
02	423	433	444	455	466	477	487	498	509	520
03	531	541	552	563	574	584	595	606	617	627
04	638	649	660	670	681	692	703	713	724	735
05	746	756	767	778	788	799	810	821	831	842
06	853	863	874	885	895	906	917	927	938	949
07	60 959	970	981	991	*002	*013	*023	*034	*045	*055
08	61 066	077	087	098	109	119	130	140	151	162
09	172	183	194	204	215	225	236	247	257	268
410	278	289	300	310	321	331	342	352	363	374
11	384	395	405	416	426	437	448	458	469	479
12	490	500	511	521	532	542	553	563	574	584
13	595	606	616	627	637	648	658	669	679	690
14	700	711	721	731	742	752	763	773	784	794
15	805	815	826	836	847	857	868	878	888	899
16	61 909	920	930	941	951	962	972	982	993	*003
17	62 014	024	034	045	055	066	076	086	097	107
18	118	128	138	149	159	170	180	190	201	211
19	221	232	242	252	263	273	284	294	304	315
420	325	335	346	356	366	377	387	397	408	418
21	428	439	449	459	469	480	490	500	511	521
22	531	542	552	562	572	583	593	603	613	624
23	634	644	655	665	675	685	696	706	716	726
24	737	747	757	767	778	788	798	808	818	829
25	839	849	859	870	880	890	900	910	921	931
26	62 941	951	961	972	982	992	*002	*012	*022	*033
27	63 043	053	063	073	083	094	104	114	124	134
28	144	155	165	175	185	195	205	215	225	236
29	246	256	266	276	286	296	306	317	327	337
430	347	357	367	377	387	397	407	417	428	438
31	448	458	468	478	488	498	508	518	528	538
32	548	558	568	579	589	599	609	619	629	639
33	649	659	669	679	689	699	709	719	729	739
34	749	759	769	779	789	799	809	819	829	839
35	849	859	869	879	889	899	909	919	929	939
36	63 949	959	969	979	988	998	*008	*018	*028	*038
37	64 048	058	068	078	088	098	108	118	128	137
38	147	157	167	177	187	197	207	217	227	237
39	246	256	266	276	286	296	306	316	326	335
440	345	355	365	375	385	395	404	414	424	434
41	444	454	464	473	483	493	503	513	523	532
42	542	552	562	572	582	591	601	611	621	631
43	640	650	660	670	680	689	699	709	719	729
44	738	748	758	768	777	787	797	807	816	826
45	836	846	856	865	875	885	895	904	914	924
46	64 933	943	953	963	972	982	992	*002	*011	*021
47	65 031	040	050	060	070	079	089	099	108	118
48	128	137	147	157	167	176	186	196	205	215
49	225	234	244	254	263	273	283	292	302	312
450	65 321	331	341	350	360	369	379	389	398	408
N	0	1	2	3	4	5	6	7	8	9

Prop. Parts

	11
1	1.1
2	2.2
3	3.3
4	4.4
5	5.5
6	6.6
7	7.7
8	8.8
9	9.9

	10
1	1.0
2	2.0
3	3.0
4	4.0
5	5.0
6	6.0
7	7.0
8	8.0
9	9.0

	9
1	0.9
2	1.8
3	2.7
4	3.6
5	4.5
6	5.4
7	6.3
8	7.2
9	8.1

Prop. Parts

Table C. Five-Place Logarithms: 450–500

N	0	1	2	3	4	5	6	7	8	9
450	65 321	331	341	350	360	369	379	389	398	408
51	418	427	437	447	456	466	475	485	495	504
52	514	523	533	543	552	562	571	581	591	600
53	610	619	629	639	648	658	667	677	686	696
54	706	715	725	734	744	753	763	772	782	792
55	801	811	820	830	839	849	858	868	877	887
56	896	906	916	925	935	944	954	963	973	982
57	65 992	*001	*011	*020	*030	*039	*049	*058	*068	*077
58	66 087	096	106	115	124	134	143	153	162	172
59	181	191	200	210	219	229	238	247	257	266
460	276	285	295	304	314	323	332	342	351	361
61	370	380	389	398	408	417	427	436	445	455
62	464	474	483	492	502	511	521	530	539	549
63	558	567	577	586	596	605	614	624	633	642
64	652	661	671	680	689	699	708	717	727	736
65	745	755	764	773	783	792	801	811	820	829
66	839	848	857	867	876	885	894	904	913	922
67	66 932	941	950	960	969	978	987	997	*006	*015
68	67 025	034	043	052	062	071	080	089	099	108
69	117	127	136	145	154	164	173	182	191	201
470	210	219	228	237	247	256	265	274	284	293
71	302	311	321	330	339	348	357	367	376	385
72	394	403	413	422	431	440	449	459	468	477
73	486	495	504	514	523	532	541	550	560	569
74	578	587	596	605	614	624	633	642	651	660
75	669	679	688	697	706	715	724	733	742	752
76	761	770	779	788	797	806	815	825	834	843
77	852	861	870	879	888	897	906	916	925	934
78	67 943	952	961	970	979	988	997	*006	*015	*024
79	68 034	043	052	061	070	079	088	097	106	115
480	124	133	142	151	160	169	178	187	196	205
81	215	224	233	242	251	260	269	278	287	296
82	305	314	323	332	341	350	359	368	377	386
83	395	404	413	422	431	440	449	458	467	476
84	485	494	502	511	520	529	538	547	556	565
85	574	583	592	601	610	619	628	637	646	655
86	664	673	681	690	699	708	717	726	735	744
87	753	762	771	780	789	797	806	815	824	833
88	842	851	860	869	878	886	895	904	913	922
89	68 931	940	949	958	966	975	984	993	*002	*011
490	69 020	028	037	046	055	064	073	082	090	099
91	108	117	126	135	144	152	161	170	179	188
92	197	205	214	223	232	241	249	258	267	276
93	285	294	302	311	320	329	338	346	355	364
94	373	381	390	399	408	417	425	434	443	452
95	461	469	478	487	496	504	513	522	531	539
96	548	557	566	574	583	592	601	609	618	627
97	636	644	653	662	671	679	688	697	705	714
98	723	732	740	749	758	767	775	784	793	801
99	810	819	827	836	845	854	862	871	880	888
500	69 897	906	914	923	932	940	949	958	966	975
N	**0**	**1**	**2**	**3**	**4**	**5**	**6**	**7**	**8**	**9**

Prop. Parts

	10
1	1.0
2	2.0
3	3.0
4	4.0
5	5.0
6	6.0
7	7.0
8	8.0
9	9.0

	9
1	0.9
2	1.8
3	2.7
4	3.6
5	4.5
6	5.4
7	6.3
8	7.2
9	8.1

	8
1	0.8
2	1.6
3	2.4
4	3.2
5	4.0
6	4.8
7	5.6
8	6.4
9	7.2

Prop. Parts

Table C. Five-Place Logarithms: 500–550

N	0	1	2	3	4	5	6	7	8	9
500	69 897	906	914	923	932	940	949	958	966	975
01	69 984	992	*001	*010	*018	*027	*036	*044	*053	*062
02	70 070	079	088	096	105	114	122	131	140	148
03	157	165	174	183	191	200	209	217	226	234
04	243	252	260	269	278	286	295	303	312	321
05	329	338	346	355	364	372	381	389	398	406
06	415	424	432	441	449	458	467	475	484	492
07	501	509	518	526	535	544	552	561	569	578
08	586	595	603	612	621	629	638	646	655	663
09	672	680	689	697	706	714	723	731	740	749
510	757	766	774	783	791	800	808	817	825	834
11	842	851	859	868	876	885	893	902	910	919
12	70 927	935	944	952	961	969	978	986	995	*003
13	71 012	020	029	037	046	054	063	071	079	088
14	096	105	113	122	130	139	147	155	164	172
15	181	189	198	206	214	223	231	240	248	257
16	265	273	282	290	299	307	315	324	332	341
17	349	357	366	374	383	391	399	408	416	425
18	433	441	450	458	466	475	483	492	500	508
19	517	525	533	542	550	559	567	575	584	592
520	600	609	617	625	634	642	650	659	667	675
21	684	692	700	709	717	725	734	742	750	759
22	767	775	784	792	800	809	817	825	834	842
23	850	858	867	875	883	892	900	908	917	925
24	71 933	941	950	958	966	975	983	991	999	*008
25	72 016	024	032	041	049	057	066	074	082	090
26	099	107	115	123	132	140	148	156	165	173
27	181	189	198	206	214	222	230	239	247	255
28	263	272	280	288	296	304	313	321	329	337
29	346	354	362	370	378	387	395	403	411	419
530	428	436	444	452	460	469	477	485	493	501
31	509	518	526	534	542	550	558	567	575	583
32	591	599	607	616	624	632	640	648	656	665
33	673	681	689	697	705	713	722	730	738	746
34	754	762	770	779	787	795	803	811	819	827
35	835	843	852	860	868	876	884	892	900	908
36	916	925	933	941	949	957	965	973	981	989
37	72 997	*006	*014	*022	*030	*038	*046	*054	*062	*070
38	73 078	086	094	102	111	119	127	135	143	151
39	159	167	175	183	191	199	207	215	223	231
540	239	247	255	263	272	280	288	296	304	312
41	320	328	336	344	352	360	368	376	384	392
42	400	408	416	424	432	440	448	456	464	472
43	480	488	496	504	512	520	528	536	544	552
44	560	568	576	584	592	600	608	616	624	632
45	640	648	656	664	672	679	687	695	703	711
46	719	727	735	743	751	759	767	775	783	791
47	799	807	815	823	830	838	846	854	862	870
48	878	886	894	902	910	918	926	933	941	949
49	73 957	965	973	981	989	997	*005	*013	*020	*028
550	74 036	044	052	060	068	076	084	092	099	107
N	**0**	**1**	**2**	**3**	**4**	**5**	**6**	**7**	**8**	**9**

Prop. Parts

	9
1	0.9
2	1.8
3	2.7
4	3.6
5	4.5
6	5.4
7	6.3
8	7.2
9	8.1

	8
1	0.8
2	1.6
3	2.4
4	3.2
5	4.0
6	4.8
7	5.6
8	6.4
9	7.2

	7
1	0.7
2	1.4
3	2.1
4	2.8
5	3.5
6	4.2
7	4.9
8	5.6
9	6.3

Prop. Parts

Table C. Five-Place Logarithms: 550–600

N	0	1	2	3	4	5	6	7	8	9
550	74 036	044	052	060	068	076	084	092	099	107
51	115	123	131	139	147	155	162	170	178	186
52	194	202	210	218	225	233	241	249	257	265
53	273	280	288	296	304	312	320	327	335	343
54	351	359	367	374	382	390	398	406	414	421
55	429	437	445	453	461	468	476	484	492	500
56	507	515	523	531	539	547	554	562	570	578
57	586	593	601	609	617	624	632	640	648	656
58	663	671	679	687	695	702	710	718	726	733
59	741	749	757	764	772	780	788	796	803	811
560	819	827	834	842	850	858	865	873	881	889
61	896	904	912	920	927	935	943	950	958	966
62	74 974	981	989	997	*005	*012	*020	*028	*035	*043
63	75 051	059	066	074	082	089	097	105	113	120
64	128	136	143	151	159	166	174	182	189	197
65	205	213	220	228	236	243	251	259	266	274
66	282	289	297	305	312	320	328	335	343	351
67	358	366	374	381	389	397	404	412	420	427
68	435	442	450	458	465	473	481	488	496	504
69	511	519	526	534	542	549	557	565	572	580
570	587	595	603	610	618	626	633	641	648	656
71	664	671	679	686	694	702	709	717	724	732
72	740	747	755	762	770	778	785	793	800	808
73	815	823	831	838	846	853	861	868	876	884
74	891	899	906	914	921	929	937	944	952	959
75	75 967	974	982	989	997	*005	*012	*020	*027	*035
76	76 042	050	057	065	072	080	087	095	103	110
77	118	125	133	140	148	155	163	170	178	185
78	193	200	208	215	223	230	238	245	253	260
79	268	275	283	290	298	305	313	320	328	335
580	343	350	358	365	373	380	388	395	403	410
81	418	425	433	440	448	455	462	470	477	485
82	492	500	507	515	522	530	537	545	552	559
83	567	574	582	589	597	604	612	619	626	634
84	641	649	656	664	671	678	686	693	701	708
85	716	723	730	738	745	753	760	768	775	782
86	790	797	805	812	819	827	834	842	849	856
87	864	871	879	886	893	901	908	916	923	930
88	76 938	945	953	960	967	975	982	989	997	*004
89	77 012	019	026	034	041	048	056	063	070	078
590	085	093	100	107	115	122	129	137	144	151
91	159	166	173	181	188	195	203	210	217	225
92	232	240	247	254	262	269	276	283	291	298
93	305	313	320	327	335	342	349	357	364	371
94	379	386	393	401	408	415	422	430	437	444
95	452	459	466	474	481	488	495	503	510	517
96	525	532	539	546	554	561	568	576	583	590
97	597	605	612	619	627	634	641	648	656	663
98	670	677	685	692	699	706	714	721	728	735
99	743	750	757	764	772	779	786	793	801	808
600	77 815	822	830	837	844	851	859	866	873	880
N	0	1	2	3	4	5	6	7	8	9

Prop. Parts

	8
1	0.8
2	1.6
3	2.4
4	3.2
5	4.0
6	4.8
7	5.6
8	6.4
9	7.2

	7
1	0.7
2	1.4
3	2.1
4	2.8
5	3.5
6	4.2
7	4.9
8	5.6
9	6.3

Prop. Parts

Table C. Five-Place Logarithms: 600–650

N	0	1	2	3	4	5	6	7	8	9
600	77 815	822	830	837	844	851	859	866	873	880
01	887	895	902	909	916	924	931	938	945	952
02	77 960	967	974	981	988	996	*003	*010	*017	*025
03	78 032	039	046	053	061	068	075	082	089	097
04	104	111	118	125	132	140	147	154	161	168
05	176	183	190	197	204	211	219	226	233	240
06	247	254	262	269	276	283	290	297	305	312
07	319	326	333	340	347	355	362	369	376	383
08	390	398	405	412	419	426	433	440	447	455
09	462	469	476	483	490	497	504	512	519	526
610	533	540	547	554	561	569	576	583	590	597
11	604	611	618	625	633	640	647	654	661	668
12	675	682	689	696	704	711	718	725	732	739
13	746	753	760	767	774	781	789	796	803	810
14	817	824	831	838	845	852	859	866	873	880
15	888	895	902	909	916	923	930	937	944	951
16	78 958	965	972	979	986	993	*000	*007	*014	*021
17	79 029	036	043	050	057	064	071	078	085	092
18	099	106	113	120	127	134	141	148	155	162
19	169	176	183	190	197	204	211	218	225	232
620	239	246	253	260	267	274	281	288	295	302
21	309	316	323	330	337	344	351	358	365	372
22	379	386	393	400	407	414	421	428	435	442
23	449	456	463	470	477	484	491	498	505	511
24	518	525	532	539	546	553	560	567	574	581
25	588	595	602	609	616	623	630	637	644	650
26	657	664	671	678	685	692	699	706	713	720
27	727	734	741	748	754	761	768	775	782	789
28	796	803	810	817	824	831	837	844	851	858
29	865	872	879	886	893	900	906	913	920	927
630	79 934	941	948	955	962	969	975	982	989	996
31	80 003	010	017	024	030	037	044	051	058	065
32	072	079	085	092	099	106	113	120	127	134
33	140	147	154	161	168	175	182	188	195	202
34	209	216	223	229	236	243	250	257	264	271
35	277	284	291	298	305	312	318	325	332	339
36	346	353	359	366	373	380	387	393	400	407
37	414	421	428	434	441	448	455	462	468	475
38	482	489	496	502	509	516	523	530	536	543
39	550	557	564	570	577	584	591	598	604	611
640	618	625	632	638	645	652	659	665	672	679
41	686	693	699	706	713	720	726	733	740	747
42	754	760	767	774	781	787	794	801	808	814
43	821	828	835	841	848	855	862	868	875	882
44	889	895	902	909	916	922	929	936	943	949
45	80 956	963	969	976	983	990	996	*003	*010	*017
46	81 023	030	037	043	050	057	064	070	077	084
47	090	097	104	111	117	124	131	137	144	151
48	158	164	171	178	184	191	198	204	211	218
49	224	231	238	245	251	258	265	271	278	285
650	81 291	298	305	311	318	325	331	338	345	351
N	**0**	**1**	**2**	**3**	**4**	**5**	**6**	**7**	**8**	**9**

Prop. Parts

	8
1	0.8
2	1.6
3	2.4
4	3.2
5	4.0
6	4.8
7	5.6
8	6.4
9	7.2

	7
1	0.7
2	1.4
3	2.1
4	2.8
5	3.5
6	4.2
7	4.9
8	5.6
9	6.3

	6
1	0.6
2	1.2
3	1.8
4	2.4
5	3.0
6	3.6
7	4.2
8	4.8
9	5.4

Prop. Parts

Table C. Five-Place Logarithms: 650–700

N	0	1	2	3	4	5	6	7	8	9
650	81 291	298	305	311	318	325	331	338	345	351
51	358	365	371	378	385	391	398	405	411	418
52	425	431	438	445	451	458	465	471	478	485
53	491	498	505	511	518	525	531	538	544	551
54	558	564	571	578	584	591	598	604	611	617
55	624	631	637	644	651	657	664	671	677	684
56	690	697	704	710	717	723	730	737	743	750
57	757	763	770	776	783	790	796	803	809	816
58	823	829	836	842	849	856	862	869	875	882
59	889	895	902	908	915	921	928	935	941	948
660	81 954	961	968	974	981	987	994	*000	*007	*014
61	82 020	027	033	040	046	053	060	066	073	079
62	086	092	099	105	112	119	125	132	138	145
63	151	158	164	171	178	184	191	197	204	210
64	217	223	230	236	243	249	256	263	269	276
65	282	289	295	302	308	315	321	328	334	341
66	347	354	360	367	373	380	387	393	400	406
67	413	419	426	432	439	445	452	458	465	471
68	478	484	491	497	504	510	517	523	530	536
69	543	549	556	562	569	575	582	588	595	601
670	607	614	620	627	633	640	646	653	659	666
71	672	679	685	692	698	705	711	718	724	730
72	737	743	750	756	763	769	776	782	789	795
73	802	808	814	821	827	834	840	847	853	860
74	866	872	879	885	892	898	905	911	918	924
75	930	937	943	950	956	963	969	975	982	988
76	82 995	*001	*008	*014	*020	*027	*033	*040	*046	*052
77	83 059	065	072	078	085	091	097	104	110	117
78	123	129	136	142	149	155	161	168	174	181
79	187	193	200	206	213	219	225	232	238	245
680	251	257	264	270	276	283	289	296	302	308
81	315	321	327	334	340	347	353	359	366	372
82	378	385	391	398	404	410	417	423	429	436
83	442	448	455	461	467	474	480	487	493	499
84	506	512	518	525	531	537	544	550	556	563
85	569	575	582	588	594	601	607	613	620	626
86	632	639	645	651	658	664	670	677	683	689
87	696	702	708	715	721	727	734	740	746	753
88	759	765	771	778	784	790	797	803	809	816
89	822	828	835	841	847	853	860	866	872	879
690	885	891	897	904	910	916	923	929	935	942
91	83 948	954	960	967	973	979	985	992	998	*004
92	84 011	017	023	029	036	042	048	055	061	067
93	073	080	086	092	098	105	111	117	123	130
94	136	142	148	155	161	167	173	180	186	192
95	198	205	211	217	223	230	236	242	248	255
96	261	267	273	280	286	292	298	305	311	317
97	323	330	336	342	348	354	361	367	373	379
98	386	392	398	404	410	417	423	429	435	442
99	448	454	460	466	473	479	485	491	497	504
700	84 510	516	522	528	535	541	547	553	559	566
N	**0**	**1**	**2**	**3**	**4**	**5**	**6**	**7**	**8**	**9**

Prop. Parts

	7
1	0.7
2	1.4
3	2.1
4	2.8
5	3.5
6	4.2
7	4.9
8	5.6
9	6.3

	6
1	0.6
2	1.2
3	1.8
4	2.4
5	3.0
6	3.6
7	4.2
8	4.8
9	5.4

Prop. Parts

Table C. Five-Place Logarithms: 700–750

N	0	1	2	3	4	5	6	7	8	9
700	84 510	516	522	528	535	541	547	553	559	566
01	572	578	584	590	597	603	609	615	621	628
02	634	640	646	652	658	665	671	677	683	689
03	696	702	708	714	720	726	733	739	745	751
04	757	763	770	776	782	788	794	800	807	813
05	819	825	831	837	844	850	856	862	868	874
06	880	887	893	899	905	911	917	924	930	936
07	84 942	948	954	960	967	973	979	985	991	997
08	85 003	009	016	022	028	034	040	046	052	058
09	065	071	077	083	089	095	101	107	114	120
710	126	132	138	144	150	156	163	169	175	181
11	187	193	199	205	211	217	224	230	236	242
12	248	254	260	266	272	278	285	291	297	303
13	309	315	321	327	333	339	345	352	358	364
14	370	376	382	388	394	400	406	412	418	425
15	431	437	443	449	455	461	467	473	479	485
16	491	497	503	509	516	522	528	534	540	546
17	552	558	564	570	576	582	588	594	600	606
18	612	618	625	631	637	643	649	655	661	667
19	673	679	685	691	697	703	709	715	721	727
720	733	739	745	751	757	763	769	775	781	788
21	794	800	806	812	818	824	830	836	842	848
22	854	860	866	872	878	884	890	896	902	908
23	914	920	926	932	938	944	950	956	962	968
24	85 974	980	986	992	998	*004	*010	*016	*022	*028
25	86 034	040	046	052	058	064	070	076	082	088
26	094	100	106	112	118	124	130	136	141	147
27	153	159	165	171	177	183	189	195	201	207
28	213	219	225	231	237	243	249	255	261	267
29	273	279	285	291	297	303	308	314	320	326
730	332	338	344	350	356	362	368	374	380	386
31	392	398	404	410	415	421	427	433	439	445
32	451	457	463	469	475	481	487	493	499	504
33	510	516	522	528	534	540	546	552	558	564
34	570	576	581	587	593	599	605	611	617	623
35	629	635	641	646	652	658	664	670	676	682
36	688	694	700	705	711	717	723	729	735	741
37	747	753	759	764	770	776	782	788	794	800
38	806	812	817	823	829	835	841	847	853	859
39	864	870	876	882	888	894	900	906	911	917
740	923	929	935	941	947	953	958	964	970	976
41	86 982	988	994	999	*005	*011	*017	*023	*029	*035
42	87 040	046	052	058	064	070	075	081	087	093
43	099	105	111	116	122	128	134	140	146	151
44	157	163	169	175	181	186	192	198	204	210
45	216	221	227	233	239	245	251	256	262	268
46	274	280	286	291	297	303	309	315	320	326
47	332	338	344	349	355	361	367	373	379	384
48	390	396	402	408	413	419	425	431	437	442
49	448	454	460	466	471	477	483	489	495	500
750	87 506	512	518	523	529	535	541	547	552	558
N	0	1	2	3	4	5	6	7	8	9

Prop. Parts

	7
1	0.7
2	1.4
3	2.1
4	2.8
5	3.5
6	4.2
7	4.9
8	5.6
9	6.3

	6
1	0.6
2	1.2
3	1.8
4	2.4
5	3.0
6	3.6
7	4.2
8	4.8
9	5.4

	5
1	0.5
2	1.0
3	1.5
4	2.0
5	2.5
6	3.0
7	3.5
8	4.0
9	4.5

Prop. Parts

Table C. Five-Place Logarithms: 750–800

N	0	1	2	3	4	5	6	7	8	9
750	87 506	512	518	523	529	535	541	547	552	558
51	564	570	576	581	587	593	599	604	610	616
52	622	628	633	639	645	651	656	662	668	674
53	679	685	691	697	703	708	714	720	726	731
54	737	743	749	754	760	766	772	777	783	789
55	795	800	806	812	818	823	829	835	841	846
56	852	858	864	869	875	881	887	892	898	904
57	910	915	921	927	933	938	944	950	955	961
58	87 967	973	978	984	990	996	*001	*007	*013	*018
59	88 024	030	036	041	047	053	058	064	070	076
760	081	087	093	098	104	110	116	121	127	133
61	138	144	150	156	161	167	173	178	184	190
62	195	201	207	213	218	224	230	235	241	247
63	252	258	264	270	275	281	287	292	298	304
64	309	315	321	326	332	338	343	349	355	360
65	366	372	377	383	389	395	400	406	412	417
66	423	429	434	440	446	451	457	463	468	474
67	480	485	491	497	502	508	513	519	525	530
68	536	542	547	553	559	564	570	576	581	587
69	593	598	604	610	615	621	627	632	638	643
770	649	655	660	666	672	677	683	689	694	700
71	705	711	717	722	728	734	739	745	750	756
72	762	767	773	779	784	790	795	801	807	812
73	818	824	829	835	840	846	852	857	863	868
74	874	880	885	891	897	902	908	913	919	925
75	930	936	941	947	953	958	964	969	975	981
76	88 986	992	997	*003	*009	*014	*020	*025	*031	*037
77	89 042	048	053	059	064	070	076	081	087	092
78	098	104	109	115	120	126	131	137	143	148
79	154	159	165	170	176	182	187	193	198	204
780	209	215	221	226	232	237	243	248	254	260
81	265	271	276	282	287	293	298	304	310	315
82	321	326	332	337	343	348	354	360	365	371
83	376	382	387	393	398	404	409	415	421	426
84	432	437	443	448	454	459	465	470	476	481
85	487	492	498	504	509	515	520	526	531	537
86	542	548	553	559	564	570	575	581	586	592
87	597	603	609	614	620	625	631	636	642	647
88	653	658	664	669	675	680	686	691	697	702
89	708	713	719	724	730	735	741	746	752	757
790	763	768	774	779	785	790	796	801	807	812
91	818	823	829	834	840	845	851	856	862	867
92	873	878	883	889	894	900	905	911	916	922
93	927	933	938	944	949	955	960	966	971	977
94	89 982	988	993	998	*004	*009	*015	*020	*026	*031
95	90 037	042	048	053	059	064	069	075	080	086
96	091	097	102	108	113	119	124	129	135	140
97	146	151	157	162	168	173	179	184	189	195
98	200	206	211	217	222	227	233	238	244	249
99	255	260	266	271	276	282	287	293	298	304
800	90 309	314	320	325	331	336	342	347	352	358
N	**0**	**1**	**2**	**3**	**4**	**5**	**6**	**7**	**8**	**9**

Prop. Parts

	6
1	0.6
2	1.2
3	1.8
4	2.4
5	3.0
6	3.6
7	4.2
8	4.8
9	5.4

	5
1	0.5
2	1.0
3	1.5
4	2.0
5	2.5
6	3.0
7	3.5
8	4.0
9	4.5

Table C. Five-Place Logarithms: 800–850

N	0	1	2	3	4	5	6	7	8	9
800	90 309	314	320	325	331	336	342	347	352	358
01	363	369	374	380	385	390	396	401	407	412
02	417	423	428	434	439	445	450	455	461	466
03	472	477	482	488	493	499	504	509	515	520
04	526	531	536	542	547	553	558	563	569	574
05	580	585	590	596	601	607	612	617	623	628
06	634	639	644	650	655	660	666	671	677	682
07	687	693	698	703	709	714	720	725	730	736
08	741	747	752	757	763	768	773	779	784	789
09	795	800	806	811	816	822	827	832	838	843
810	849	854	859	865	870	875	881	886	891	897
11	902	907	913	918	924	929	934	940	945	950
12	90 956	961	966	972	977	982	988	993	998	*004
13	91 009	014	020	025	030	036	041	046	052	057
14	062	068	073	078	084	089	094	100	105	110
15	116	121	126	132	137	142	148	153	158	164
16	169	174	180	185	190	196	201	206	212	217
17	222	228	233	238	243	249	254	259	265	270
18	275	281	286	291	297	302	307	312	318	323
19	328	334	339	344	350	355	360	365	371	376
820	381	387	392	397	403	408	413	418	424	429
21	434	440	445	450	455	461	466	471	477	482
22	487	492	498	503	508	514	519	524	529	535
23	540	545	551	556	561	566	572	577	582	587
24	593	598	603	609	614	619	624	630	635	640
25	645	651	656	661	666	672	677	682	687	693
26	698	703	709	714	719	724	730	735	740	745
27	751	756	761	766	772	777	782	787	793	798
28	803	808	814	819	824	829	834	840	845	850
29	855	861	866	871	876	882	887	892	897	903
830	908	913	918	924	929	934	939	944	950	955
31	91 960	965	971	976	981	986	991	997	*002	*007
32	92 012	018	023	028	033	038	044	049	054	059
33	065	070	075	080	085	091	096	101	106	111
34	117	122	127	132	137	143	148	153	158	163
35	169	174	179	184	189	195	200	205	210	215
36	221	226	231	236	241	247	252	257	262	267
37	273	278	283	288	293	298	304	309	314	319
38	324	330	335	340	345	350	355	361	366	371
39	376	381	387	392	397	402	407	412	418	423
840	428	433	438	443	449	454	459	464	469	474
41	480	485	490	495	500	505	511	516	521	526
42	531	536	542	547	552	557	562	567	572	578
43	583	588	593	598	603	609	614	619	624	629
44	634	639	645	650	655	660	665	670	675	681
45	686	691	696	701	706	711	716	722	727	732
46	737	742	747	752	758	763	768	773	778	783
47	788	793	799	804	809	814	819	824	829	834
48	840	845	850	855	860	865	870	875	881	886
49	891	896	901	906	911	916	921	927	932	937
850	92 942	947	952	957	962	967	973	978	983	988
N	0	1	2	3	4	5	6	7	8	9

Prop. Parts

	6
1	0.6
2	1.2
3	1.8
4	2.4
5	3.0
6	3.6
7	4.2
8	4.8
9	5.4

	5
1	0.5
2	1.0
3	1.5
4	2.0
5	2.5
6	3.0
7	3.5
8	4.0
9	4.5

Prop. Parts

N	0	1	2	3	4	5	6	7	8	9
850	92 942	947	952	957	962	967	973	978	983	988
51	92 993	998	*003	*008	*013	*018	*024	*029	*034	*039
52	93 044	049	054	059	064	069	075	080	085	090
53	095	100	105	110	115	120	125	131	136	141
54	146	151	156	161	166	171	176	181	186	192
55	197	202	207	212	217	222	227	232	237	242
56	247	252	258	263	268	273	278	283	288	293
57	298	303	308	313	318	323	328	334	339	344
58	349	354	359	364	369	374	379	384	389	394
59	399	404	409	414	420	425	430	435	440	445
860	450	455	460	465	470	475	480	485	490	495
61	500	505	510	515	520	526	531	536	541	546
62	551	556	561	566	571	576	581	586	591	596
63	601	606	611	616	621	626	631	636	641	646
64	651	656	661	666	671	676	682	687	692	697
65	702	707	712	717	722	727	732	737	742	747
66	752	757	762	767	772	777	782	787	792	797
67	802	807	812	817	822	827	832	837	842	847
68	852	857	862	867	872	877	882	887	892	897
69	902	907	912	917	922	927	932	937	942	947
870	93 952	957	962	967	972	977	982	987	992	997
71	94 002	007	012	017	022	027	032	037	042	047
72	052	057	062	067	072	077	082	086	091	096
73	101	106	111	116	121	126	131	136	141	146
74	151	156	161	166	171	176	181	186	191	196
75	201	206	211	216	221	226	231	236	240	245
76	250	255	260	265	270	275	280	285	290	295
77	300	305	310	315	320	325	330	335	340	345
78	349	354	359	364	369	374	379	384	389	394
79	399	404	409	414	419	424	429	433	438	443
880	448	453	458	463	468	473	478	483	488	493
81	498	503	507	512	517	522	527	532	537	542
82	547	552	557	562	567	571	576	581	586	591
83	596	601	606	611	616	621	626	630	635	640
84	645	650	655	660	665	670	675	680	685	689
85	694	699	704	709	714	719	724	729	734	738
86	743	748	753	758	763	768	773	778	783	787
87	792	797	802	807	812	817	822	827	832	836
88	841	846	851	856	861	866	871	876	880	885
89	890	895	900	905	910	915	919	924	929	934
890	939	944	949	954	959	963	968	973	978	983
91	94 988	993	998	*002	*007	*012	*017	*022	*027	*032
92	95 036	041	046	051	056	061	066	071	075	080
93	085	090	095	100	105	109	114	119	124	129
94	134	139	143	148	153	158	163	168	173	177
95	182	187	192	197	202	207	211	216	221	226
96	231	236	240	245	250	255	260	265	270	274
97	279	284	289	294	299	303	308	313	318	323
98	328	332	337	342	347	352	357	361	366	371
99	376	381	386	390	395	400	405	410	415	419
900	95 424	429	434	439	444	448	453	458	463	468
N	0	1	2	3	4	5	6	7	8	9

Prop. Parts

	6
1	0.6
2	1.2
3	1.8
4	2.4
5	3.0
6	3.6
7	4.2
8	4.8
9	5.4

	5
1	0.5
2	1.0
3	1.5
4	2.0
5	2.5
6	3.0
7	3.5
8	4.0
9	4.5

	4
1	0.4
2	0.8
3	1.2
4	1.6
5	2.0
6	2.4
7	2.8
8	3.2
9	3.6

Prop. Parts

Table C. Five-Place Logarithms: 900–950

N	0	1	2	3	4	5	6	7	8	9
900	95 424	429	434	439	444	448	453	458	463	468
01	472	477	482	487	492	497	501	506	511	516
02	521	525	530	535	540	545	550	554	559	564
03	569	574	578	583	588	593	598	602	607	612
04	617	622	626	631	636	641	646	650	655	660
05	665	670	674	679	684	689	694	698	703	708
06	713	718	722	727	732	737	742	746	751	756
07	761	766	770	775	780	785	789	794	799	804
08	809	813	818	823	828	832	837	842	847	852
09	856	861	866	871	875	880	885	890	895	899
910	904	909	914	918	923	928	933	938	942	947
11	952	957	961	966	971	976	980	985	990	995
12	95 999	*004	*009	*014	*019	*023	*028	*033	*038	*042
13	96 047	052	057	061	066	071	076	080	085	090
14	095	099	104	109	114	118	123	128	133	137
15	142	147	152	156	161	166	171	175	180	185
16	190	194	199	204	209	213	218	223	227	232
17	237	242	246	251	256	261	265	270	275	280
18	284	289	294	298	303	308	313	317	322	327
19	332	336	341	346	350	355	360	365	369	374
920	379	384	388	393	398	402	407	412	417	421
21	426	431	435	440	445	450	454	459	464	468
22	473	478	483	487	492	497	501	506	511	515
23	520	525	530	534	539	544	548	553	558	562
24	567	572	577	581	586	591	595	600	605	609
25	614	619	624	628	633	638	642	647	652	656
26	661	666	670	675	680	685	689	694	699	703
27	708	713	717	722	727	731	736	741	745	750
28	755	759	764	769	774	778	783	788	792	797
29	802	806	811	816	820	825	830	834	839	844
930	848	853	858	862	867	872	876	881	886	890
31	895	900	904	909	914	918	923	928	932	937
32	942	946	951	956	960	965	970	974	979	984
33	96 988	993	997	*002	*007	*011	*016	*021	*025	*030
34	97 035	039	044	049	053	058	063	067	072	077
35	081	086	090	095	100	104	109	114	118	123
36	128	132	137	142	146	151	155	160	165	169
37	174	179	183	188	192	197	202	206	211	216
38	220	225	230	234	239	243	248	253	257	262
39	267	271	276	280	285	290	294	299	304	308
940	313	317	322	327	331	336	340	345	350	354
41	359	364	368	373	377	382	387	391	396	400
42	405	410	414	419	424	428	433	437	442	447
43	451	456	460	465	470	474	479	483	488	493
44	497	502	506	511	516	520	525	529	534	539
45	543	548	552	557	562	566	571	575	580	585
46	589	594	598	603	607	612	617	621	626	630
47	635	640	644	649	653	658	663	667	672	676
48	681	685	690	695	699	704	708	713	717	722
49	727	731	736	740	745	749	754	759	763	768
950	97 772	777	782	786	791	795	800	804	809	813
N	**0**	**1**	**2**	**3**	**4**	**5**	**6**	**7**	**8**	**9**

Prop. Parts

	5
1	0.5
2	1.0
3	1.5
4	2.0
5	2.5
6	3.0
7	3.5
8	4.0
9	4.5

	4
1	0.4
2	0.8
3	1.2
4	1.6
5	2.0
6	2.4
7	2.8
8	3.2
9	3.6

Prop. Parts

Table C. Five-Place Logarithms: 950–1000

N	0	1	2	3	4	5	6	7	8	9
950	97 772	777	782	786	791	795	800	804	809	813
51	818	823	827	832	836	841	845	850	855	859
52	864	868	873	877	882	886	891	896	900	905
53	909	914	918	923	928	932	937	941	946	950
54	97 955	959	964	968	973	978	982	987	991	996
55	98 000	005	009	014	019	023	028	032	037	041
56	046	050	055	059	064	068	073	078	082	087
57	091	096	100	105	109	114	118	123	127	132
58	137	141	146	150	155	159	164	168	173	177
59	182	186	191	195	200	204	209	214	218	223
960	227	232	236	241	245	250	254	259	263	268
61	272	277	281	286	290	295	299	304	308	313
62	318	322	327	331	336	340	345	349	354	358
63	363	367	372	376	381	385	390	394	399	403
64	408	412	417	421	426	430	435	439	444	448
65	453	457	462	466	471	475	480	484	489	493
66	498	502	507	511	516	520	525	529	534	538
67	543	547	552	556	561	565	570	574	579	583
68	588	592	597	601	605	610	614	619	623	628
69	632	637	641	646	650	655	659	664	668	673
970	677	682	686	691	695	700	704	709	713	717
71	722	726	731	735	740	744	749	753	758	762
72	767	771	776	780	784	789	793	798	802	807
73	811	816	820	825	829	834	838	843	847	851
74	856	860	865	869	874	878	883	887	892	896
75	900	905	909	914	918	923	927	932	936	941
76	945	949	954	958	963	967	972	976	981	985
77	98 989	994	998	*003	*007	*012	*016	*021	*025	*029
78	99 034	038	043	047	052	056	061	065	069	074
79	078	083	087	092	096	100	105	109	114	118
980	123	127	131	136	140	145	149	154	158	162
81	167	171	176	180	185	189	193	198	202	207
82	211	216	220	224	229	233	238	242	247	251
83	255	260	264	269	273	277	282	286	291	295
84	300	304	308	313	317	322	326	330	335	339
85	344	348	352	357	361	366	370	374	379	383
86	388	392	396	401	405	410	414	419	423	427
87	432	436	441	445	449	454	458	463	467	471
88	476	480	484	489	493	498	502	506	511	515
89	520	524	528	533	537	542	546	550	555	559
990	564	568	572	577	581	585	590	594	599	603
91	607	612	616	621	625	629	634	638	642	647
92	651	656	660	664	669	673	677	682	686	691
93	695	699	704	708	712	717	721	726	730	734
94	739	743	747	752	756	760	765	769	774	778
95	782	787	791	795	800	804	808	813	817	822
96	826	830	835	839	843	848	852	856	861	865
97	870	874	878	883	887	891	896	900	904	909
98	913	917	922	926	930	935	939	944	948	952
99	99 957	961	965	970	974	978	983	987	991	996
1000	00 000	004	009	013	017	022	026	030	035	039
N	**0**	**1**	**2**	**3**	**4**	**5**	**6**	**7**	**8**	**9**

Prop. Parts

	5
1	0.5
2	1.0
3	1.5
4	2.0
5	2.5
6	3.0
7	3.5
8	4.0
9	4.5

	4
1	0.4
2	0.8
3	1.2
4	1.6
5	2.0
6	2.4
7	2.8
8	3.2
9	3.6

Prop. Parts

Table D. Logarithms of Trigonometric Functions to Five Decimal Places[1] (Subtract 10 from each entry)

Special Interpolation in Table D. In the first three columns on pages 223, 224, and 225, the tabular differences are so large that linear interpolation gives inaccurate results. Since every entry for the logarithm of the cosine of an angle near 90° can be thought of as the logarithm of the sine of an angle near 0°, it is sufficient if we consider only the sines of small angles. In like manner, since the tangent and cotangent are both reciprocals and cofunctions, it is sufficient to consider interpolation for tangents of very small angles, for we have

$$\log \tan A = -\log \cot A = -\log \tan (90° - A) = \log \cot (90° - A).$$

If A and B are sufficiently small angles, both expressed in minutes, it can be shown that the following relations are accurate to five places of decimals.

$$(a) \log \sin A = \log \sin B + \log A - \log B;$$

$$(b) \log \tan A = \log \tan B + \log A - \log B.$$

In particular, these relations will be reliable to five places of decimals if both A and B are less than 3° and $A - B$ is less than 1′. Since these conditions are true for interpolation problems for the sine and tangent in the first columns on pages 223, 224, and 225, these formulas may be used.

Example 1. Find log cos 89° 27.5′. This is the same as finding

$$\log \sin 0° \, 32.5'.$$

Let $A = 32.5'$, and let $B = 32'$. Then

$$\log \sin 32.5' = \log \sin 32' + \log 32.5 - \log 32,$$

whence $\log \cos 89° \, 27.5' = 7.97560 - 10$.

Example 2. Find log tan 1° 15.2′. Let $A = 1° \, 15.2' = 75.2'$, and let $B = 1° \, 15' = 75'$. Then

$$\log \tan 1° \, 15.2' = \log \tan 1° \, 15' + \log 75.2 - \log 75 = 8.34002 - 10.$$

Note. Ordinary linear interpolation in the first example would have given the result 7.97555 − 10, with an error of 5 in the last place. Linear interpolation in the last example would have given the result 8.34001 − 10, with an error of 1 in the last place.

[1] Reprinted by permission from *The McGraw-Hill Five-Place Logarithmic and Trigonometric Tables*, edited by R. D. Beetle, copyright 1933 by McGraw-Hill.

Table D (Continued)

0°

′	L Sin	d	L Tan	c d	L Cot	L Cos	
0	———		———		———	0.00 000	**60**
1	6.46 373	30103	6.46 373	30103	13.53 627	0.00 000	59
2	6.76 476	17609	6.76 476	17609	13.23 524	0.00 000	58
3	6.94 085	12494	6.94 085	12494	13.05 915	0.00 000	57
4	7.06 579	9691	7.06 579	9691	12.93 421	0.00 000	56
5	7.16 270	7918	7.16 270	7918	12.83 730	0.00 000	55
6	7.24 188	6694	7.24 188	6694	12.75 812	0.00 000	54
7	7.30 882	5800	7.30 882	5800	12.69 118	0.00 000	53
8	7.36 682	5115	7.36 682	5115	12.63 318	0.00 000	52
9	7.41 797	4576	7.41 797	4576	12.58 203	0.00 000	51
10	7.46 373	4139	7.46 373	4139	12.53 627	0.00 000	**50**
11	7.50 512	3779	7.50 512	3779	12.49 488	0.00 000	49
12	7.54 291	3476	7.54 291	3476	12.45 709	0.00 000	48
13	7.57 767	3218	7.57 767	3219	12.42 233	0.00 000	47
14	7.60 985	2997	7.60 986	2996	12.39 014	0.00 000	46
15	7.63 982	2802	7.63 982	2803	12.36 018	0.00 000	45
16	7.66 784	2633	7.66 785	2633	12.33 215	0.00 000	44
17	7.69 417	2483	7.69 418	2482	12.30 582	9.99 999	43
18	7.71 900	2348	7.71 900	2348	12.28 100	9.99 999	42
19	7.74 248	2227	7.74 248	2228	12.25 752	9.99 999	41
20	7.76 475	2119	7.76 476	2119	12.23 524	9.99 999	**40**
21	7.78 594	2021	7.78 595	2020	12.21 405	9.99 999	39
22	7.80 615	1930	7.80 615	1931	12.19 385	9.99 999	38
23	7.82 545	1848	7.82 546	1848	12.17 454	9.99 999	37
24	7.84 393	1773	7.84 394	1773	12.15 606	9.99 999	36
25	7.86 166	1704	7.86 167	1704	12.13 833	9.99 999	35
26	7.87 870	1639	7.87 871	1639	12.12 129	9.99 999	34
27	7.89 509	1579	7.89 510	1579	12.10 490	9.99 999	33
28	7.91 088	1524	7.91 089	1524	12.08 911	9.99 999	32
29	7.92 612	1472	7.92 613	1473	12.07 387	9.99 998	31
30	7.94 084	1424	7.94 086	1424	12.05 914	9.99 998	**30**
31	7.95 508	1379	7.95 510	1379	12.04 490	9.99 998	29
32	7.96 887	1336	7.96 889	1336	12.03 111	9.99 998	28
33	7.98 223	1297	7.98 225	1297	12.01 775	9.99 998	27
34	7.99 520	1259	7.99 522	1259	12.00 478	9.99 998	26
35	8.00 779	1223	8.00 781	1223	11.99 219	9.99 998	25
36	8.02 002	1190	8.02 004	1190	11.97 996	9.99 998	24
37	8.03 192	1158	8.03 194	1159	11.96 806	9.99 997	23
38	8.04 350	1128	8.04 353	1128	11.95 647	9.99 997	22
39	8.05 478	1100	8.05 481	1100	11.94 519	9.99 997	21
40	8.06 578	1072	8.06 581	1072	11.93 419	9.99 997	**20**
41	8.07 650	1046	8.07 653	1047	11.92 347	9.99 997	19
42	8.08 696	1022	8.08 700	1022	11.91 300	9.99 997	18
43	8.09 718	999	8.09 722	998	11.90 278	9.99 997	17
44	8.10 717	976	8.10 720	976	11.89 280	9.99 996	16
45	8.11 693	954	8.11 696	955	11.88 304	9.99 996	15
46	8.12 647	934	8.12 651	934	11.87 349	9.99 996	14
47	8.13 581	914	8.13 585	915	11.86 415	9.99 996	13
48	8.14 495	896	8.14 500	895	11.85 500	9.99 996	12
49	8.15 391	877	8.15 395	878	11.84 605	9.99 996	11
50	8.16 268	860	8.16 273	860	11.83 727	9.99 995	**10**
51	8.17 128	843	8.17 133	843	11.82 867	9.99 995	9
52	8.17 971	827	8.17 976	828	11.82 024	9.99 995	8
53	8.18 798	812	8.18 804	812	11.81 196	9.99 995	7
54	8.19 610	797	8.19 616	797	11.80 384	9.99 995	6
55	8.20 407	782	8.20 413	782	11.79 587	9.99 994	5
56	8.21 189	769	8.21 195	769	11.78 805	9.99 994	4
57	8.21 958	755	8.21 964	756	11.78 036	9.99 994	3
58	8.22 713	743	8.22 720	742	11.77 280	9.99 994	2
59	8.23 456	730	8.23 462	730	11.76 538	9.99 994	1
60	8.24 186		8.24 192		11.75 808	9.99 993	**0**
	L Cos	d	L Cot	c d	L Tan	L Sin	′

89°

Since the tabular differences in the first three columns of this page, and on each of the two pages following, are so large and change so rapidly in value that ordinary linear interpolation does not give results accurate to five places of decimals, special methods of interpolation are necessary. A brief account of these special methods is given on page 222.

Table D (Continued)

1°

′	L Sin	d	L Tan	c d	L Cot	L Cos	
0	8.24 186	717	8.24 192	718	11.75 808	9.99 993	**60**
1	8.24 903	706	8.24 910	706	11.75 090	9.99 993	59
2	8.25 609	695	8.25 616	696	11.74 384	9.99 993	58
3	8.26 304	684	8.26 312	684	11.73 688	9.99 993	57
4	8.26 988	673	8.26 996	673	11.73 004	9.99 992	56
5	8.27 661	663	8.27 669	663	11.72 331	9.99 992	55
6	8.28 324	653	8.28 332	654	11.71 668	9.99 992	54
7	8.28 977	644	8.28 986	643	11.71 014	9.99 992	53
8	8.29 621	634	8.29 629	634	11.70 371	9.99 992	52
9	8.30 255	624	8.30 263	625	11.69 737	9.99 991	51
10	8.30 879	616	8.30 888	617	11.69 112	9.99 991	**50**
11	8.31 495	608	8.31 505	607	11.68 495	9.99 991	49
12	8.32 103	599	8.32 112	599	11.67 888	9.99 990	48
13	8.32 702	590	8.32 711	591	11.67 289	9.99 990	47
14	8.33 292	583	8.33 302	584	11.66 698	9.99 990	46
15	8.33 875	575	8.33 886	575	11.66 114	9.99 990	45
16	8.34 450	568	8.34 461	568	11.65 539	9.99 989	44
17	8.35 018	560	8.35 029	561	11.64 971	9.99 989	43
18	8.35 578	553	8.35 590	553	11.64 410	9.99 989	42
19	8.36 131	547	8.36 143	546	11.63 857	9.99 989	41
20	8.36 678	539	8.36 689	540	11.63 311	9.99 988	**40**
21	8.37 217	533	8.37 229	533	11.62 771	9.99 988	39
22	8.37 750	526	8.37 762	527	11.62 238	9.99 988	38
23	8.83 276	520	8.38 289	520	11.61 711	9.99 987	37
24	8.38 796	514	8.38 809	514	11.61 191	9.99 987	36
25	8.39 310	508	8.39 323	509	11.60 677	9.99 987	35
26	8.39 818	502	8.39 832	502	11.60 168	9.99 986	34
27	8.40 320	496	8.40 334	496	11.59 666	9.99 986	33
28	8.40 816	491	8.40 830	491	11.59 170	9.99 986	32
29	8.41 307	485	8.41 321	486	11.58 679	9.99 985	31
30	8.41 792	480	8.41 807	480	11.58 193	9.99 985	**30**
31	8.42 272	474	8.42 287	475	11.57 713	9.99 985	29
32	8.42 746	470	8.42 762	470	11.57 238	9.99 984	28
33	8.43 216	464	8.43 232	464	11.56 768	9.99 984	27
34	8.43 680	459	8.43 696	460	11.56 304	9.99 984	26
35	8.44 139	455	8.44 156	455	11.55 844	9.99 983	25
36	8.44 594	450	8.44 611	450	11.55 389	9.99 983	24
37	8.45 044	445	8.45 061	446	11.54 939	9.99 983	23
38	8.45 489	441	8.45 507	441	11.54 493	9.99 982	22
39	8.45 930	436	8.45 948	437	11.54 052	9.99 982	21
40	8.46 366	433	8.46 385	432	11.53 615	9.99 982	**20**
41	8.46 799	427	8.46 817	428	11.53 183	9.99 981	19
42	8.47 226	424	8.47 245	424	11.52 755	9.99 981	18
43	8.47 650	419	8.47 669	420	11.52 331	9.99 981	17
44	8.48 069	416	8.48 089	416	11.51 911	9.99 980	16
45	8.48 485	411	8.48 505	412	11.51 495	9.99 980	15
46	8.48 896	408	8.48 917	408	11.51 083	9.99 979	14
47	8.49 304	404	8.49 325	404	11.50 675	9.99 979	13
48	8.49 708	400	8.49 729	401	11.50 271	9.99 979	12
49	8.50 108	396	8.50 130	397	11.49 870	9.99 978	11
50	8.50 504	393	8.50 527	393	11.49 473	9.99 978	**10**
51	8.50 897	390	8.50 920	390	11.49 080	9.99 977	9
52	8.51 287	386	8.51 310	386	11.48 690	9.99 977	8
53	8.51 673	382	8.51 696	383	11.48 304	9.99 977	7
54	8.52 055	379	8.52 079	380	11.47 921	9.99 976	6
55	8.52 434	376	8.52 459	376	11.47 541	9.99 976	5
56	8.52 810	373	8.52 835	373	11.47 165	9.99 975	4
57	8.53 183	369	8.53 208	370	11.46 792	9.99 975	3
58	8.53 552	367	8.53 578	367	11.46 422	9.99 974	2
59	8.53 919	363	8.53 945	363	11.46 055	9.99 974	1
60	8.54 282		8.54 308		11.45 692	9.99 974	**0**
	L Cos	d	L Cot	c d	L Tan	L Sin	′

88°

If ordinary linear interpolation is not sufficiently accurate, use the special methods described on page 222.

Table D (Continued)

2°

′	L Sin	d	L Tan	c d	L Cot	L Cos	
0	8.54 282	360	8.54 308	361	11.45 692	9.99 974	**60**
1	8.54 642	357	8.54 669	358	11.45 331	9.99 973	59
2	8.54 999	355	8.55 027	355	11.44 973	9.99 973	58
3	8.55 354	351	8.55 382	352	11.44 618	9.99 972	57
4	8.55 705	349	8.55 734	349	11.44 266	9.99 972	56
5	8.56 054	346	8.56 083	346	11.43 917	9.99 971	55
6	8.56 400	343	8.56 429	344	11.43 571	9.99 971	54
7	8.56 743	341	8.56 773	341	11.43 227	9.99 970	53
8	8.57 084	337	8.57 114	338	11.42 886	9.99 970	52
9	8.57 421	336	8.57 452	336	11.42 548	9.99 969	51
10	8.57 757	332	8.57 788	333	11.42 212	9.99 969	**50**
11	8.58 089	330	8.58 121	330	11.41 879	9.99 968	49
12	8.58 419	328	8.58 451	328	11.41 549	9.99 968	48
13	8.58 747	325	8.58 779	326	11.41 221	9.99 967	47
14	8.59 072	323	8.59 105	323	11.40 895	9.99 967	46
15	8.59 395	320	8.59 428	321	11.40 572	9.99 967	45
16	8.59 715	318	8.59 749	319	11.40 251	9.99 966	44
17	8.60 033	316	8.60 068	316	11.39 932	9.99 966	43
18	8.60 349	313	8.60 384	314	11.39 616	9.99 965	42
19	8.60 662	311	8.60 698	311	11.39 302	9.99 964	41
20	8.60 973	309	8.61 009	310	11.38 991	9.99 964	**40**
21	8.61 282	307	8.61 319	307	11.38 681	9.99 963	39
22	8.61 589	305	8.61 626	305	11.38 374	9.99 963	38
23	8.61 894	302	8.61 931	303	11.38 069	9.99 962	37
24	8.62 196	301	8.62 234	301	11.37 766	9.99 962	36
25	8.62 497	298	8.62 535	299	11.37 465	9.99 961	35
26	8.62 795	296	8.62 834	297	11.37 166	9.99 961	34
27	8.63 091	294	8.63 131	295	11.36 869	9.99 960	33
28	8.63 385	293	8.63 426	292	11.36 574	9.99 960	32
29	8.63 678	290	8.63 718	291	11.36 282	9.99 959	31
30	8.63 968	288	8.64 009	289	11.35 991	9.99 959	**30**
31	8.64 256	287	8.64 298	287	11.35 702	9.99 958	29
32	8.64 543	284	8.64 585	285	11.35 415	9.99 958	28
33	8.64 827	283	8.64 870	284	11.35 130	9.99 957	27
34	8.65 110	281	8.65 154	281	11.34 846	9.99 956	26
35	8.65 391	279	8.65 435	280	11.34 565	9.99 956	25
36	8.65 670	277	8.65 715	278	11.34 285	9.99 955	24
37	8.65 947	276	8.65 993	276	11.34 007	9.99 955	23
38	8.66 223	274	8.66 269	274	11.33 731	9.99 954	22
39	8.66 497	272	8.66 543	273	11.33 457	9.99 954	21
40	8.66 769	270	8.66 816	271	11.33 184	9.99 953	**20**
41	8.67 039	269	8.67 087	269	11.32 913	9.99 952	19
42	8.67 308	267	8.67 356	268	11.32 644	9.99 952	18
43	8.67 575	266	8.67 624	266	11.32 376	9.99 951	17
44	8.67 841	263	8.67 890	264	11.32 110	9.99 951	16
45	8.68 104	263	8.68 154	263	11.31 846	9.99 950	15
46	8.68 367	260	8.68 417	261	11.31 583	9.99 949	14
47	8.68 627	259	8.68 678	260	11.31 322	9.99 949	13
48	8.68 886	258	8.68 938	258	11.31 062	9.99 948	12
49	8.69 144	256	8.69 196	257	11.30 804	9.99 948	11
50	8.69 400	254	8.69 453	255	11.30 547	9.99 947	**10**
51	8.69 654	253	8.69 708	254	11.30 292	9.99 946	9
52	8.69 907	252	8.69 962	252	11.30 038	9.99 946	8
53	8.70 159	250	8.70 214	251	11.29 786	9.99 945	7
54	8.70 409	249	8.70 465	249	11.29 535	9.99 944	6
55	8.70 658	247	8.70 714	248	11.29 286	9.99 944	5
56	8.70 905	246	8.70 962	246	11.29 038	9.99 943	4
57	8.71 151	244	8.71 208	245	11.28 792	9.99 942	3
58	8.71 395	243	8.71 453	244	11.28 547	9.99 942	2
59	8.71 638	242	8.71 697	243	11.28 303	9.99 941	1
60	8.71 880		8.71 940		11.28 060	9.99 940	**0**
	L Cos	d	L Cot	c d	L Tan	L Sin	′

87°

If ordinary linear interpolation is not sufficiently accurate, use the special methods described on page 222.

Table D (Continued)

3°

′	L Sin	d	L Tan	c d	L Cot	L Cos	′
0	8.71 880	240	8.71 940	241	11.28 060	9.99 940	**60**
1	8.72 120	239	8.72 181	239	11.27 819	9.99 940	59
2	8.72 359	238	8.72 420	239	11.27 580	9.99 939	58
3	8.72 597	237	8.72 659	237	11.27 341	9.99 938	57
4	8.72 834	235	8.72 896	236	11.27 104	9.99 938	56
5	8.73 069	234	8.73 132	234	11.26 868	9.99 937	55
6	8.73 303	232	8.73 366	234	11.26 634	9.99 936	54
7	8.73 535	232	8.73 600	232	11.26 400	9.99 936	53
8	8.73 767	230	8.73 832	231	11.26 168	9.99 935	52
9	8.73 997	229	8.74 063	229	11.25 937	9.99 934	51
10	8.74 226	228	8.74 292	229	11.25 708	9.99 934	**50**
11	8.74 454	226	8.74 521	227	11.25 479	9.99 933	49
12	8.74 680	226	8.74 748	226	11.25 252	9.99 932	48
13	8.74 906	224	8.74 974	225	11.25 026	9.99 932	47
14	8.75 130	223	8.75 199	224	11.24 801	9.99 931	46
15	8.75 353	222	8.75 423	222	11.24 577	9.99 930	45
16	8.75 575	220	8.75 645	222	11.24 355	9.99 929	44
17	8.75 795	220	8.75 867	220	11.24 133	9.99 929	43
18	8.76 015	219	8.76 087	219	11.23 913	9.99 928	42
19	8.76 234	217	8.76 306	219	11.23 694	9.99 927	41
20	8.76 451	216	8.76 525	217	11.23 475	9.99 926	**40**
21	8.76 667	216	8.76 742	216	11.23 258	9.99 926	39
22	8.76 883	214	8.76 958	215	11.23 042	9.99 925	38
23	8.77 097	213	8.77 173	214	11.22 827	9.99 924	37
24	8.77 310	212	8.77 387	213	11.22 613	9.99 923	36
25	8.77 522	211	8.77 600	211	11.22 400	9.99 923	35
26	8.77 733	210	8.77 811	211	11.22 189	9.99 922	34
27	8.77 943	209	8.78 022	210	11.21 978	9.99 921	33
28	8.78 152	208	8.78 232	209	11.21 768	9.99 920	32
29	8.78 360	208	8.78 441	208	11.21 559	9.99 920	31
30	8.78 568	206	8.78 649	206	11.21 351	9.99 919	**30**
31	8.78 774	205	8.78 855	206	11.21 145	9.99 918	29
32	8.78 979	204	8.79 061	205	11.20 939	9.99 917	28
33	8.79 183	203	8.79 266	204	11.20 734	9.99 917	27
34	8.79 386	202	8.79 470	203	11.20 530	9.99 916	26
35	8.79 588	201	8.79 673	202	11.20 327	9.99 915	25
36	8.79 789	201	8.79 875	201	11.20 125	9.99 914	24
37	8.79 990	199	8.80 076	201	11.19 924	9.99 913	23
38	8.80 189	199	8.80 277	199	11.19 723	9.99 913	22
39	8.80 388	197	8.80 476	198	11.19 524	9.99 912	21
40	8.80 585	197	8.80 674	198	11.19 326	9.99 911	**20**
41	8.80 782	196	8.80 872	196	11.19 128	9.99 910	19
42	8.80 978	195	8.81 068	196	11.18 932	9.99 909	18
43	8.81 173	194	8.81 264	195	11.18 736	9.99 909	17
44	8.81 367	193	8.81 459	194	11.18 541	9.99 908	16
45	8.81 560	192	8.81 653	193	11.18 347	9.99 907	15
46	8.81 752	192	8.81 846	192	11.18 154	9.99 906	14
47	8.81 944	190	8.82 038	192	11.17 962	9.99 905	13
48	8.82 134	190	8.82 230	190	11.17 770	9.99 904	12
49	8.82 324	189	8.82 420	190	11.17 580	9.99 904	11
50	8.82 513	188	8.82 610	189	11.17 390	9.99 903	**10**
51	8.82 701	187	8.82 799	188	11.17 201	9.99 902	9
52	8.82 888	187	8.82 987	188	11.17 013	9.99 901	8
53	8.83 075	186	8.83 175	186	11.16 825	9.99 900	7
54	8.83 261	185	8.83 361	186	11.16 639	9.99 899	6
55	8.83 446	184	8.83 547	185	11.16 453	9.99 898	5
56	8.83 630	183	8.83 732	184	11.16 268	9.99 898	4
57	8.83 813	183	8.83 916	184	11.16 084	9.99 897	3
58	8.83 996	181	8.84 100	182	11.15 900	9.99 896	2
59	8.84 177	181	8.84 282	182	11.15 718	9.99 895	1
60	8.84 358		8.84 464		11.15 536	9.99 894	**0**
	L Cos	d	L Cot	c d	L Tan	L Sin	′

Prop. Pts.

	239	**237**	**235**	**234**
2	47.8	47.4	47.0	46.8
3	71.7	71.1	70.5	70.2
4	95.6	94.8	94.0	93.6
5	119.5	118.5	117.5	117.0
6	143.4	142.2	141.0	140.4
7	167.3	165.9	164.5	163.8
8	191.2	189.6	188.0	187.2
9	215.1	213.3	211.5	210.6
	232	**229**	**227**	**226**
2	46.4	45.8	45.4	45.2
3	69.6	68.7	68.1	67.8
4	92.8	91.6	90.8	90.4
5	116.0	114.5	113.5	113.0
6	139.2	137.4	136.2	135.6
7	162.4	160.3	158.9	158.2
8	185.6	183.2	181.6	180.8
9	208.8	206.1	204.3	203.4
	224	**222**	**220**	**219**
2	44.8	44.4	44.0	43.8
3	67.2	66.6	66.0	65.7
4	89.6	88.8	88.0	87.6
5	112.0	111.0	110.0	109.5
6	134.4	133.2	132.0	131.4
7	156.8	155.4	154.0	153.3
8	179.2	177.6	176.0	175.2
9	201.6	199.8	198.0	197.1
	217	**215**	**213**	**211**
2	43.4	43.0	42.6	42.2
3	65.1	64.5	63.9	63.3
4	86.8	86.0	85.2	84.4
5	108.5	107.5	106.5	105.5
6	130.2	129.0	127.8	126.6
7	151.9	150.5	149.1	147.7
8	173.6	172.0	170.4	168.8
9	195.3	193.5	191.7	189.9
	208	**206**	**203**	**201**
2	41.6	41.2	40.6	40.2
3	62.4	61.8	60.9	60.3
4	83.2	82.4	81.2	80.4
5	104.0	103.0	101.5	100.5
6	124.8	123.6	121.8	120.6
7	145.6	144.2	142.1	140.7
8	166.4	164.8	162.4	160.8
9	187.2	185.4	182.7	180.9
	199	**197**	**195**	**193**
2	39.8	39.4	39.0	38.6
3	59.7	59.1	58.5	57.9
4	79.6	78.8	78.0	77.2
5	99.5	98.5	97.5	96.5
6	119.4	118.2	117.0	115.8
7	139.3	137.9	136.5	135.1
8	159.2	157.6	156.0	154.4
9	179.1	177.3	175.5	173.7
	192	**190**	**188**	**186**
2	38.4	38.0	37.6	37.2
3	57.6	57.0	56.4	55.8
4	76.8	76.0	75.2	74.4
5	96.0	95.0	94.0	93.0
6	115.2	114.0	112.8	111.6
7	134.4	133.0	131.6	130.2
8	153.6	152.0	150.4	148.8
9	172.8	171.0	169.2	167.4
	184	**183**	**182**	**181**
2	36.8	36.6	36.4	36.2
3	55.2	54.9	54.6	54.3
4	73.6	73.2	72.8	72.4
5	92.0	91.5	91.0	90.5
6	110.4	109.8	109.2	108.6
7	128.8	128.1	127.4	126.7
8	147.2	146.4	145.6	144.8
9	165.6	164.7	163.8	162.9

Prop. Pts.

86°

Table D (Continued)

4°

′	L Sin	d	L Tan	c d	L Cot	L Cos	
0	8.84 358	181	8.84 464	182	11.15 536	9.99 894	60
1	8.84 539	179	8.84 646	180	11.15 354	9.99 893	59
2	8.84 718	179	8.84 826	180	11.15 174	9.99 892	58
3	8.84 897	178	8.85 006	179	11.14 994	9.99 891	57
4	8.85 075	177	8.85 185	178	11.14 815	9.99 891	56
5	8.85 252	177	8.85 363	177	11.14 637	9.99 890	55
6	8.85 429	176	8.85 540	177	11.14 460	9.99 889	54
7	8.85 605	175	8.85 717	176	11.14 283	9.99 888	53
8	8.85 780	175	8.85 893	176	11.14 107	9.99 887	52
9	8.85 955	173	8.86 069	174	11.13 931	9.99 886	51
10	8.86 128	173	8.86 243	174	11.13 757	9.99 885	**50**
11	8.86 301	173	8.86 417	174	11.13 583	9.99 884	49
12	8.86 474	171	8.86 591	172	11.13 409	9.99 883	48
13	8.86 645	171	8.86 763	172	11.13 237	9.99 882	47
14	8.86 816	171	8.86 935	171	11.13 065	9.99 881	46
15	8.86 987	169	8.87 106	171	11.12 894	9.99 880	45
16	8.87 156	169	8.87 277	170	11.12 723	9.99 879	44
17	8.87 325	169	8.87 447	169	11.12 553	9.99 879	43
18	8.87 494	167	8.87 616	169	11.12 384	9.99 878	42
19	8.87 661	168	8.87 785	168	11.12 215	9.99 877	41
20	8.87 829	166	8.87 953	167	11.12 047	9.99 876	**40**
21	8.87 995	166	8.88 120	167	11.11 880	9.99 875	39
22	8.88 161	165	8.88 287	166	11.11 713	9.99 874	38
23	8.88 326	164	8.88 453	165	11.11 547	9.99 873	37
24	8.88 490	164	8.88 618	165	11.11 382	9.99 872	36
25	8.88 654	163	8.88 783	165	11.11 217	9.99 871	35
26	8.88 817	163	8.88 948	163	11.11 052	9.99 870	34
27	8.88 980	162	8.89 111	163	11.10 889	9.99 869	33
28	8.89 142	162	8.89 274	163	11.10 726	9.99 868	32
29	8.89 304	160	8.89 437	161	11.10 563	9.99 867	31
30	8.89 464	161	8.89 598	162	11.10 402	9.99 866	**30**
31	8.89 625	159	8.89 760	160	11.10 240	9.99 865	29
32	8.89 784	159	8.89 920	160	11.10 080	9.99 864	28
33	8.89 943	159	8.90 080	160	11.09 920	9.99 863	27
34	8.90 102	158	8.90 240	159	11.09 760	9.99 862	26
35	8.90 260	157	8.90 399	158	11.09 601	9.99 861	25
36	8.90 417	157	8.90 557	158	11.09 443	9.99 860	24
37	8.90 574	156	8.90 715	157	11.09 285	9.99 859	23
38	8.90 730	155	8.90 872	157	11.09 128	9.99 858	22
39	8.90 885	155	8.91 029	156	11.08 971	9.99 857	21
40	8.91 040	155	8.91 185	155	11.08 815	9.99 856	**20**
41	8.91 195	154	8.91 340	155	11.08 660	9.99 855	19
42	8.91 349	153	8.91 495	155	11.08 505	9.99 854	18
43	8.91 502	153	8.91 650	153	11.08 350	9.99 853	17
44	8.91 655	152	8.91 803	154	11.08 197	9.99 852	16
45	8.91 807	152	8.91 957	153	11.08 043	9.99 851	15
46	8.91 959	151	8.92 110	152	11.07 890	9.99 850	14
47	8.92 110	151	8.92 262	152	11.07 738	9.99 848	13
48	8.92 261	150	8.92 414	151	11.07 586	9.99 847	12
49	8.92 411	150	8.92 565	151	11.07 435	9.99 846	11
50	8.92 561	149	8.92 716	150	11.07 284	9.99 845	**10**
51	8.92 710	149	8.92 866	150	11.07 134	9.99 844	9
52	8.92 859	148	8.93 016	149	11.06 984	9.99 843	8
53	8.93 007	147	8.93 165	148	11.06 835	9.99 842	7
54	8.93 154	147	8.93 313	149	11.06 687	9.99 841	6
55	8.93 301	147	8.93 462	147	11.06 538	9.99 840	5
56	8.93 448	146	8.93 609	147	11.06 391	9.99 839	4
57	8.93 594	146	8.93 756	147	11.06 244	9.99 838	3
58	8.93 740	145	8.93 903	146	11.06 097	9.99 837	2
59	8.93 885	145	8.94 049	146	11.05 951	9.99 836	1
60	8.94 030		8.94 195		11.05 805	9.99 834	**0**
	L Cos	d	L Cot	c d	L Tan	L Sin	′

Prop. Pts.

	182	181	180	179
2	36.4	36.2	36.0	35.8
3	54.6	54.3	54.0	53.7
4	72.8	72.4	72.0	71.6
5	91.0	90.5	90.0	89.5
6	109.2	108.6	108.0	107.4
7	127.4	126.7	126.0	125.3
8	145.6	144.8	144.0	143.2
9	163.8	162.9	162.0	161.1

	178	177	176	175
2	35.6	35.4	35.2	35.0
3	53.4	53.1	52.8	52.5
4	71.2	70.8	70.4	70.0
5	89.0	88.5	88.0	87.5
6	106.8	106.2	105.6	105.0
7	124.6	123.9	123.2	122.5
8	142.4	141.6	140.8	140.0
9	160.2	159.3	158.4	157.5

	174	173	172	171
2	34.8	34.6	34.4	34.2
3	52.2	51.9	51.6	51.3
4	69.6	69.2	68.8	68.4
5	87.0	86.5	86.0	85.5
6	104.4	103.8	103.2	102.6
7	121.8	121.1	120.4	119.7
8	139.2	138.4	137.6	136.8
9	156.6	155.7	154.8	153.9

	170	169	168	167
2	34.0	33.8	33.6	33.4
3	51.0	50.7	50.4	50.1
4	68.0	67.6	67.2	66.8
5	85.0	84.5	84.0	83.5
6	102.0	101.4	100.8	100.2
7	119.0	118.3	117.6	116.9
8	136.0	135.2	134.4	133.6
9	153.0	152.1	151.2	150.3

	166	165	164	163
2	33.2	33.0	32.8	32.6
3	49.8	49.5	49.2	48.9
4	66.4	66.0	65.6	65.2
5	83.0	82.5	82.0	81.5
6	99.6	99.0	98.4	97.8
7	116.2	115.5	114.8	114.1
8	132.8	132.0	131.2	130.4
9	149.4	148.5	147.6	146.7

	162	161	160	159
2	32.4	32.2	32.0	31.8
3	48.6	48.3	48.0	47.7
4	64.8	64.4	64.0	63.6
5	81.0	80.5	80.0	79.5
6	97.2	96.6	96.0	95.4
7	113.4	112.7	112.0	111.3
8	129.6	128.8	128.0	127.2
9	145.8	144.9	144.0	143.1

	158	157	156	155
2	31.6	31.4	31.2	31.0
2	47.4	47.1	46.8	46.5
4	63.2	62.8	62.4	62.0
5	79.0	78.5	78.0	77.5
6	94.8	94.2	93.6	93.0
7	110.6	109.9	109.2	108.5
8	126.4	125.6	124.8	124.0
9	142.2	141.3	140.4	139.5

	154	153	152
2	30.8	30.6	30.4
3	46.2	45.9	45.6
4	61.6	61.2	60.8
5	77.0	76.5	76.0
6	92.4	91.8	91.2
7	107.8	107.1	106.4
8	123.2	122.4	121.6
9	138.6	137.7	136.8

Prop. Pts.

85°

Table D (Continued)

5°

′	L Sin	d	L Tan	c d	L Cot	L Cos	
0	8.94 030	144	8.94 195	145	11.05 805	9.99 834	**60**
1	8.94 174	143	8.94 340	145	11.05 660	9.99 833	59
2	8.94 317	144	8.94 485	145	11.05 515	9.99 832	58
3	8.94 461	142	8.94 630	143	11.05 370	9.99 831	57
4	8.94 603	143	8.94 773	144	11.05 227	9.99 830	56
5	8.94 746	141	8.94 917	143	11.05 083	9.99 829	55
6	8.94 887	142	8.95 060	142	11.04 940	9.99 828	54
7	8.95 029	141	8.95 202	142	11.04 798	9.99 827	53
8	8.95 170	140	8.95 344	142	11.04 656	9.99 825	52
9	8.95 310	140	8.95 486	141	11.04 514	9.99 824	51
10	8.95 450	139	8.95 627	140	11.04 373	9.99 823	**50**
11	8.95 589	139	8.95 767	141	11.04 233	9.99 822	49
12	8.95 728	139	8.95 908	139	11.04 092	9.99 821	48
13	8.95 867	138	8.96 047	140	11.03 953	9.99 820	47
14	8.96 005	138	8.96 187	138	11.03 813	9.99 819	46
15	8.96 143	137	8.96 325	139	11.03 675	9.99 817	45
16	8.96 280	137	8.96 464	138	11.03 536	9.99 816	44
17	8.96 417	136	8.96 602	137	11.03 398	9.99 815	43
18	8.96 553	136	8.96 739	138	11.03 261	9.99 814	42
19	8.96 689	136	8.96 877	136	11.03 123	9.99 813	41
20	8.96 825	135	8.97 013	137	11.02 987	9.99 812	**40**
21	8.96 960	135	8.97 150	135	11.02 850	9.99 810	39
22	8.97 095	134	8.97 285	136	11.02 715	9.99 809	38
23	8.97 229	134	8.97 421	135	11.02 579	9.99 808	37
24	8.97 363	133	8.97 556	135	11.02 444	9.99 807	36
25	8.97 496	133	8.97 691	134	11.02 309	9.99 806	35
26	8.97 629	133	8.97 825	134	11.02 175	9.99 804	34
27	8.97 762	132	8.97 959	133	11.02 041	9.99 803	33
28	8.97 894	132	8.98 092	133	11.01 908	9.99 802	32
29	8.98 026	131	8.98 225	133	11.01 775	9.99 801	31
30	8.98 157	131	8.98 358	132	11.01 642	9.99 800	**30**
31	8.98 288	131	8.98 490	132	11.01 510	9.99 798	29
32	8.98 419	130	8.98 622	131	11.01 378	9.99 797	28
33	8.98 549	130	8.98 753	131	11.01 247	9.99 796	27
34	8.98 679	129	8.98 884	131	11.01 116	9.99 795	26
35	8.98 808	129	8.99 015	130	11.00 985	9.99 793	25
36	8.98 937	129	8.99 145	139	11.00 855	9.99 792	24
37	8.99 066	128	8.99 275	130	11.00 725	9.99 791	23
38	8.99 194	128	8.99 405	129	11.00 595	9.99 790	22
39	8.99 322	128	8.99 534	128	11.00 466	9.99 788	21
40	8.99 450	127	8.99 662	129	11.00 338	9.99 787	**20**
41	8.99 577	127	8.99 791	128	11.00 209	9.99 786	19
42	8.99 704	126	8.99 919	127	11.00 081	9.99 785	18
43	8.99 830	126	9.00 046	128	10.99 954	9.99 783	17
44	8.99 956	126	9.00 174	127	10.99 826	9.99 782	16
45	9.00 082	125	9.00 301	126	10.99 699	9.99 781	15
46	9.00 207	125	9.00 427	126	10.99 573	9.99 780	14
47	9.00 332	124	9.00 553	126	10.99 447	9.99 778	13
48	9.00 456	125	9.00 679	126	10.99 321	9.99 777	12
49	9.00 581	123	9.00 805	125	10.99 195	9.99 776	11
50	9.00 704	124	9.00 930	125	10.99 070	9.99 775	**10**
51	9.00 828	123	9.01 055	124	10.98 945	9.99 773	9
52	9.00 951	123	9.01 179	124	10.98 821	9.99 772	8
53	9.01 074	122	9.01 303	124	10.98 697	9.99 771	7
54	9.01 196	122	9.01 427	123	10.98 573	9.99 769	6
55	9.01 318	122	9.01 550	123	10.98 450	9.99 768	5
56	9.01 440	121	9.01 673	123	10.98 327	9.99 767	4
57	9.01 561	121	9.01 796	122	10.98 204	9.99 765	3
58	9.01 682	121	9.01 918	122	10.98 082	9.99 764	2
59	9.01 803	120	9.02 040	122	10.97 960	9.99 763	1
60	9.01 923		9.02 162		10.97 838	9.99 761	**0**
	L Cos	d	L Cot	c d	L Tan	L Sin	′

Prop. Pts.

	151	150	149	148
2	30.2	30.0	29.8	29.6
3	45.3	45.0	44.7	44.4
4	60.4	60.0	59.6	59.2
5	75.5	75.0	74.5	74.0
6	90.6	90.0	89.4	88.8
7	105.7	105.0	104.3	103.6
8	120.8	120.0	119.2	118.4
9	135.9	135.0	134.1	133.2

	147	146	145	144
2	29.4	29.2	29.0	28.8
3	44.1	43.8	43.5	43.2
4	58.8	58.4	58.0	57.6
5	73.5	73.0	72.5	72.0
6	88.2	87.6	87.0	86.4
7	102.9	102.2	101.5	100.8
8	117.6	116.8	116.0	115.2
9	132.3	131.4	130.5	129.6

	143	142	141	140
2	28.6	28.4	28.2	28.0
3	42.9	42.6	42.3	42.0
4	57.2	56.8	56.4	56.0
5	71.5	71.0	70.5	70.0
6	85.8	85.2	84.6	84.0
7	100.1	99.4	98.7	98.0
8	114.4	113.6	112.8	112.0
9	128.7	127.8	126.9	126.0

	139	138	137	136
2	27.8	27.6	27.4	27.2
3	41.7	41.4	41.1	40.8
4	55.6	55.2	54.8	54.4
5	69.5	69.0	68.5	68.0
6	83.4	82.8	82.2	81.6
7	97.3	96.6	95.9	95.2
8	111.2	110.4	109.6	108.8
9	125.1	124.2	123.3	122.4

	135	134	133	132
2	27.0	26.8	26.6	26.4
3	40.5	40.2	39.9	39.6
4	54.0	53.6	53.2	52.8
5	67.5	67.0	66.5	66.0
6	81.0	80.4	79.8	79.2
7	94.5	93.8	93.1	92.4
8	108.0	107.2	106.4	105.6
9	121.5	120.6	119.7	118.8

	131	130	129	128
2	26.2	26.0	25.8	25.6
3	39.3	39.0	38.7	38.4
4	52.4	52.0	51.6	51.2
5	65.5	65.0	64.5	64.0
6	78.6	78.0	77.4	76.8
7	91.7	91.0	90.3	89.6
8	104.8	104.0	103.2	102.4
9	117.9	117.0	116.1	115.2

	127	126	125	124
2	25.4	25.2	25.0	24.8
3	38.1	37.8	37.5	37.2
4	50.8	50.4	50.0	49.6
5	63.5	63.0	62.5	62.0
6	76.2	75.6	75.0	74.4
7	88.9	88.2	87.5	86.8
8	101.6	100.8	100.0	99.2
9	114.3	113.4	112.5	111.6

	123	122	121	120
2	24.6	24.4	24.2	24.0
3	36.9	36.6	36.3	36.0
4	49.2	48.8	48.4	48.0
5	61.5	61.0	60.5	60.0
6	73.8	73.2	72.6	72.0
7	86.1	85.4	84.7	84.0
8	98.4	97.6	96.8	96.0
9	110.7	109.8	108.9	108.0

Prop. Pts.

84°

Table D (Continued)

6°

′	L Sin	d	L Tan	c d	L Cot	L Cos	
0	9.01 923	120	9.02 162	121	10.97 838	9.99 761	**60**
1	9.02 043	120	9.02 283	121	10.97 717	9.99 760	59
2	9.02 163	120	9.02 404	121	10.97 596	9.99 759	58
3	9.02 283	119	9.02 525	120	10.97 475	9.99 757	57
4	9.02 402	118	9.02 645	121	10.97 355	9.99 756	56
5	9.02 520	119	9.02 766	119	10.97 234	9.99 755	55
6	9.02 639	118	9.02 885	120	10.97 115	9.99 753	54
7	9.02 757	117	9.03 005	119	10.96 995	9.99 752	53
8	9.02 874	118	9.03 124	118	10.96 876	9.99 751	52
9	9.02 992	117	9.03 242	119	10.96 758	9.99 749	51
10	9.03 109	117	9.03 361	118	10.96 639	9.99 748	**50**
11	9.03 226	116	9.03 479	118	10.96 521	9.99 747	49
12	9.03 342	116	9.03 597	117	10.96 403	9.99 745	48
13	9.03 458	116	9.03 714	118	10.96 286	9.99 744	47
14	9.03 574	116	9.03 832	116	10.96 168	9.99 742	46
15	9.03 690	115	9.03 948	117	10.96 052	9.99 741	45
16	9.03 805	115	9.04 065	116	10.95 935	9.99 740	44
17	9.03 920	114	9.04 181	116	10.95 819	9.99 738	43
18	9.04 034	115	9.04 297	116	10.95 703	9.99 737	42
19	9.04 149	113	9.04 413	115	10.95 587	9.99 736	41
20	9.04 262	114	9.04 528	115	10.95 472	9.99 734	**40**
21	9.04 376	114	9.04 643	115	10.95 357	9.99 733	39
22	9.04 490	113	9.04 758	115	10.95 242	9.99 731	38
23	9.04 603	112	9.04 873	114	10.95 127	9.99 730	37
24	9.04 715	113	9.04 987	114	10.95 013	9.99 728	36
25	9.04 828	112	9.05 101	113	10 94 899	9.99 727	35
26	9.04 940	112	9.05 214	114	10.94 786	9.99 726	34
27	9.05 052	112	9.05 328	113	10.94 672	9.99 724	33
28	9.05 164	111	9.05 441	112	10.94 559	9.99 723	32
29	9.05 275	111	9.05 553	113	10.94 447	9.99 721	31
30	9.05 386	111	9.05 666	112	10.94 334	9.99 720	**30**
31	9.05 497	110	9.05 778	112	10.94 222	9.99 718	29
32	9.05 607	110	9.05 890	112	10.94 110	9.99 717	28
33	9.05 717	110	9.06 002	111	10.93 998	9.99 716	27
34	9.05 827	110	9.06 113	111	10.93 887	9.99 714	26
35	9.05 937	109	9.06 224	111	10.93 776	9.99 713	25
36	9.06 046	109	9.06 335	110	10.93 665	9.99 711	24
37	9.06 155	109	9.06 445	111	10.93 555	9.99 710	23
38	9.06 264	108	9.06 556	110	10.93 444	9.99 708	22
39	9.06 372	109	9.06 666	109	10.93 334	9.99 707	21
40	9.06 481	108	9.06 775	110	10.93 225	9.99 705	**20**
41	9.06 589	107	9.06 885	109	10.93 115	9.99 704	19
42	9.06 696	108	9.06 994	109	10.93 006	9.99 702	18
43	9.06 804	107	9.07 103	108	10.92 897	9.99 701	17
44	9.06 911	107	9.07 211	109	10.92 789	9.99 699	16
45	9.07 018	106	9.07 320	108	10.92 680	9.99 698	15
46	9.07 124	107	9.07 428	108	10.92 572	9.99 696	14
47	9.07 231	106	9.07 536	107	10.92 464	9.99 695	13
48	9.07 337	105	9.07 643	108	10.92 357	9.99 693	12
49	9.07 442	106	9.07 751	107	10.92 249	9.99 692	11
50	9.07 548	105	9.07 858	106	10.92 142	9.99 690	**10**
51	9.07 653	105	9.07 964	107	10.92 036	9.99 689	9
52	9.07 758	105	9.08 071	106	10.91 929	9.99 687	8
53	9.07 863	105	9.08 177	106	10.91 823	9.99 686	7
54	9.07 968	104	9.08 283	106	10.91 717	9.99 684	6
55	9.08 072	104	9.08 389	106	10.91 611	9.99 683	5
56	9.08 176	104	9.08 495	105	10.91 505	9.99 681	4
57	9.08 280	103	9.08 600	105	10.91 400	9.99 680	3
58	9.08 383	103	9.08 705	105	10.91 295	9.99 678	2
59	9.08 486	103	9.08 810	104	10.91 190	9.99 677	1
60	9.08 589		9.08 914		10.91 086	9.99 675	**0**
	L Cos	d	L Cot	c d	L Tan	L Sin	′

Prop. Pts.

	121	120	119
1	12.1	12.0	11.9
2	24.2	24.0	23.8
3	36.3	36.0	35.7
4	48.4	48.0	47.6
5	60.5	60.0	59.5
6	72.6	72.0	71.4
7	84.7	84.0	83.3
8	96.8	96.0	95.2
9	108.9	108.0	107.1

	118	117	116
1	11.8	11.7	11.6
2	23.6	23.4	23.2
3	35.4	35.1	34.8
4	47.2	46.8	46.4
5	59.0	58.5	58.0
6	70.8	70.2	69.6
7	82.6	81.9	81.2
8	94.4	93.6	92.8
9	106.2	105.3	104.4

	115	114	113
1	11.5	11.4	11.3
2	23.0	22.8	22.6
3	34.5	34.2	33.9
4	46.0	45.6	45.2
5	57.5	57.0	56.5
6	69.0	68.4	67.8
7	80.5	79.8	79.1
8	92.0	91.2	90.4
9	103.5	102.6	101.7

	112	111	110
1	11.2	11.1	11.0
2	22.4	22.2	22.0
3	33.6	33.3	33.0
4	44.8	44.4	44.0
5	56.0	55.5	55.0
6	67.2	66.6	66.0
7	78.4	77.7	77.0
8	89.6	88.8	88.0
9	100.8	99.9	99.0

	109	108	107	106
1	10.9	10.8	10.7	10.6
2	21.8	21.6	21.4	21.2
3	32.7	32.4	32.1	31.8
4	43.6	43.2	42.8	42.4
5	54.5	54.0	53.5	53.0
6	65.4	64.8	64.2	63.6
7	76.3	75.6	74.9	74.2
8	87.2	86.4	85.6	84.8
9	98.1	97.2	96.3	95.4

Prop. Pts.

83°

Table D (Continued)

7°

′	L Sin	d	L Tan	c d	L Cot	L Cos	
0	9.08 589		9.08 914		10.91 086	9.99 675	**60**
1	9.08 692	103	9.09 019	105	10.90 981	9.99 674	59
2	9.08 795	103	9.09 123	104	10.90 877	9 99 672	58
3	9.08 897	102	9.09 227	104	10.90 773	9.99 670	57
4	9.08 999	102	9.09 330	103	10.90 670	9.99 669	56
5	9.09 101	102	9.09 434	104	10.90 566	9.99 667	55
6	9.09 202	101	9.09 537	103	10.90 463	9.99 666	54
7	9.09 304	102	9.09 640	103	10.90 360	9.99 664	53
8	9.09 405	101	9.09 742	102	10.90 258	9.99 663	52
9	9.09 506	101	9.09 845	103	10.90 155	9.99 661	51
10	9.09 606	100	9.09 947	102	10.90 053	9.99 659	**50**
11	9.09 707	101	9.10 049	102	10.89 951	9.99 658	49
12	9.09 807	100	9.10 150	101	10.89 850	9.99 656	48
13	9.09 907	100	9.10 252	102	10.89 748	9.99 655	47
14	9.10 006	99	9.10 353	101	10.89 647	9.99 653	46
15	9.10 106	100	9.10 454	101	10.89 546	9.99 651	45
16	9.10 205	99	9.10 555	101	10.89 445	9.99 650	44
17	9.10 304	99	9.10 656	101	10.89 344	9.99 648	43
18	9.10 402	98	9.10 756	100	10.89 244	9.99 647	42
19	9.10 501	99	9.10 856	100	10.89 144	9.99 645	41
20	9.10 599	98	9.10 956	100	10.89 044	9.99 643	**40**
21	9.10 697	98	9.11 056	100	10.88 944	9.99 642	39
22	9.10 795	98	9.11 155	99	10.88 845	9.99 640	38
23	9.10 893	98	9.11 254	99	10.88 746	9.99 638	37
24	9.10 990	97	9.11 353	99	10.88 647	9.99 637	36
25	9.11 087	97	9.11 452	99	10.88 548	9.99 635	35
26	9.11 184	97	9.11 551	99	10.88 449	9.99 633	34
27	9.11 281	97	9.11 649	98	10.88 351	9.99 632	33
28	9.11 377	96	9.11 747	98	10.88 253	9.99 630	32
29	9.11 474	97	9.11 845	98	10.88 155	9.99 629	31
30	9.11 570	96	9.11 943	98	10.88 057	9.99 627	**30**
31	9.11 666	96	9.12 040	97	10.87 960	9.99 625	29
32	9.11 761	95	9.12 138	98	10.87 862	9.99 624	28
33	9.11 857	96	9.12 235	97	10.87 765	9.99 622	27
34	9.11 952	95	9.12 332	97	10.87 668	9.99 620	26
35	9.12 047	95	9.12 428	96	10.87 572	9.99 618	25
36	9.12 142	95	9.12 525	97	10.87 475	9.99 617	24
37	9.12 236	94	9.12 621	96	10.87 379	9.99 615	23
38	9.12 331	95	9.12 717	96	10.87 283	9.99 613	22
39	9.12 425	94	9.12 813	96	10.87 187	9.99 612	21
40	9.12 519	94	9.12 909	96	10.87 091	9.99 610	**20**
41	9.12 612	93	9.13 004	95	10.86 996	9.99 608	19
42	9.12 706	94	9.13 099	95	10.86 901	9.99 607	18
43	9.12 799	93	9.13 194	95	10.86 806	9.99 605	17
44	9.12 892	93	9.13 289	95	10.86 711	9.99 603	16
45	9.12 985	93	9.13 384	95	10.86 616	9.99 601	15
46	9.13 078	93	9.13 478	94	10.86 522	9.99 600	14
47	9 13 171	93	9.13 573	95	10.86 427	9.99 598	13
48	9.13 263	92	9.13 667	94	10.86 333	9.99 596	12
49	9.13 355	92	9.13 761	94	10.86 239	9.99 595	11
50	9.13 447	92	9.13 854	93	10.86 146	9.99 593	**10**
51	9.13 539	92	9.13 948	94	10.86 052	9.99 591	9
52	9.13 630	91	9.14 041	93	10.85 959	9.99 589	8
53	9.13 722	92	9.14 134	93	10.85 866	9.99 588	7
54	9.13 813	91	9.14 227	93	10.85 773	9.99 586	6
55	9.13 904	91	9.14 320	93	10.85 680	9.99 584	5
56	9.13 994	90	9.14 412	92	10.85 588	9.99 582	4
57	9.14 085	91	9.14 504	92	10.85 496	9.99 581	3
58	9.14 175	90	9.14 597	93	10.85 403	9.99 579	2
59	9.14 266	91	9.14 688	91	10.85 312	9.99 577	1
60	9.14 356	90	9.14 780	92	10.85 220	9.99 575	**0**
	L Cos	d	L Cot	c d	L Tan	L Sin	′

Prop. Pts.

	105	104	103
1	10.5	10.4	10.3
2	21.0	20.8	20.6
3	31.5	31.2	30.9
4	42.0	41.6	41.2
5	52.5	52.0	51.5
6	63.0	62.4	61.8
7	73.5	72.8	72.1
8	84.0	83.2	82.4
9	94.5	93.6	92.7

	102	101	99
1	10.2	10.1	9.9
2	20.4	20.2	19.8
3	30.6	30.3	29.7
4	40.8	40.4	39.6
5	51.0	50.5	49.5
6	61.2	60.6	59.4
7	71.4	70.7	69.3
8	81.6	80.8	79.2
9	91.8	90.9	89.1

	98	97	96
1	9.8	9.7	9.6
2	19.6	19.4	19.2
3	29.4	29.1	28.8
4	39.2	38.8	38.4
5	49.0	48.5	48.0
6	58.8	58.2	57.6
7	68.6	67.9	67.2
8	78.4	77.6	76.8
9	88.2	87.3	86.4

	95	94	93
1	9.5	9.4	9.3
2	19.0	18.8	18.6
3	28.5	28.2	27.9
4	38.0	37.6	37.2
5	47.5	47.0	46.5
6	57.0	56.4	55.8
7	66.5	65.8	65.1
8	76.0	75.2	74.4
9	85.5	84.6	83.7

	92	91	90
1	9.2	9.1	9.0
2	18.4	18.2	18.0
3	27.6	27.3	27.0
4	36.8	36.4	36.0
5	46.0	45.5	45.0
6	55.2	54.6	54.0
7	64.4	63.7	63.0
8	73.6	72.8	72.0
9	82.8	81.9	81.0

Prop. Pts.

82°

Table D (Continued)

8°

′	L Sin	d	L Tan	c d	L Cot	L Cos	
0	9.14 356	89	9.14 780	92	10.85 220	9.99 575	**60**
1	9.14 445	90	9.14 872	91	10.85 128	9.99 574	59
2	9.14 535	89	9.14 963	91	10.85 037	9.99 572	58
3	9.14 624	90	9.15 054	91	10.84 946	9.99 570	57
4	9.14 714	89	9.15 145	91	10.84 855	9.99 568	56
5	9.14 803	88	9.15 236	91	10.84 764	9.99 566	55
6	9.14 891	89	9.15 327	90	10.84 673	9.99 565	54
7	9.14 980	89	9.15 417	91	10.84 583	9.99 563	53
8	9.15 069	88	9.15 508	90	10.84 492	9.99 561	52
9	9.15 157	88	9.15 598	90	10.84 402	9.99 559	51
10	9.15 245	88	9.15 688	89	10.84 312	9.99 557	**50**
11	9.15 333	88	9.15 777	90	10.84 223	9.99 556	49
12	9.15 421	87	9.15 867	89	10.84 133	9.99 554	48
13	9.15 508	88	9.15 956	90	10.84 044	9.99 552	47
14	9.15 596	87	9.16 046	89	10.83 954	9.99 550	46
15	9.15 683	87	9.16 135	89	10.83 865	9.99 548	45
16	9.15 770	87	9.16 224	88	10.83 776	9.99 546	44
17	9.15 857	87	9.16 312	89	10.83 688	9.99 545	43
18	9.15 944	86	9.16 401	88	10.83 599	9.99 543	42
19	9.16 030	86	9.16 489	88	10.83 511	9.99 541	41
20	9.16 116	87	9.16 577	88	10.83 423	9.99 539	**40**
21	9.16 203	86	9.16 665	88	10.83 335	9.99 537	39
22	9.16 289	85	9.16 753	88	10.83 247	9.99 535	38
23	9.16 374	86	9.16 841	87	10.83 159	9.99 533	37
24	9.16 460	85	9.16 928	88	10.83 072	9.99 532	36
25	9.16 545	86	9.17 016	87	10.82 984	9.99 530	35
26	9.16 631	85	9.17 103	87	10.82 897	9.99 528	34
27	9.16 716	85	9.17 190	87	10.82 810	9.99 526	33
28	9.16 801	85	9.17 277	86	10.82 723	9.99 524	32
29	9.16 886	84	9.17 363	87	10.82 637	9.99 522	31
30	9.16 970	85	9.17 450	86	10.82 550	9.99 520	**30**
31	9.17 055	84	9.17 536	86	10.82 464	9.99 518	29
32	9.17 139	84	9.17 622	86	10.82 378	9.99 517	28
33	9.17 223	84	9.17 708	86	10.82 292	9.99 515	27
34	9.17 307	84	9.17 794	86	10.82 206	9.99 513	26
35	9.17 391	83	9.17 880	85	10.82 120	9.99 511	25
36	9.17 474	84	9.17 965	86	10.82 035	9.99 509	24
37	9.17 558	83	9.18 051	85	10.81 949	9.99 507	23
38	9.17 641	83	9.18 136	85	10.81 864	9.99 505	22
39	9.17 724	83	9.18 221	85	10.81 779	9.99 503	21
40	9.17 807	83	9.18 306	85	10.81 694	9.99 501	**20**
41	9.17 890	83	9.18 391	84	10.81 609	9.99 499	19
42	9.17 983	82	9.18 475	85	10.81 525	9.99 497	18
43	9.18 055	82	9.18 560	84	10.81 440	9.99 495	17
44	9.18 137	83	9.18 644	84	10.81 356	9.99 494	16
45	9.18 220	82	9.18 728	84	10.81 272	9.99 492	15
46	9.18 302	81	9.18 812	84	10.81 188	9.99 490	14
47	9.18 383	82	9.18 896	83	10.81 104	9.99 488	13
48	9.18 465	82	9.18 979	84	10.81 021	9.99 486	12
49	9.18 547	81	9.19 063	83	10.80 937	9.99 484	11
50	9.18 628	81	9.19 146	83	10.80 854	9.99 482	**10**
51	9.18 709	81	9.19 229	83	10.80 771	9.99 480	9
52	9.18 790	81	9.19 312	83	10.80 688	9.99 478	8
53	9.18 871	81	9.19 395	83	10.80 605	9.99 476	7
54	9.18 952	81	9.19 478	83	10.80 522	9.99 474	6
55	9.19 033	80	9.19 561	82	10.80 439	9.99 472	5
56	9.19 113	80	9.19 643	82	10.80 357	9.99 470	4
57	9.19 193	80	9.19 725	82	10.80 275	9.99 468	3
58	9.19 273	80	9.19 807	82	10.80 193	9.99 466	2
59	9.19 353	80	9.19 889	82	10.80 111	9.99 464	1
60	9.19 433		9.19 971		10.80 029	9.99 462	**0**
	L Cos	d	L Cot	c d	L Tan	L Sin	′

Prop. Pts.

	92	91	90
1	9.2	9.1	9.0
2	18.4	18.2	18.0
3	27.6	27.3	27.0
4	36.8	36.4	36.0
5	46.0	45.5	45.0
6	55.2	54.6	54.0
7	64.4	63.7	63.0
8	73.6	72.8	72.0
9	82.8	81.9	81.0

	89	88	87
1	8.9	8.8	8.7
2	17.8	17.6	17.4
3	26.7	26.4	26.1
4	35.6	35.2	34.8
5	44.5	44.0	43.5
6	53.4	52.8	52.2
7	62.3	61.6	60.9
8	71.2	70.4	69.6
9	80.1	79.2	78.3

	86	85	84
1	8.6	8.5	8.4
2	17.2	17.0	16.8
3	25.8	25.5	25.2
4	34.4	34.0	33.6
5	43.0	42.5	42.0
6	51.6	51.0	50.4
7	60.2	59.5	58.8
8	68.8	68.0	67.2
9	77.4	76.5	75.6

	83	82	81	80
1	8.3	8.2	8.1	8.0
2	16.6	16.4	16.2	16.0
3	24.9	24.6	24.3	24.0
4	33.2	32.8	32.4	32.0
5	41.5	41.0	40.5	40.0
6	49.8	49.2	48.6	48.0
7	58.1	57.4	56.7	56.0
8	66.4	65.6	64.8	64.0
9	74.7	73.8	72.9	72.0

Prop. Pts.

81°

Table D (Continued)

9°

′	L Sin	d	L Tan	c d	L Cot	L Cos	′
0	9.19 433	80	9.19 971	82	10.80 029	9.99 462	**60**
1	9.19 513	79	9.20 053	81	10.79 947	9.99 460	59
2	9.19 592	80	9.20 134	82	10.79 866	9.99 458	58
3	9.19 672	79	9.20 216	81	10.79 784	9.99 456	57
4	9.19 751	79	9.20 297	81	10.79 703	9.99 454	56
5	9.19 830	79	9.20 378	81	10.79 622	9.99 452	55
6	9.19 909	79	9.20 459	81	10.79 541	9.99 450	54
7	9.19 988	79	9.20 540	81	10.79 460	9.99 448	53
8	9.20 067	78	9.20 621	80	10.79 379	9.99 446	52
9	9.20 145	78	9.20 701	81	10.79 299	9.99 444	51
10	9.20 223	79	9.20 782	80	10.79 218	9.99 442	**50**
11	9.20 302	78	9.20 862	80	10.79 138	9.99 440	49
12	9.20 380	78	9.20 942	80	10.79 058	9.99 438	48
13	9.20 458	77	9.21 022	80	10.78 978	9.99 436	47
14	9.20 535	78	9.21 102	80	10.78 898	9.99 434	46
15	9.20 613	78	9.21 182	79	10.78 818	9.99 432	45
16	9.20 691	77	9.21 261	80	10.78 739	9.99 429	44
17	9.20 768	77	9.21 341	79	10.78 659	9.99 427	43
18	9.20 845	77	9.21 420	79	10.78 580	9.99 425	42
19	9.20 922	77	9.21 499	79	10.78 501	9.99 423	41
20	9.20 999	77	9.21 578	79	10.78 422	9.99 421	**40**
21	9.21 076	77	9.21 657	79	10.78 343	9.99 419	39
22	9.21 153	76	9.21 736	78	10.78 264	9.99 417	38
23	9.21 229	77	9.21 814	79	10.78 186	9.99 415	37
24	9.21 306	76	9.21 893	78	10.78 107	9.99 413	36
25	9.21 382	76	9.21 971	78	10.78 029	9.99 411	35
26	9.21 458	76	9.22 049	78	10.77 951	9.99 409	34
27	9.21 534	76	9.22 127	78	10.77 873	9.99 407	33
28	9.21 610	75	9.22 205	78	10.77 795	9.99 404	32
29	9.21 685	76	9.22 283	78	10.77 717	9.99 402	31
30	9.21 761	75	9.22 361	77	10.77 639	9.99 400	**30**
31	9.21 836	76	9.22 438	78	10.77 562	9.99 398	29
32	9.21 912	75	9.22 516	77	10.77 484	9.99 396	28
33	9.21 987	75	9.22 593	77	10.77 407	9.99 394	27
34	9.22 062	75	9.22 670	77	10.77 330	9.99 392	26
35	9.22 137	74	9.22 747	77	10.77 253	9.99 390	25
36	9.22 211	75	9.22 824	77	10.77 176	9.99 388	24
37	9.22 286	75	9.22 901	76	10.77 099	9.99 385	23
38	9.22 361	74	9.22 977	77	10.77 023	9.99 383	22
39	9.22 435	74	9.23 054	76	10.76 946	9.99 381	21
40	9.22 509	74	9.23 130	76	10.76 870	9.99 379	**20**
41	9.22 583	74	9.23 206	77	10.76 794	9.99 377	19
42	9.22 657	74	9.23 283	76	10.76 717	9.99 375	18
43	9.22 731	74	9.23 359	76	10.76 641	9.99 372	17
44	9.22 805	73	9.23 435	75	10.76 565	9.99 370	16
45	9.22 878	74	9.23 510	76	10.76 490	9.99 368	15
46	9.22 952	73	9.23 586	75	10.76 414	9.99 366	14
47	9.23 025	73	9.23 661	76	10.76 339	9.99 364	13
48	9.23 098	73	9.23 737	75	10.76 263	9.99 362	12
49	9.23 171	73	9.23 812	75	10.76 188	9.99 359	11
50	9.23 244	73	9.23 887	75	10.76 113	9.99 357	**10**
51	9.23 317	73	9.23 962	75	10.76 038	9.99 355	9
52	9.23 390	72	9.24 037	75	10.75 963	9.99 353	8
53	9.23 462	73	9.24 112	74	10.75 888	9.99 351	7
54	9.23 535	72	9.24 186	75	10.75 814	9.99 348	6
55	9.23 607	72	9.24 261	74	10.75 739	9.99 346	5
56	9.23 679	73	9.24 335	75	10.75 665	9.99 344	4
57	9.23 752	71	9.24 410	74	10.75 590	9.99 342	3
58	9.23 823	72	9.24 484	74	10.75 516	9.99 340	2
59	9.23 895	72	9.24 558	74	10.75 442	9.99 337	1
60	9.23 967		9.24 632		10.75 368	9.99 335	**0**
	L Cos	d	L Cot	c d	L Tan	L Sin	′

Prop. Pts.

	82	81	80
1	8.2	8.1	8.0
2	16.4	16.2	16.0
3	24.6	24.3	24.0
4	32.8	32.4	32.0
5	41.0	40.5	40.0
6	49.2	48.6	48.0
7	57.4	56.7	56.0
8	65.6	64.8	64.0
9	73.8	72.9	72.0

	79	78	77
1	7.9	7.8	7.7
2	15.8	15.6	15.4
3	23.7	23.4	23.1
4	31.6	31.2	30.8
5	39.5	39.0	38.5
6	47.4	46.8	46.2
7	55.3	54.6	53.9
8	63.2	62.4	61.6
9	71.1	70.2	69.3

	76	75	74
1	7.6	7.5	7.4
2	15.2	15.0	14.8
3	22.8	22.5	22.2
4	30.4	30.0	29.6
5	38.0	37.5	37.0
6	45.6	45.0	44.4
7	53.2	52.5	51.8
8	60.8	60.0	59.2
9	68.4	67.5	66.6

	73	72	71
1	7.3	7.2	7.1
2	14.6	14.4	14.2
3	21.9	21.6	21.3
4	29.2	28.8	28.4
5	36.5	36.0	35.5
6	43.8	43.2	42.6
7	51.1	50.4	49.7
8	58.4	57.6	56.8
9	65.7	64.8	63.9

	3	2
1	0.3	0.2
2	0.6	0.4
3	0.9	0.6
4	1.2	0.8
5	1.5	1.0
6	1.8	1.2
7	2.1	1.4
8	2.4	1.6
9	2.7	1.8

Prop. Pts.

80°

Table D (Continued)

10°

′	L Sin	d	L Tan	c d	L Cot	L Cos	d	
0	9.23 967	72	9.24 632	74	10.75 368	9.99 335	2	60
1	9.24 039	71	9.24 706	73	10.75 294	9.99 333	2	59
2	9.24 110	71	9.24 779	74	10.75 221	9.99 331	3	58
3	9.24 181	72	9.24 853	73	10.75 147	9.99 328	2	57
4	9.24 253	71	9.24 926	74	10.75 074	9.99 326	2	56
5	9.24 324	71	9.25 000	73	10.75 000	9.99 324	2	55
6	9.24 395	71	9.25 073	73	10.74 927	9.99 322	3	54
7	9.24 466	70	9.25 146	73	10.74 854	9.99 319	2	53
8	9.24 536	71	9.25 219	73	10.74 781	9.99 317	2	52
9	9.24 607	70	9.25 292	73	10.74 708	9.99 315	2	51
10	9.24 677	71	9.25 365	72	10.74 635	9.99 313	3	50
11	9.24 748	70	9.25 437	73	10.74 563	9.99 310	2	49
12	9.24 818	70	9.25 510	72	10.74 490	9.99 308	2	48
13	9.24 888	70	9.25 582	73	10.74 418	9.99 306	2	47
14	9.24 958	70	9.25 655	72	10.74 345	9.99 304	3	46
15	9.25 028	70	9.25 727	72	10.74 273	9.99 301	2	45
16	9.25 098	70	9.25 799	72	10.74 201	9.99 299	2	44
17	9.25 168	69	9.25 871	72	10.74 129	9.99 297	3	43
18	9.25 237	70	9.25 943	72	10.74 057	9.99 294	2	42
19	9.25 307	69	9.26 015	71	10.73 985	9.99 292	2	41
20	9.25 376	69	9.26 086	72	10.73 914	9.99 290	2	40
21	9.25 445	69	9.26 158	71	10.73 842	9.99 288	3	39
22	9.25 514	69	9.26 229	72	10.73 771	9.99 285	2	38
23	9.25 583	69	9.26 301	71	10.73 699	9.99 283	2	37
24	9.25 652	69	9.26 372	71	10.73 628	9.99 281	3	36
25	9.25 721	69	9.26 443	71	10.73 557	9.99 278	2	35
26	9.25 790	68	9.26 514	71	10.73 486	9.99 276	2	34
27	9.25 858	69	9.26 585	70	10.73 415	9.99 274	3	33
28	9.25 927	68	9.26 655	71	10.73 345	9.99 271	2	32
29	9.25 995	68	9.26 726	71	10.73 274	9.99 269	2	31
30	9.26 063	68	9.26 797	70	10.73 203	9.99 267	3	30
31	9.26 131	68	9.26 867	70	10.73 133	9.99 264	2	29
32	9.26 199	68	9.26 937	71	10.73 063	9.99 262	2	28
33	9.26 267	68	9.27 008	70	10.72 992	9.99 260	3	27
34	9.26 335	68	9.27 078	70	10.72 922	9.99 257	2	26
35	9.26 403	67	9.27 148	70	10.72 852	9.99 255	3	25
36	9.26 470	68	9.27 218	70	10.72 782	9.99 252	2	24
37	9.26 538	67	9.27 288	69	10.72 712	9.99 250	2	23
38	9.26 605	67	9.27 357	70	10.72 643	9.99 248	3	22
39	9.26 672	67	9.27 427	69	10.72 573	9.99 245	2	21
40	9.26 739	67	9.27 496	70	10.72 504	9.99 243	2	20
41	9.26 806	67	9.27 566	69	10.72 434	9.99 241	3	19
42	9.26 873	67	9.27 635	69	10.72 365	9.99 238	2	18
43	9.26 940	67	9.27 704	69	10.72 296	9.99 236	3	17
44	9.27 007	66	9.27 773	69	10.72 227	9.99 233	2	16
45	9.27 073	67	9.27 842	69	10.72 158	9.99 231	2	15
46	9.27 140	66	9.27 911	69	10.72 089	9.99 229	3	14
47	9.27 206	67	9.27 980	69	10.72 020	9.99 226	2	13
48	9.27 273	66	9.28 049	68	10.71 951	9.99 224	3	12
49	9.27 339	66	9.28 117	69	10.71 883	9.99 221	2	11
50	9.27 405	66	9.28 186	68	10.71 814	9.99 219	2	10
51	9.27 471	66	9.28 254	69	10.71 746	9.99 217	3	9
52	9.27 537	65	9.28 323	68	10.71 677	9.99 214	2	8
53	9.27 602	66	9.28 391	68	10.71 609	9.99 212	3	7
54	9.27 668	66	9.28 459	68	10.71 541	9.99 209	2	6
55	9.27 734	65	9.28 527	68	10.71 473	9.99 207	3	5
56	9.27 799	65	9.28 595	67	10.71 405	9.99 204	2	4
57	9.27 864	66	9.28 662	68	10.71 338	9.99 202	2	3
58	9.27 930	65	9.28 730	68	10.71 270	9.99 200	3	2
59	9.27 995	65	9.28 798	67	10.71 202	9.99 197	2	1
60	9.28 060		9.28 865		10.71 135	9.99 195		0
	L Cos	d	L Cot	c d	L Tan	L Sin	d	′

Prop. Pts.

	74	73	72
1	7.4	7.3	7.2
2	14.8	14.6	14.4
3	22.2	21.9	21.6
4	29.6	29.2	28.8
5	37.0	36.5	36.0
6	44.4	43.8	43.2
7	51.8	51.1	50.4
8	59.2	58.4	57.6
9	66.6	65.7	64.8

	71	70	69
1	7.1	7.0	6.9
2	14.2	14.0	13.8
3	21.3	21.0	20.7
4	28.4	28.0	27.6
5	35.5	35.0	34.5
6	42.6	42.0	41.4
7	49.7	49.0	48.3
8	56.8	56.0	55.2
9	63.9	63.0	62.1

	68	67	66
1	6.8	6.7	6.6
2	13.6	13.4	13.2
3	20.4	20.1	19.8
4	27.2	26.8	26.4
5	34.0	33.5	33.0
6	40.8	40.2	39.6
7	47.6	46.9	46.2
8	54.4	53.6	52.8
9	61.2	60.3	59.4

	65	3	2
1	6.5	0.3	0.2
2	13.0	0.6	0.4
3	19.5	0.9	0.6
4	26.0	1.2	0.8
5	32.5	1.5	1.0
6	39.0	1.8	1.2
7	45.5	2.1	1.4
8	52.0	2.4	1.6
9	58.5	2.7	1.8

Prop. Pts.

79°

Table D (Continued)

11°

′	L Sin	d	L Tan	c d	L Cot	L Cos	d	′
0	9.28 060	65	9.28 865	68	10.71 135	9.99 195	3	**60**
1	9.28 125	65	9.28 933	67	10.71 067	9.99 192	2	59
2	9.28 190	64	9.29 000	67	10.71 000	9.99 190	3	58
3	9.28 254	65	9.29 067	67	10.70 933	9.99 187	2	57
4	9.28 319	65	9.29 134	67	10.70 866	9.99 185	3	56
5	9.28 384	64	9.29 201	67	10.70 799	9.99 182	2	55
6	9.28 448	64	9.29 268	67	10.70 732	9.99 180	3	54
7	9.28 512	65	9.29 335	67	10.70 665	9.99 177	2	53
8	9.28 577	64	9.29 402	66	10.70 598	9.99 175	3	52
9	9.28 641	64	9.29 468	67	10.70 532	9.99 172	2	51
10	9.28 705	64	9.29 535	66	10.70 465	9.99 170	3	**50**
11	9.28 769	64	9.29 601	67	10.70 399	9.99 167	2	49
12	9.28 833	63	9.29 668	66	10.70 332	9.99 165	3	48
13	9.28 896	64	9.29 734	66	10.70 266	9.99 162	2	47
14	9.28 960	64	9.29 800	66	10.70 200	9.99 160	3	46
15	9.29 024	63	9.29 866	66	10.70 134	9.99 157	2	45
16	9.29 087	63	9.29 932	66	10.70 068	9.99 155	3	44
17	9.29 150	64	9.29 998	66	10.70 002	9.99 152	2	43
18	9.29 214	63	9.30 064	66	10.69 936	9.99 150	3	42
19	9.29 277	63	9.30 130	65	10.69 870	9.99 147	2	41
20	9.29 340	63	9.30 195	66	10.69 805	9.99 145	3	**40**
21	9.29 403	63	9.30 261	65	10.69 739	9.99 142	2	39
22	9.29 466	63	9.30 326	65	10.69 674	9.99 140	3	38
23	9.29 529	62	9.30 391	66	10.69 609	9.99 137	2	37
24	9.29 591	63	9.30 457	65	10.69 543	9.99 135	3	36
25	9.29 654	62	9.30 522	65	10.69 478	9.99 132	2	35
26	9.29 716	63	9.30 587	65	10.69 413	9.99 130	3	34
27	9.29 779	62	9.30 652	65	10.69 348	9.99 127	3	33
28	9.29 841	62	9.30 717	65	10.69 283	9.99 124	2	32
29	9.29 903	63	9.30 782	64	10.69 218	9.99 122	3	31
30	9.29 966	62	9.30 846	65	10.69 154	9.99 119	2	**30**
31	9.30 028	62	9.30 911	64	10.69 089	9.99 117	3	29
32	9.30 090	61	9.30 975	65	10.69 025	9.99 114	2	28
33	9.30 151	62	9.31 040	64	10.68 960	9.99 112	3	27
34	9.30 213	62	9.31 104	64	10.68 896	9.99 109	3	26
35	9.30 275	61	9.31 168	65	10.68 832	9.99 106	2	25
36	9.30 336	62	9.31 233	64	10.68 767	9.99 104	3	24
37	9.30 398	61	9.31 297	64	10.68 703	9.99 101	2	23
38	9.30 459	62	9.31 361	64	10.68 639	9.99 099	3	22
39	9.30 521	61	9.31 425	64	10.68 575	9.99 096	3	21
40	9.30 582	61	9.31 489	63	10.68 511	9.99 093	2	**20**
41	9.30 643	61	9.31 552	64	10.68 448	9.99 091	3	19
42	9.30 704	61	9.31 616	63	10.68 384	9.99 088	2	18
43	9.30 765	61	9.31 679	64	10.68 321	9.99 086	3	17
44	9.30 826	61	9.31 743	63	10.68 257	9.99 083	3	16
45	9.30 887	60	9.31 806	64	10.68 194	9.99 080	2	15
46	9.30 947	61	9.31 870	63	10.68 130	9.99 078	3	14
47	9.31 008	60	9.31 933	63	10.68 067	9.99 075	3	13
48	9.31 068	61	9.31 996	63	10.68 004	9.99 072	2	12
49	9.31 129	60	9.32 059	63	10.67 941	9.99 070	3	11
50	9.31 189	61	9.32 122	63	10.67 878	9.99 067	3	**10**
51	9.31 250	60	9.32 185	63	10.67 815	9.99 064	2	9
52	9.31 310	60	9.32 248	63	10.67 752	9.99 062	3	8
53	9.31 370	60	9.32 311	62	10.67 689	9.99 059	3	7
54	9.31 430	60	9.32 373	63	10.67 627	9.99 056	2	6
55	9.31 490	59	9.32 436	62	10.67 564	9.99 054	3	5
56	9.31 549	60	9.32 498	63	10.67 502	9.99 051	3	4
57	9.31 609	60	9.32 561	62	10.67 439	9.99 048	2	3
58	9.31 669	59	9.32 623	62	10.67 377	9.99 046	3	2
59	9.31 728	60	9.32 685	62	10.67 315	9.99 043	3	1
60	9.31 788		9.32 747		10.67 253	9.99 040		**0**
	L Cos	d	L Cot	c d	L Tan	L Sin	d	′

78°

Prop. Pts.

	68	67	66
1	6.8	6.7	6.6
2	13.6	13.4	13.2
3	20.4	20.1	19.8
4	27.2	26.8	26.4
5	34.0	33.5	33.0
6	40.8	40.2	39.6
7	47.6	46.9	46.2
8	54.4	53.6	52.8
9	61.2	60.3	59.4

	65	64	63
1	6.5	6.4	6.3
2	13.0	12.8	12.6
3	19.5	19.2	18.9
4	26.0	25.6	25.2
5	32.5	32.0	31.5
6	39.0	38.4	37.8
7	45.5	44.8	44.1
8	52.0	51.2	50.4
9	58.5	57.6	56.7

	62	61	60
1	6.2	6.1	6.0
2	12.4	12.2	12.0
3	18.6	18.3	18.0
4	24.8	24.4	24.0
5	31.0	30.5	30.0
6	37.2	36.6	36.0
7	43.4	42.7	42.0
8	49.6	48.8	48.0
9	55.8	54.9	54.0

	59	3	2
1	5.9	0.3	0.2
2	11.8	0.6	0.4
3	17.7	0.9	0.6
4	23.6	1.2	0.8
5	29.5	1.5	1.0
6	35.4	1.8	1.2
7	41.3	2.1	1.4
8	47.2	2.4	1.6
9	53.1	2.7	1.8

Table D (Continued)

12°

′	L Sin	d	L Tan	c d	L Cot	L Cos	d	′
0	9.31 788		9.32 747		10.67 253	9.99 040		**60**
1	9.31 847	59	9.32 810	63	10.67 190	9.99 038	2	59
2	9.31 907	60	9.32 872	62	10.67 128	9.99 035	3	58
3	9.31 966	59	9.32 933	61	10.67 067	9.99 032	3	57
4	9.32 025	59	9.32 995	62	10.67 005	9.99 030	2	56
5	9.32 084	59	9.33 057	62	10.66 943	9.99 027	3	55
6	9.32 143	59	9.33 119	62	10.66 881	9.99 024	3	54
7	9.32 202	59	9.33 180	61	10.66 820	9.99 022	2	53
8	9.32 261	59	9.33 242	62	10.66 758	9.99 019	3	52
9	9.32 319	58	9.33 303	61	10.66 697	9.99 016	3	51
10	9.32 378	59	9.33 365	62	10.66 635	9.99 013	3	**50**
11	9.32 437	59	9.33 426	61	10.66 574	9.99 011	2	49
12	9.32 495	58	9.33 487	61	10.66 513	9.99 008	3	48
13	9.32 553	58	9.33 548	61	10.66 452	9.99 005	3	47
14	9.32 612	59	9.33 609	61	10.66 391	9.99 002	3	46
15	9.32 670	58	9.33 670	61	10.66 330	9.99 000	2	45
16	9.32 728	58	9.33 731	61	10.66 269	9.98 997	3	44
17	9.32 786	58	9.33 792	61	10.66 208	9.98 994	3	43
18	9.32 844	58	9.33 853	61	10.66 147	9.98 991	3	42
19	9.32 902	58	9.33 913	60	10.66 087	9.98 989	2	41
20	9.32 960	58	9.33 974	61	10.66 026	9.98 986	3	**40**
21	9.33 018	58	9.34 034	60	10.65 966	9.98 983	3	39
22	9.33 075	57	9.34 095	61	10.65 905	9.98 980	3	38
23	9.33 133	58	9.34 155	60	10.65 845	9.98 978	2	37
24	9.33 190	57	9.34 215	60	10.65 785	9.98 975	3	36
25	9.33 248	58	9.34 276	61	10.65 724	9.98 972	3	35
26	9.33 305	57	9.34 336	60	10.65 664	9.98 969	3	34
27	9.33 362	57	9.34 396	60	10.65 604	9.98 967	2	33
28	9.33 420	58	9.34 456	60	10.65 544	9.98 964	3	32
29	9.33 477	57	9.34 516	60	10.65 484	9.98 961	3	31
30	9.33 534	57	9.34 576	60	10.65 424	9.98 958	3	**30**
31	9.33 591	57	9.34 635	59	10.65 365	9.98 955	3	29
32	9.33 647	56	9.34 695	60	10.65 305	9.98 953	2	28
33	9.33 704	57	9.34 755	60	10.65 245	9.98 950	3	27
34	9.33 761	57	9.34 814	59	10.65 186	9.98 947	3	26
35	9.33 818	57	9.34 874	60	10.65 126	9.98 944	3	25
36	9.33 874	56	9.34 933	59	10.65 067	9.98 941	3	24
37	9.33 931	57	9.34 992	59	10.65 008	9.98 938	3	23
38	9.33 987	56	9.35 051	59	10.64 949	9.98 936	2	22
39	9.34 043	56	9.35 111	60	10.64 889	9.98 933	3	21
40	9.34 100	57	9.35 170	59	10.64 830	9.98 930	3	**20**
41	9.34 156	56	9.35 229	59	10.64 771	9.98 927	3	19
42	9.34 212	56	9.35 288	59	10.64 712	9.98 924	3	18
43	9.34 268	56	9.35 347	59	10.64 653	9.98 921	3	17
44	9.34 324	56	9.35 405	58	10.64 595	9.98 919	2	16
45	9.34 380	56	9.35 464	59	10.64 536	9.98 916	3	15
46	9.34 436	56	9.35 523	59	10.64 477	9.98 913	3	14
47	9.34 491	55	9.35 581	58	10.64 419	9.98 910	3	13
48	9.34 547	56	9.35 640	59	10.64 360	9.98 907	3	12
49	9.34 602	55	9.35 698	58	10.64 302	9.98 904	3	11
50	9.34 658	56	9.35 757	59	10.64 243	9.98 901	3	**10**
51	9.34 713	55	9.35 815	58	10.64 185	9.98 898	3	9
52	9.34 769	56	9.35 873	58	10.64 127	9.98 896	2	8
53	9.34 824	55	9.35 931	58	10.64 069	9.98 893	3	7
54	9.34 879	55	9.35 989	58	10.64 011	9.98 890	3	6
55	9.34 934	55	9.36 047	58	10.63 953	9.98 887	3	5
56	9.34 989	55	9.36 105	58	10.63 895	9.98 884	3	4
57	9.35 044	55	9.36 163	58	10.63 837	9.98 881	3	3
58	9.35 099	55	9.36 221	58	10.63 779	9.98 878	3	2
59	9.35 154	55	9.36 279	58	10.63 721	9.98 875	3	1
60	9.35 209	55	9.36 336	57	10.63 664	9.98 872	3	**0**
	L Cos	d	L Cot	c d	L Tan	L Sin	d	′

Prop. Pts.

	63	62	61
1	6.3	6.2	6.1
2	12.6	12.4	12.2
3	18.9	18.6	18.3
4	25.2	24.8	24.4
5	31.5	31.0	30.5
6	37.8	37.2	36.6
7	44.1	43.4	42.7
8	50.4	49.6	48.8
9	56.7	55.8	54.9

	60	59	58
1	6.0	5.9	5.8
2	12.0	11.8	11.6
3	18.0	17.7	17.4
4	24.0	23.6	23.2
5	30.0	29.5	29.0
6	36.0	35.4	34.8
7	42.0	41.3	40.6
8	48.0	47.2	46.4
9	54.0	53.1	52.2

	57	56	55
1	5.7	5.6	5.5
2	11.4	11.2	11.0
3	17.1	16.8	16.5
4	22.8	22.4	22.0
5	28.5	28.0	27.5
6	34.2	33.6	33.0
7	39.9	39.2	38.5
8	45.6	44.8	44.0
9	51.3	50.4	49.5

	3	2
1	0.3	0.2
2	0.6	0.4
3	0.9	0.6
4	1.2	0.8
5	1.5	1.0
6	1.8	1.2
7	2.1	1.4
8	2.4	1.6
9	2.7	1.8

Prop. Pts.

77°

Table D (Continued)

13°

′	L Sin	d	L Tan	c d	L Cot	L Cos	d	
0	9.35 209	54	9.36 336	58	10.63 664	9.98 872	3	**60**
1	9.35 263	55	9.36 394	58	10.63 606	9.98 869	2	59
2	9.35 318	55	9.36 452	57	10.63 548	9.98 867	3	58
3	9.35 373	54	9.36 509	57	10.63 491	9.98 864	3	57
4	9.35 427	54	9.36 566	58	10.63 434	9.98 861	3	56
5	9.35 481	55	9.36 624	57	10.63 376	9.98 858	3	55
6	9.35 536	54	9.36 681	57	10.63 319	9.98 855	3	54
7	9.35 590	54	9.36 738	57	10.63 262	9.98 852	3	53
8	9.35 644	54	9.36 795	57	10.63 205	9.98 849	3	52
9	9.35 698	54	9.36 852	57	10.63 148	9.98 846	3	51
10	9.35 752	54	9.36 909	57	10.63 091	9.98 843	3	**50**
11	9.35 806	54	9.36 966	57	10.63 034	9.98 840	3	49
12	9.35 860	54	9.37 023	57	10.62 977	9.98 837	3	48
13	9.35 914	54	9.37 080	57	10.62 920	9.98 834	3	47
14	9.35 968	54	9.37 137	56	10.62 863	9.98 831	3	46
15	9.36 022	53	9.37 193	57	10.62 807	9.98 828	3	45
16	9.36 075	54	9.37 250	56	10.62 750	9.98 825	3	44
17	9.36 129	53	9.37 306	57	10.62 694	9.98 822	3	43
18	9.36 182	54	9.37 363	56	10.62 637	9.98 819	3	42
19	9.36 236	53	9.37 419	57	10.62 581	9.98 816	3	41
20	9.36 289	53	9.37 476	56	10.62 524	9.98 813	3	**40**
21	9.36 342	53	9.37 532	56	10.62 468	9.98 810	3	39
22	9.36 395	54	9.37 588	56	10.62 412	9.98 807	3	38
23	9.36 449	53	9.37 644	56	10.62 356	9.98 804	3	37
24	9.36 502	53	9.37 700	56	10.62 300	9.98 801	3	36
25	9.36 555	53	9.37 756	56	10.62 244	9.98 798	3	35
26	9.36 608	52	9.37 812	56	10.62 188	9.98 795	3	34
27	9.36 660	53	9.37 868	56	10.62 132	9.98 792	3	33
28	9.36 713	53	9.37 924	56	10.62 076	9.98 789	3	32
29	9.36 766	53	9.37 980	55	10.62 020	9.98 786	3	31
30	9.36 819	52	9.38 035	56	10.61 965	9.98 783	3	**30**
31	9.36 871	53	9.38 091	56	10.61 909	9.98 780	3	29
32	9.36 924	52	9.38 147	55	10.61 853	9.98 777	3	28
33	9.36 976	52	9.38 202	55	10.61 798	9.98 774	3	27
34	9.37 028	53	9.38 257	56	10.61 743	9.98 771	3	26
35	9.37 081	52	9.38 313	55	10.61 687	9.98 768	3	25
36	9.37 133	52	9.38 368	55	10.61 632	9.98 765	3	24
37	9.37 185	52	9.38 423	56	10.61 577	9.98 762	3	23
38	9.37 237	52	9.38 479	55	10.61 521	9.98 759	3	22
39	9.37 289	52	9.38 534	55	10.61 466	9.98 756	3	21
40	9.37 341	52	9.38 589	55	10.61 411	9.98 753	3	**20**
41	9.37 393	52	9.38 644	55	10.61 356	9.98 750	4	19
42	9.37 445	52	9.38 699	55	10.61 301	9.98 746	3	18
43	9.37 497	52	9.38 754	54	10.61 246	9.98 743	3	17
44	9.37 549	51	9.38 808	55	10.61 192	9.98 740	3	16
45	9.37 600	52	9.38 863	55	10.61 137	9.98 737	3	15
46	9.37 652	51	9.38 918	54	10.61 082	9.98 734	3	14
47	9.37 703	52	9.38 972	55	10.61 028	9.98 731	3	13
48	9.37 755	51	9.39 027	55	10.60 973	9.98 728	3	12
49	9.37 806	52	9.39 082	54	10.60 918	9.98 725	3	11
50	9.37 858	51	9.39 136	54	10.60 864	9.98 722	3	**10**
51	9.37 909	51	9.39 190	55	10.60 810	9.98 719	4	9
52	9.37 960	51	9.39 245	54	10.60 755	9.98 715	3	8
53	9.38 011	51	9.39 299	54	10.60 701	9.98 712	3	7
54	9.38 062	51	9.39 353	54	10.60 647	9.98 709	3	6
55	9.38 113	51	9.39 407	54	10.60 593	9.98 706	3	5
56	9.38 164	51	9.39 461	54	10.60 539	9.98 703	3	4
57	9.38 215	51	9.39 515	54	10.60 485	9.98 700	3	3
58	9.38 266	51	9.39 569	54	10.60 431	9.98 697	3	2
59	9.38 317	51	9.39 623	54	10.60 377	9.98 694	4	1
60	9.38 368		9.39 677		10.60 323	9.98 690		**0**
	L Cos	**d**	**L Cot**	**c d**	**L Tan**	**L Sin**	**d**	**′**

76°

Prop. Pts.

	58	57	56
1	5.8	5.7	5.6
2	11.6	11.4	11.2
3	17.4	17.1	16.8
4	23.2	22.8	22.4
5	29.0	28.5	28.0
6	34.8	34.2	33.6
7	40.6	39.9	39.2
8	46.4	45.6	44.8
9	52.2	51.3	50.4

	55	54	53
1	5.5	5.4	5.3
2	11.0	10.8	10.6
3	16.5	16.2	15.9
4	22.0	21.6	21.2
5	27.5	27.0	26.5
6	33.0	32.4	31.8
7	38.5	37.8	37.1
8	44.0	43.2	42.4
9	49.5	48.6	47.7

	52	51
1	5.2	5.1
2	10.4	10.2
3	15.6	15.3
4	20.8	20.4
5	26.0	25.5
6	31.2	30.6
7	36.4	35.7
8	41.6	40.8
9	46.8	45.9

	4	3	2
1	0.4	0.3	0.2
2	0.8	0.6	0.4
3	1.2	0.9	0.6
4	1.6	1.2	0.8
5	2.0	1.5	1.0
6	2.4	1.8	1.2
7	2.8	2.1	1.4
8	3.2	2.4	1.6
9	3.6	2.7	1.8

Prop. Pts.

Table D (Continued)

14°

′	L Sin	d	L Tan	c d	L Cot	L Cos	d	
0	9.38 368		9.39 677		10.60 323	9.98 690		**60**
1	9.38 418	50	9.39 731	54	10.60 269	9.98 687	3	59
2	9.38 469	51	9.39 785	54	10.60 215	9.98 684	3	58
3	9.38 519	50	9.39 838	53	10.60 162	9.98 681	3	57
4	9.38 570	51	9.39 892	54	10.60 108	9.98 678	3	56
5	9.38 620	50	9.39 945	53	10.60 055	9.98 675	3	55
6	9.38 670	50	9.39 999	54	10.60 001	9.98 671	4	54
7	9.38 721	51	9.40 052	53	10.59 948	9.98 668	3	53
8	9.38 771	50	9.40 106	54	10.59 894	9.98 665	3	52
9	9.38 821	50	9.40 159	53	10.59 841	9.98 662	3	51
10	9.38 871	50	9.40 212	53	10.59 788	9.98 659	3	**50**
11	9.38 921	50	9.40 266	54	10.59 734	9.98 656	3	49
12	9.38 971	50	9.40 319	53	10.59 681	9.98 652	4	48
13	9.39 021	50	9.40 372	53	10.59 628	9.98 649	3	47
14	9.39 071	50	9.40 425	53	10.59 575	9.98 646	3	46
15	9.39 121	50	9.40 478	53	10.59 522	9.98 643	3	45
16	9.39 170	49	9.40 531	53	10.59 469	9.98 640	3	44
17	9.39 220	50	9.40 584	53	10.59 416	9.98 636	4	43
18	9.39 270	50	9.40 636	52	10.59 364	9.98 633	3	42
19	9.39 319	49	9.40 689	53	10.59 311	9.98 630	3	41
20	9.39 369	50	9.40 742	53	10.59 258	9.98 627	3	**40**
21	9.39 418	49	9.40 795	53	10.59 205	9.98 623	4	39
22	9.39 467	49	9.40 847	52	10.59 153	9.98 620	3	38
23	9.39 517	50	9.40 900	53	10.59 100	9.98 617	3	37
24	9.39 566	49	9.40 952	52	10.59 048	9.98 614	3	36
25	9.39 615	49	9.41 005	53	10.58 995	9.98 610	4	35
26	9.39 664	49	9.41 057	52	10.58 943	9.98 607	3	34
27	9.39 713	49	9.41 109	52	10.58 891	9.98 604	3	33
28	9.39 762	49	9.41 161	52	10.58 839	9.98 601	3	32
29	9.39 811	49	9.41 214	53	10.58 786	9.98 597	4	31
30	9.39 860	49	9.41 266	52	10.58 734	9.98 594	3	**30**
31	9.39 909	49	9.41 318	52	10.58 682	9.98 591	3	29
32	9.93 958	49	9.41 370	52	10.58 630	9.98 588	3	28
33	9.40 006	48	9.41 422	52	10.58 578	9.98 584	4	27
34	9.40 055	49	9.41 474	52	10.58 526	9.98 581	3	26
35	9.40 103	48	9.41 526	52	10.58 474	9.98 578	3	25
36	9.40 152	49	9.41 578	52	10.58 422	9.98 574	4	24
37	9.40 200	48	9.41 629	51	10.58 371	9.98 571	3	23
38	9.40 249	49	9.41 681	52	10.58 319	9.98 568	3	22
39	9.40 297	48	9.41 733	52	10.58 267	9.98 565	3	21
40	9.40 346	49	9.41 784	51	10.58 216	9.98 561	4	**20**
41	9.40 394	48	9.41 836	52	10.58 164	9.98 558	3	19
42	9.40 442	48	9.41 887	51	10.58 113	9.98 555	3	18
43	9.40 490	48	9.41 939	52	10.58 061	9.98 551	4	17
44	9.40 538	48	9.41 990	51	10.58 010	9.98 548	3	16
45	9.40 586	48	9.42 041	51	10.57 959	9.98 545	3	15
46	9.40 634	48	9.42 093	52	10.57 907	9.98 541	4	14
47	9.40 682	48	9.42 144	51	10.57 856	9.98 538	3	13
48	9.40 730	48	9.42 195	51	10.57 805	9.98 535	3	12
49	9.40 778	48	9.42 246	51	10.57 754	9.98 531	4	11
50	9.40 825	47	9.42 297	51	10.57 703	9.98 528	3	**10**
51	9.40 873	48	9.42 348	51	10.57 652	9.98 525	3	9
52	9.40 921	48	9.42 399	51	10.57 601	9.98 521	4	8
53	9.40 968	47	9.42 450	51	10.57 550	9.98 518	3	7
54	9.41 016	48	9.42 501	51	10.57 499	9.98 515	3	6
55	9.41 063	47	9.42 552	51	10.57 448	9.98 511	4	5
56	9.41 111	48	9.42 603	51	10.57 397	9.98 508	3	4
57	9.41 158	47	9.42 653	50	10.57 347	9.98 505	3	3
58	9.41 205	47	9.42 704	51	10.57 296	9.98 501	4	2
59	9.41 252	47	9.42 755	51	10.57 245	9.98 498	3	1
60	9.41 300	48	9.42 805	50	10.57 195	9.98 494	4	**0**
	L Cos	d	L Cot	c d	L Tan	L Sin	d	′

Prop. Pts.

	54	53	52
1	5.4	5.3	5.2
2	10.8	10.6	10.4
3	16.2	15.9	15.6
4	21.6	21.2	20.8
5	27.0	26.5	26.0
6	32.4	31.8	31.2
7	37.8	37.1	36.4
8	43.2	42.4	41.6
9	48.6	47.7	46.8

	51	50	49
1	5.1	5.0	4.9
2	10.2	10.0	9.8
3	15.3	15.0	14.7
4	20.4	20.0	19.6
5	25.5	25.0	24.5
6	30.6	30.0	29.4
7	35.7	35.0	34.3
8	40.8	40.0	39.2
9	45.9	45.0	44.1

	48	47
1	4.8	4.7
2	9.6	9.4
3	14.4	14.1
4	19.2	18.8
5	24.0	23.5
6	28.8	28.2
7	33.6	32.9
8	38.4	37.6
9	43.2	42.3

	4	3
1	0.4	0.3
2	0.8	0.6
3	1.2	0.9
4	1.6	1.2
5	2.0	1.5
6	2.4	1.8
7	2.8	2.1
8	3.2	2.4
9	3.6	2.7

Prop. Pts.

75°

Table D (Continued)

15°

′	L Sin	d	L Tan	c d	L Cot	L Cos	d	
0	9.41 300	47	9.42 805	51	10.57 195	9.98 494	3	**60**
1	9.41 347	47	9.42 856	50	10.57 144	9.98 491	3	59
2	9.41 394	47	9.42 906	51	10.57 094	9.98 488	4	58
3	9.41 441	47	9.42 957	50	10.57 043	9.98 484	3	57
4	9.41 488	47	9.43 007	50	10.56 993	9.98 481	4	56
5	9.41 535	47	9.43 057	51	10.56 943	9.98 477	3	55
6	9.41 582	46	9.43 108	50	10.56 892	9.98 474	3	54
7	9.41 628	47	9.43 158	50	10.56 842	9.98 471	4	53
8	9.41 675	47	9.43 208	50	10.56 792	9.98 467	3	52
9	9.41 722	46	9.43 258	50	10.56 742	9.98 464	4	51
10	9.41 768	47	9.43 308	50	10.56 692	9.98 460	3	**50**
11	9.41 815	46	9.43 358	50	10.56 642	9.98 457	4	49
12	9.41 861	47	9.43 408	50	10.56 592	9.98 453	3	48
13	9.41 908	46	9.43 458	50	10.56 542	9.98 450	3	47
14	9.41 954	47	9.43 508	50	10.56 492	9.98 447	4	46
15	9.42 001	46	9.43 558	49	10.56 442	9.98 443	3	45
16	9.42 047	46	9.43 607	50	10.56 393	9.98 440	4	44
17	9.42 093	47	9.43 657	50	10.56 343	9.98 436	3	43
18	9.42 140	46	9.43 707	49	10.56 293	9.98 433	4	42
19	9.42 186	46	9.43 756	50	10.56 244	9.98 429	3	41
20	9.42 232	46	9.43 806	49	10.56 194	9.98 426	4	**40**
21	9.42 278	46	9.43 855	50	10.56 145	9.98 422	3	39
22	9.42 324	46	9.43 905	49	10.56 095	9.98 419	4	38
23	9.42 370	46	9.43 954	50	10.56 046	9.98 415	3	37
24	9.42 416	45	9.44 004	49	10.55 996	9.98 412	3	36
25	9.42 461	46	9.44 053	49	10.55 947	9.98 409	4	35
26	9.42 507	46	9.44 102	49	10.55 898	9.98 405	3	34
27	9.42 553	46	9.44 151	50	10.55 849	9.98 402	4	33
28	9.42 599	45	9.44 201	49	10.55 799	9.98 398	3	32
29	9.42 644	46	9.44 250	49	10.55 750	9.98 395	4	31
30	9.42 690	45	9.44 299	49	10.55 701	9.98 391	3	**30**
31	9.42 735	46	9.44 348	49	10.55 652	9.98 388	4	29
32	9.42 781	45	9.44 397	49	10.55 603	9.98 384	3	28
33	9.42 826	46	9.44 446	49	10.55 554	9.98 381	4	27
34	9.42 872	45	9.44 495	49	10.55 505	9.98 377	4	26
35	9.42 917	45	9.44 544	48	10.55 456	9.98 373	3	25
36	9.42 962	46	9.44 592	49	10.55 408	9.98 370	4	24
37	9.43 008	45	9.44 641	49	10.55 359	9.98 366	3	23
38	9.43 053	45	9.44 690	48	10.55 310	9.98 363	4	22
39	9.43 098	45	9.44 738	49	10.55 262	9.98 359	3	21
40	9.43 143	45	9.44 787	49	10.55 213	9.98 356	4	**20**
41	9.43 188	45	9.44 836	48	10.55 164	9.98 352	3	19
42	9.43 233	45	9.44 884	49	10.55 116	9.98 349	4	18
43	9.43 278	45	9.44 933	48	10.55 067	9.98 345	3	17
44	9.43 323	44	9.44 981	48	10.55 019	9.98 342	4	16
45	9.43 367	45	9.45 029	49	10.54 971	9.98 338	4	15
46	9.43 412	45	9.45 078	48	10.54 922	9.98 334	3	14
47	9.43 457	45	9.45 126	48	10.54 874	9.98 331	4	13
48	9.43 502	44	9.45 174	48	10.54 826	9.98 327	3	12
49	9.43 546	45	9.45 222	49	10.54 778	9.98 324	4	11
50	9.43 591	44	9.45 271	48	10.54 729	9.98 320	3	**10**
51	9.43 635	45	9.45 319	48	10.54 681	9.98 317	4	9
52	9.43 680	44	9.45 367	48	10.54 633	9.98 313	4	8
53	9.43 724	45	9.45 415	48	10.54 585	9.98 309	3	7
54	9.43 769	44	9.45 463	48	10.54 537	9.98 306	4	6
55	9.43 813	44	9.45 511	48	10.54 489	9.98 302	3	5
56	9.43 857	44	9.45 559	47	10.54 441	9.98 299	4	4
57	9.43 901	45	9.45 606	48	10.54 394	9.98 295	4	3
58	9.43 946	44	9.45 654	48	10.54 346	9.98 291	3	2
59	9.43 990	44	9.45 702	48	10.54 298	9.98 288	4	1
60	9.44 034		9.45 750		10.54 250	9.98 284		**0**
	L Cos	d	L Cot	c d	L Tan	L Sin	d	′

74°

Prop. Pts.

	51	50	49
1	5.1	5.0	4.9
2	10.2	10.0	9.8
3	15.3	15.0	14.7
4	20.4	20.0	19.6
5	25.5	25.0	24.5
6	30.6	30.0	29.4
7	35.7	35.0	34.3
8	40.8	40.0	39.2
9	45.9	45.0	44.1

	48	47	46
1	4.8	4.7	4.6
2	9.6	9.4	9.2
3	14.4	14.1	13.8
4	19.2	18.8	18.4
5	24.0	23.5	23.0
6	28.8	28.2	27.6
7	33.6	32.9	32.2
8	38.4	37.6	36.8
9	43.2	42.3	41.4

	45	44
1	4.5	4.4
2	9.0	8.8
3	13.5	13.2
4	18.0	17.6
5	22.5	22.0
6	27.0	26.4
7	31.5	30.8
8	36.0	35.2
9	40.5	39.6

	4	3
1	0.4	0.3
2	0.8	0.6
3	1.2	0.9
4	1.6	1.2
5	2.0	1.5
6	2.4	1.8
7	2.8	2.1
8	3.2	2.4
9	3.6	2.7

Prop. Pts.

Table D (Continued)

16°

′	L Sin	d	L Tan	c d	L Cot	L Cos	d	
0	9.44 034	44	9.45 750	47	10.54 250	9.98 284	3	**60**
1	9.44 078	44	9.45 797	48	10.54 203	9.98 281	4	59
2	9.44 122	44	9.45 845	47	10.54 155	9.98 277	4	58
3	9.44 166	44	9.45 892	48	10.54 108	9.98 273	3	57
4	9.44 210	43	9.45 940	47	10.54 060	9.98 270	4	56
5	9.44 253	44	9.45 987	48	10.54 013	9.98 266	4	55
6	9.44 297	44	9.46 035	47	10.53 965	9.98 262	3	54
7	9.44 341	44	9.46 082	48	10.53 918	9.98 259	4	53
8	9.44 385	43	9.46 130	47	10.53 870	9.98 255	4	52
9	9.44 428	44	9.46 177	47	10.53 823	9.98 251	3	51
10	9.44 472	44	9.46 224	47	10.53 776	9.98 248	4	**50**
11	9.44 516	43	9.46 271	48	10.53 729	9.98 244	4	49
12	9.44 559	43	9.46 319	47	10.53 681	9.98 240	3	48
13	9.44 602	44	9.46 366	47	10.53 634	9.98 237	4	47
14	9.44 646	43	9.46 413	47	10.53 587	9.98 233	4	46
15	9.44 689	44	9.46 460	47	10.53 540	9.98 229	3	45
16	9.44 733	43	9.46 507	47	10.53 493	9.98 226	4	44
17	9.44 776	43	9.46 554	47	10.53 446	9.98 222	4	43
18	9.44 819	43	9.46 601	47	10.53 399	9.98 218	3	42
19	9.44 862	43	9.46 648	46	10.53 352	9.98 215	4	41
20	9.44 905	43	9.46 694	47	10.53 306	9.98 211	4	**40**
21	9.44 948	44	9.46 741	47	10.53 259	9.98 207	3	39
22	9.44 992	43	9.46 788	47	10.53 212	9.98 204	4	38
23	9.45 035	42	9.46 835	46	10.53 165	9.98 200	4	37
24	9.45 077	43	9.46 881	47	10.53 119	9.98 196	4	36
25	9.45 120	43	9.46 928	47	10.53 072	9.98 192	3	35
26	9.45 163	43	9.46 975	46	10.53 025	9.98 189	4	34
27	9.45 206	43	9.47 021	47	10.52 979	9.98 185	4	33
28	9.45 249	43	9.47 068	46	10.52 932	9.98 181	4	32
29	9.45 292	42	9.47 114	46	10.52 886	9.98 177	3	31
30	9.45 334	43	9.47 160	47	10.52 840	9.98 174	4	**30**
31	9.45 377	42	9.47 207	46	10.52 793	9.98 170	4	29
32	9.45 419	43	9.47 253	46	10.52 747	9.98 166	4	28
33	9.45 462	42	9.47 299	47	10.52 701	9.98 162	3	27
34	9.45 504	43	9.47 346	46	10.52 654	9.98 159	4	26
35	9.45 547	42	9.47 392	46	10.52 608	9.98 155	4	25
36	9.45 589	43	9.47 438	46	10.52 562	9.98 151	4	24
37	9.45 632	42	9.47 484	46	10.52 516	9.98 147	3	23
38	9.45 674	42	9.47 530	46	10.52 470	9.98 144	4	22
39	9.45 716	42	9.47 576	46	10.52 424	9.98 140	4	21
40	9.45 758	43	9.47 622	46	10.52 378	9.98 136	4	**20**
41	9.45 801	42	9.47 668	46	10.52 332	9.98 132	3	19
42	9.45 843	42	9.47 714	46	10.52 286	9.98 129	4	18
43	9.45 885	42	9.47 760	46	10.52 240	9.98 125	4	17
44	9.45 927	42	9.47 806	46	10.52 194	9.98 121	4	16
45	9.45 969	42	9.47 852	45	10.52 148	9.98 117	4	15
46	9.46 011	42	9.47 897	46	10.52 103	9.98 113	3	14
47	9.46 053	42	9.47 943	46	10.52 057	9.98 110	4	13
48	9.46 095	41	9.47 989	46	10.52 011	9.98 106	4	12
49	9.46 136	42	9.48 035	45	10.51 965	9.98 102	4	11
50	9.46 178	42	9.48 080	46	10.51 920	9.98 098	4	**10**
51	9.46 220	42	9.48 126	45	10.51 874	9.98 094	4	9
52	9.46 262	41	9.48 171	46	10.51 829	9.98 090	3	8
53	9.46 303	42	9.48 217	45	10.51 783	9.98 087	4	7
54	9.46 345	41	9.48 262	45	10.51 738	9.98 083	4	6
55	9.46 386	42	9.48 307	46	10.51 693	9.98 079	4	5
56	9.46 428	41	9.48 353	45	10.51 647	9.98 075	4	4
57	9.46 469	42	9.48 398	45	10.51 602	9.98 071	4	3
58	9.46 511	41	9.48 443	46	10.51 557	9.98 067	4	2
59	9.46 552	42	9.48 489	45	10.51 511	9.98 063	3	1
60	9.46 594		9.48 534		10.51 466	9.98 060		**0**
	L Cos	d	L Cot	c d	L Tan	L Sin	d	′

Prop. Pts.

	48	47	46
1	4.8	4.7	4.6
2	9.6	9.4	9.2
3	14.4	14.1	13.8
4	19.2	18.8	18.4
5	24.0	23.5	23.0
6	28.8	28.2	27.6
7	33.6	32.9	32.2
8	38.4	37.6	36.8
9	43.2	42.3	41.4

	45	44	43
1	4.5	4.4	4.3
2	9.0	8.8	8.6
3	13.5	13.2	12.9
4	18.0	17.6	17.2
5	22.5	22.0	21.5
6	27.0	26.4	25.8
7	31.5	30.8	30.1
8	36.0	35.2	34.4
9	40.5	39.6	38.7

	42	41
1	4.2	4.1
2	8.4	8.2
3	12.6	12.3
4	16.8	16.4
5	21.0	20.5
6	25.2	24.6
7	29.4	28.7
8	33.6	32.8
9	37.8	36.9

	4	3
1	0.4	0.3
2	0.8	0.6
3	1.2	0.9
4	1.6	1.2
5	2.0	1.5
6	2.4	1.8
7	2.8	2.1
8	3.2	2.4
9	3.6	2.7

73°

Table D (Continued)

17°

′	L Sin	d	L Tan	c d	L Cot	L Cos	d	
0	9.46 594	41	9.48 534	45	10.51 466	9.98 060	4	**60**
1	9.46 635	41	9.48 579	45	10.51 421	9.98 056	4	59
2	9.46 676	41	9.48 624	45	10.51 376	9.98 052	4	58
3	9.46 717	41	9.48 669	45	10.51 331	9.98 048	4	57
4	9.46 758	42	9.48 714	45	10.51 286	9.98 044	4	56
5	9.46 800	41	9.48 759	45	10.51 241	9.98 040	4	55
6	9.46 841	41	9.48 804	45	10.51 196	9.98 036	4	54
7	9.46 882	41	9.48 849	45	10.51 151	9.98 032	3	53
8	9.46 923	41	9.48 894	45	10.51 106	9.98 029	4	52
9	9.46 964	41	9.48 939	45	10.51 061	9.98 025	4	51
10	9.47 005	40	9.48 984	45	10.51 016	9.98 021	4	**50**
11	9.47 045	41	9.49 029	44	10.50 971	9.98 017	4	49
12	9.47 086	41	9.49 073	45	10.50 927	9.98 013	4	48
13	9.47 127	41	9.49 118	45	10.50 882	9.98 009	4	47
14	9.47 168	41	9.49 163	44	10.50 837	9.98 005	4	46
15	9.47 209	40	9.49 207	45	10.50 793	9.98 001	4	45
16	9.47 249	41	9.49 252	44	10.50 748	9.97 997	4	44
17	9.47 290	40	9.49 296	45	10.50 704	9.97 993	4	43
18	9.47 330	41	9.49 341	44	10.50 659	9.97 989	3	42
19	9.47 371	40	9.49 385	45	10.50 615	9.97 986	4	41
20	9.47 411	41	9.49 430	44	10.50 570	9.97 982	4	**40**
21	9.47 452	40	9.49 474	45	10.50 526	9.97 978	4	39
22	9.47 492	41	9.49 519	44	10.50 481	9.97 974	4	38
23	9.47 533	40	9.49 563	44	10.50 437	9.97 970	4	37
24	9.47 573	40	9.49 607	45	10.50 393	9.97 966	4	36
25	9.47 613	41	9.49 652	44	10.50 348	9.97 962	4	35
26	9.47 654	40	9.49 696	44	10.50 304	9.97 958	4	34
27	9.47 694	40	9.49 740	44	10.50 260	9.97 954	4	33
28	9.47 734	40	9.49 784	44	10.50 216	9.97 950	4	32
29	9.47 774	40	9.49 828	44	10.50 172	9.97 946	4	31
30	9.47 814	40	9.49 872	44	10.50 128	9.97 942	4	**30**
31	9.47 854	40	9.49 916	44	10.50 084	9.97 938	4	29
32	9.47 894	40	9.49 960	44	10.50 040	9.97 934	4	28
33	9.47 934	40	9.50 004	44	10.49 996	9.97 930	4	27
34	9.47 974	40	9.50 048	44	10.49 952	9.97 926	4	26
35	9.48 014	40	9.50 092	44	10.49 908	9.97 922	4	25
36	9.48 054	40	9.50 136	44	10.49 864	9.97 918	4	24
37	9.48 094	39	9.50 180	43	10.49 820	9.97 914	4	23
38	9.48 133	40	9.50 223	44	10.49 777	9.97 910	4	22
39	9.48 173	40	9.50 267	44	10.49 733	9.97 906	4	21
40	9.48 213	39	9.50 311	44	10.49 689	9.97 902	4	**20**
41	9.48 252	40	9.50 355	43	10.49 645	9.97 898	4	19
42	9.48 292	40	9.50 398	44	10.49 602	9.97 894	4	18
43	9.48 332	39	9.50 442	43	10.49 558	9.97 890	4	17
44	9.48 371	40	9.50 485	44	10.49 515	9.97 886	4	16
45	9.48 411	39	9.50 529	43	10.49 471	9.97 882	4	15
46	9.48 450	40	9.50 572	44	10.49 428	9.97 878	4	14
47	9.48 490	39	9.50 616	43	10.49 384	9.97 874	4	13
48	9.48 529	39	9.50 659	44	10.49 341	9.97 870	4	12
49	9.48 568	39	9.50 703	43	10.49 297	9.97 866	5	11
50	9.48 607	40	9.50 746	43	10.49 254	9.97 861	4	**10**
51	9.48 647	39	9.50 789	44	10.49 211	9.97 857	4	9
52	9.48 686	39	9.50 833	43	10.49 167	9.97 853	4	8
53	9.48 725	39	9.50 876	43	10.49 124	9.97 849	4	7
54	9.48 764	39	9.50 919	43	10.49 081	9.97 845	4	6
55	9.48 803	39	9.50 962	43	10.49 038	9.97 841	4	5
56	9.48 842	39	9.51 005	43	10.48 995	9.97 837	4	4
57	9.48 881	39	9.51 048	44	10.48 952	9.97 833	4	3
58	9.48 920	39	9.51 092	43	10.48 908	9.97 829	4	2
59	9.48 959	39	9.51 135	43	10.48 865	9.97 825	4	1
60	9.48 998		9.51 178		10.48 822	9.97 821		**0**
	L Cos	d	L Cot	c d	L Tan	L Sin	d	′

Prop. Pts.

	45	44	43
1	4.5	4.4	4.3
2	9.0	8.8	8.6
3	13.5	13.2	12.9
4	18.0	17.6	17.2
5	22.5	22.0	21.5
6	27.0	26.4	25.8
7	31.5	30.8	30.1
8	36.0	35.2	34.4
9	40.5	39.6	38.7

	42	41
1	4.2	4.1
2	8.4	8.2
3	12.6	12.3
4	16.8	16.4
5	21.0	20.5
6	25.2	24.6
7	29.4	28.7
8	33.6	32.8
9	37.8	36.9

	40	39
1	4.0	3.9
2	8.0	7.8
3	12.0	11.7
4	16.0	15.6
5	20.0	19.5
6	24.0	23.4
7	28.0	27.3
8	32.0	31.2
9	36.0	35.1

	5	4	3
1	0.5	0.4	0.3
2	1.0	0.8	0.6
3	1.5	1.2	0.9
4	2.0	1.6	1.2
5	2.5	2.0	1.5
6	3.0	2.4	1.8
7	3.5	2.8	2.1
8	4.0	3.2	2.4
9	4.5	3.6	2.7

Prop. Pts.

72°

Table D (Continued)

18°

′	L Sin	d	L Tan	c d	L Cot	L Cos	d	
0	9.48 998	39	9.51 178	43	10.48 822	9.97 821	4	**60**
1	9.49 037	39	9.51 221	43	10.48 779	9.97 817	5	59
2	9.49 076	39	9.51 264	42	10.48 736	9.97 812	4	58
3	9.49 115	38	9.51 306	43	10.48 694	9.97 808	4	57
4	9.49 153	39	9.51 349	43	10.48 651	9.97 804	4	56
5	9.49 192	39	9.51 392	43	10.48 608	9.97 800	4	55
6	9.49 231	38	9.51 435	43	10.48 565	9.97 796	4	54
7	9.49 269	39	9.51 478	42	10.48 522	9.97 792	4	53
8	9.49 308	39	9.51 520	43	10.48 480	9.97 788	4	52
9	9.49 347	38	9.51 563	43	10.48 437	9.97 784	5	51
10	9.49 385	39	9.51 606	42	10.48 394	9.97 779	4	**50**
11	9.49 424	38	9.51 648	43	10.48 352	9.97 775	4	49
12	9.49 462	38	9.51 691	43	10.48 309	9.97 771	4	48
13	9.49 500	39	9.51 734	42	10.48 266	9.97 767	4	47
14	9.49 539	38	9.51 776	43	10.48 224	9.97 763	4	46
15	9.49 577	38	9.51 819	42	10.48 181	9.97 759	5	45
16	9.49 615	39	9.51 861	42	10.48 139	9.97 754	4	44
17	9.49 654	38	9.51 903	43	10.48 097	9.97 750	4	43
18	9.49 692	38	9.51 946	42	10.48 054	9.97 746	4	42
19	9.49 730	38	9.51 988	43	10.48 012	9.97 742	4	41
20	9.49 768	38	9.52 031	42	10.47 969	9.97 738	4	**40**
21	9.49 806	38	9.52 073	42	10.47 927	9.97 734	5	39
22	9.49 844	38	9.52 115	42	10.47 885	9.97 729	4	38
23	9.49 882	38	9.52 157	43	10.47 843	9.97 725	4	37
24	9.49 920	38	9.52 200	42	10.47 800	9.97 721	4	36
25	9.49 958	38	9.52 242	42	10.47 758	9.97 717	4	35
26	9.49 996	38	9.52 284	42	10.47 716	9.97 713	5	34
27	9.50 034	38	9.52 326	42	10.47 674	9.97 708	4	33
28	9.50 072	38	9.52 368	42	10.47 632	9.97 704	4	32
29	9.50 110	38	9.52 410	42	10.47 590	9.97 700	4	31
30	9.50 148	37	9.52 452	42	10.47 548	9.97 696	5	**30**
31	9.50 185	38	9.52 494	42	10.47 506	9.97 691	4	29
32	9.50 223	38	9.52 536	42	10.47 464	9.97 687	4	28
33	9.50 261	37	9.52 578	42	10.47 422	9.97 683	4	27
34	9.50 298	38	9.52 620	41	10.47 380	9.97 679	5	26
35	9.50 336	38	9.52 661	42	10.47 339	9.97 674	4	25
36	9.50 374	37	9.52 703	42	10.47 297	9.97 670	4	24
37	9.50 411	38	9.52 745	42	10.47 255	9.97 666	4	23
38	9.50 449	37	9.52 787	42	10.47 213	9.97 662	5	22
39	9.50 486	37	9.52 829	41	10.47 171	9.97 657	4	21
40	9.50 523	38	9.52 870	42	10.47 130	9.97 653	4	**20**
41	9.50 561	37	9.52 912	41	10.47 088	9.97 649	4	19
42	9.50 598	37	9.52 953	42	10.47 047	9.97 645	5	18
43	9.50 635	38	9.52 995	42	10.47 005	9.97 640	4	17
44	9.50 673	37	9.53 037	41	10.46 963	9.97 636	4	16
45	9.50 710	37	9.53 078	42	10.46 922	9.97 632	4	15
46	9.50 747	37	9.53 120	41	10.46 880	9.97 628	5	14
47	9.50 784	37	9.53 161	41	10.46 839	9.97 623	4	13
48	9.50 821	37	9.53 202	42	10.46 798	9.97 619	4	12
49	9.50 858	38	9.53 244	41	10.46 756	9.97 615	5	11
50	9.50 896	37	9.53 285	42	10.46 715	9.97 610	4	**10**
51	9.50 933	37	9.53 327	41	10.46 673	9.97 606	4	9
52	9.50 970	37	9.53 368	41	10.46 632	9.97 602	5	8
53	9.51 007	36	9.53 409	41	10.46 591	9.97 597	4	7
54	9.51 043	37	9.53 450	42	10.46 550	9.97 593	4	6
55	9.51 080	37	9.53 492	41	10.46 508	9.97 589	5	5
56	9.51 117	37	9.53 533	41	10.46 467	9.97 584	4	4
57	9.51 154	37	9.53 574	41	10.46 426	9.97 580	4	3
58	9.51 191	36	9.53 615	41	10.46 385	9.97 576	5	2
59	9.51 227	37	9.53 656	41	10.46 344	9.97 571	4	1
60	9.51 264		9.53 697		10.46 303	9.97 567		**0**
	L Cos	d	L Cot	c d	L Tan	L Sin	d	′

Prop. Pts.

	43	42	41
1	4.3	4.2	4.1
2	8.6	8.4	8.2
3	12.9	12.6	12.3
4	17.2	16.8	16.4
5	21.5	21.0	20.5
6	25.8	25.2	24.6
7	30.1	29.4	28.7
8	34.4	33.6	32.8
9	38.7	37.8	36.9

	39	38	37
1	3.9	3.8	3.7
2	7.8	7.6	7.4
3	11.7	11.4	11.1
4	15.6	15.2	14.8
5	19.5	19.0	18.5
6	23.4	22.8	22.2
7	27.3	26.6	25.9
8	31.2	30.4	29.6
9	35.1	34.2	33.3

	36	5	4
1	3.6	0.5	0.4
2	7.2	1.0	0.8
3	10.8	1.5	1.2
4	14.4	2.0	1.6
5	18.0	2.5	2.0
6	21.6	3.0	2.4
7	25.2	3.5	2.8
8	28.8	4.0	3.2
9	32.4	4.5	3.6

Prop. Pts.

71°

Table D (Continued)

19°

′	L Sin	d	L Tan	c d	L Cot	L Cos	d	
0	9.51 264	37	9.53 697	41	10.46 303	9.97 567	4	**60**
1	9.51 301	37	9.53 738	41	10.46 262	9.97 563	5	59
2	9.51 338	36	9.53 779	41	10.46 221	9.97 558	4	58
3	9.51 374	37	9.53 820	41	10.46 180	9.97 554	4	57
4	9.51 411	36	9.53 861	41	10.46 139	9.97 550	5	56
5	9.51 447	37	9.53 902	41	10.46 098	9.97 545	4	55
6	9.51 484	36	9.53 943	41	10.46 057	9.97 541	5	54
7	9.51 520	37	9.53 984	41	10.46 016	9.97 536	4	53
8	9.51 557	36	9.54 025	40	10.45 975	9.97 532	4	52
9	9.51 593	36	9.54 065	41	10.45 935	9.97 528	5	51
10	9.51 629	37	9.54 106	41	10.45 894	9.97 523	4	**50**
11	9.51 666	36	9.54 147	40	10.45 853	9.97 519	4	49
12	9.51 702	36	9.54 187	41	10.45 813	9.97 515	5	48
13	9.51 738	36	9.54 228	41	10.45 772	9.97 510	4	47
14	9.51 774	37	9.54 269	40	10.45 731	9.97 506	5	46
15	9.51 811	36	9.54 309	41	10.45 691	9.97 501	4	45
16	9.51 847	36	9.54 350	40	10.45 650	9.97 497	5	44
17	9.51 883	36	9.54 390	41	10.45 610	9.97 492	4	43
18	9.51 919	36	9.54 431	40	10.45 569	9.97 488	4	42
19	9.51 955	36	9.54 471	41	10.45 529	9.97 484	5	41
20	9.51 991	36	9.54 512	40	10.45 488	9.97 479	4	**40**
21	9.52 027	36	9.54 552	41	10.45 448	9.97 475	5	39
22	9.52 063	36	9.54 593	40	10.45 407	9.97 470	4	38
23	9.52 099	36	9.54 633	40	10.45 367	9.97 466	5	37
24	9.52 135	36	9.54 673	41	10.45 327	9.97 461	4	36
25	9.52 171	36	9.54 714	40	10.45 286	9.97 457	4	35
26	9.52 207	35	9.54 754	40	10.45 246	9.97 453	5	34
27	9.52 242	36	9.54 794	41	10.45 206	9.97 448	4	33
28	9.52 278	36	9.54 835	40	10.45 165	9.97 444	5	32
29	9.52 314	36	9.54 875	40	10.45 125	9.97 439	4	31
30	9.52 350	35	9.54 915	40	10.45 085	9.97 435	5	**30**
31	9.52 385	36	9.54 955	40	10.45 045	9.97 430	4	29
32	9.52 421	35	9.54 995	40	10.45 005	9.97 426	5	28
33	9.52 456	36	9.55 035	40	10.44 965	9.97 421	4	27
34	9.52 492	35	9.55 075	40	10.44 925	9.97 417	5	26
35	9.52 527	36	9.55 115	40	10.44 885	9.97 412	4	25
36	9.52 563	35	9.55 155	40	10.44 845	9.97 408	5	24
37	9.52 598	36	9.55 195	40	10.44 805	9.97 403	4	23
38	9.52 634	35	9.55 235	40	10.44 765	9.97 399	5	22
39	9.52 669	36	9.55 275	40	10.44 725	9.97 394	4	21
40	9.52 705	35	9.55 315	40	10.44 685	9.97 390	5	**20**
41	9.52 740	35	9.55 355	40	10.44 645	9.97 385	4	19
42	9.52 775	36	9.55 395	39	10.44 605	9.97 381	5	18
43	9.52 811	35	9.55 434	40	10.44 566	9.97 376	4	17
44	9.52 846	35	9.55 474	40	10.44 526	9.97 372	5	16
45	9.52 881	35	9.55 514	40	10.44 486	9.97 367	4	15
46	9.52 916	35	9.55 554	39	10.44 446	9.97 363	5	14
47	9.52 951	35	9.55 593	40	10.44 407	9.97 358	5	13
48	9.52 986	35	9.55 633	40	10.44 367	9.97 353	4	12
49	9.53 021	35	9.55 673	39	10.44 327	9.97 349	5	11
50	9.53 056	36	9.55 712	40	10.44 288	9.97 344	4	**10**
51	9.53 092	34	9.55 752	39	10.44 248	9.97 340	5	9
52	9.53 126	35	9.55 791	40	10.44 209	9.97 335	4	8
53	9.53 161	35	9.55 831	39	10.44 169	9.97 331	5	7
54	9.53 196	35	9.55 870	40	10.44 130	9.97 326	4	6
55	9.53 231	35	9.55 910	39	10.44 090	9.97 322	5	5
56	9.53 266	35	9.55 949	40	10.44 051	9.97 317	5	4
57	9.53 301	35	9.55 989	39	10.44 011	9.97 312	4	3
58	9.53 336	34	9.56 028	39	10.43 972	9.97 308	5	2
59	9.53 370	35	9.56 067	40	10.43 933	9.97 303	4	1
60	9.53 405		9.56 107		10.43 893	9.97 299		**0**
	L Cos	d	L Cot	c d	L Tan	L Sin	d	′

70°

Prop. Pts.

	41	40	39
1	4.1	4.0	3.9
2	8.2	8.0	7.8
3	12.3	12.0	11.7
4	16.4	16.0	15.6
5	20.5	20.0	19.5
6	24.6	24.0	23.4
7	28.7	28.0	27.3
8	32.8	32.0	31.2
9	36.9	36.0	35.1

	37	36	35
1	3.7	3.6	3.5
2	7.4	7.2	7.0
3	11.1	10.8	10.5
4	14.8	14.4	14.0
5	18.5	18.0	17.5
6	22.2	21.6	21.0
7	25.9	25.2	24.5
8	29.6	28.8	28.0
9	33.3	32.4	31.5

	34	5	4
1	3.4	0.5	0.4
2	6.8	1.0	0.8
3	10.2	1.5	1.2
4	13.6	2.0	1.6
5	17.0	2.5	2.0
6	20.4	3.0	2.4
7	23.8	3.5	2.8
8	27.2	4.0	3.2
9	30.6	4.5	3.6

Prop. Pts.

Table D (Continued)

20°

′	L Sin	d	L Tan	c d	L Cot	L Cos	d	
0	9.53 405	35	9.56 107	39	10.43 893	9.97 299	5	**60**
1	9.53 440	35	9.56 146	39	10.43 854	9.97 294	5	59
2	9.53 475	34	9.56 185	39	10.43 815	9.97 289	4	58
3	9.53 509	35	9.56 224	40	10.43 776	9.97 285	5	57
4	9.53 544	34	9.56 264	39	10.43 736	9.97 280	4	56
5	9.53 578	35	9.56 303	39	10.43 697	9.97 276	5	55
6	9.53 613	34	9.56 342	39	10.43 658	9.97 271	5	54
7	9.53 647	35	9.56 381	39	10.43 619	9.97 266	4	53
8	9.53 682	34	9.56 420	39	10.43 580	9.97 262	5	52
9	9.53 716	35	9.56 459	39	10.43 541	9.97 257	5	51
10	9.53 751	34	9.56 498	39	10.43 502	9.97 252	4	**50**
11	9.53 785	34	9.56 537	39	10.43 463	9.97 248	5	49
12	9.53 819	35	9.56 576	39	10.43 424	9.97 243	5	48
13	9.53 854	34	9.56 615	39	10.43 385	9.97 238	4	47
14	9.53 888	34	9.56 654	39	10.43 346	9.97 234	5	46
15	9.53 922	35	9.56 693	39	10.43 307	9.97 229	5	45
16	9.53 957	34	9.56 732	39	10.43 268	9.97 224	4	44
17	9.53 991	34	9.56 771	39	10.43 229	9.97 220	5	43
18	9.54 025	34	9.56 810	39	10.43 190	9.97 215	5	42
19	9.54 059	34	9.56 849	38	10.43 151	9.97 210	4	41
20	9.54 093	34	9.56 887	39	10.43 113	9.97 206	5	**40**
21	9.54 127	34	9.56 926	39	10.43 074	9.97 201	5	39
22	9.54 161	34	9.56 965	39	10.43 035	9.97 196	4	38
23	9.54 195	34	9.57 004	38	10.42 996	9.97 192	5	37
24	9.54 229	34	9.57 042	39	10.42 958	9.97 187	5	36
25	9.54 263	34	9.57 081	39	10.42 919	9.97 182	4	35
26	9.54 297	34	9.57 120	38	10.42 880	9.97 178	5	34
27	9.54 331	34	9.57 158	39	10.42 842	9.97 173	5	33
28	9.54 365	34	9.57 197	38	10.42 803	9.97 168	5	32
29	9.54 399	34	9.57 235	39	10.42 765	9.97 163	4	31
30	9.54 433	33	9.57 274	38	10.42 726	9.97 159	5	**30**
31	9.54 466	34	9.57 312	39	10.42 688	9.97 154	5	29
32	9.54 500	34	9.57 351	38	10.42 649	9.97 149	4	28
33	9.54 534	33	9.57 389	39	10.42 611	9.97 145	5	27
34	9.54 567	34	9.57 428	38	10.42 572	9.97 140	5	26
35	9.54 601	34	9.57 466	38	10.42 534	9.97 135	5	25
36	9.54 635	33	9.57 504	39	10.42 496	9.97 130	4	24
37	9.54 668	34	9.57 543	38	10.42 457	9.97 126	5	23
38	9.54 702	33	9.57 581	38	10.42 419	9.97 121	5	22
39	9.54 735	34	9.57 619	39	10.42 381	9.97 116	5	21
40	9.54 769	33	9.57 658	38	10.42 342	9.97 111	4	**20**
41	9.54 802	34	9.57 696	38	10.42 304	9.97 107	5	19
42	9.54 836	33	9.57 734	38	10.42 266	9.97 102	5	18
43	9.54 869	34	9.57 772	38	10.42 228	9.97 097	5	17
44	9.54 903	33	9.57 810	39	10.42 190	9.97 092	5	16
45	9.54 936	33	9.57 849	38	10.42 151	9.97 087	4	15
46	9.54 969	34	9.57 887	38	10.42 113	9.97 083	5	14
47	9.55 003	33	9.57 925	38	10.42 075	9.97 078	5	13
48	9.55 036	33	9.57 963	38	10.42 037	9.97 073	5	12
49	9.55 069	33	9.58 001	38	10.41 999	9.97 068	5	11
50	9.55 102	34	9.58 039	38	10.41 961	9.97 063	4	**10**
51	9.55 136	33	9.58 077	38	10.41 923	9.97 059	5	9
52	9.55 169	33	9.58 115	38	10.41 885	9.97 054	5	8
53	9.55 202	33	9.58 153	38	10.41 847	9.97 049	5	7
54	9.55 235	33	9.58 191	38	10.41 809	9.97 044	5	6
55	9.55 268	33	9.58 229	38	10.41 771	9.97 039	4	5
56	9.55 301	33	9.58 267	37	10.41 733	9.97 035	5	4
57	9.55 334	33	9.58 304	38	10.41 696	9.97 030	5	3
58	9.55 367	33	9.58 342	38	10.41 658	9.97 025	5	2
59	9.55 400	33	9.58 380	38	10.41 620	9.97 020	5	1
60	9.55 433		9.58 418		10.41 582	9.97 015		**0**
	L Cos	d	L Cot	c d	L Tan	L Sin	d	′

Prop. Pts.

	40	39	38
1	4.0	3.9	3.8
2	8.0	7.8	7.6
3	12.0	11.7	11.4
4	16.0	15.6	15.2
5	20.0	19.5	19.0
6	24.0	23.4	22.8
7	28.0	27.3	26.6
8	32.0	31.2	30.4
9	36.0	35.1	34.2

	37	35	34
1	3.7	3.5	3.4
2	7.4	7.0	6.8
3	11.1	10.5	10.2
4	14.8	14.0	13.6
5	18.5	17.5	17.0
6	22.2	21.0	20.4
7	25.9	24.5	23.8
8	29.6	28.0	27.2
9	33.3	31.5	30.6

	33	5	4
1	3.3	0.5	0.4
2	6.6	1.0	0.8
3	9.9	1.5	1.2
4	13.2	2.0	1.6
5	16.5	2.5	2.0
6	19.8	3.0	2.4
7	23.1	3.5	2.8
8	26.4	4.0	3.2
9	29.7	4.5	3.6

Prop. Pts.

69°

Table D (Continued)

21°

′	L Sin	d	L Tan	c d	L Cot	L Cos	d	
0	9.55 433	33	9.58 418	37	10.41 582	9.97 015	5	**60**
1	9.55 466	33	9.58 455	38	10.41 545	9.97 010	5	59
2	9.55 499	33	9.58 493	38	10.41 507	9.97 005	4	58
3	9.55 532	32	9.58 531	38	10.41 469	9.97 001	5	57
4	9.55 564	33	9.58 569	37	10.41 431	9.96 996	5	56
5	9.55 597	33	9.58 606	38	10.41 394	9.96 991	5	55
6	9.55 630	33	9.58 644	37	10.41 356	9.96 986	5	54
7	9.55 663	32	9.58 681	38	10.41 319	9.96 981	5	53
8	9.55 695	33	9.58 719	38	10.41 281	9.96 976	5	52
9	9.55 728	33	9.58 757	37	10.41 243	9.96 971	5	51
10	9.55 761	32	9.58 794	38	10.41 206	9.96 966	4	**50**
11	9.55 793	33	9.58 832	37	10.41 168	9.96 962	5	49
12	9.55 826	32	9.58 869	38	10.41 131	9.96 957	5	48
13	9.55 858	33	9.58 907	37	10.41 093	9.96 952	5	47
14	9.55 891	32	9.58 944	37	10.41 056	9.96 947	5	46
15	9.55 923	33	9.58 981	38	10.41 019	9.96 942	5	45
16	9.55 956	32	9.59 019	37	10.40 981	9.96 937	5	44
17	9.55 988	33	9.59 056	38	10.40 944	9.96 932	5	43
18	9.56 021	32	9.59 094	37	10.40 906	9.96 927	5	42
19	9.56 053	32	9.59 131	37	10.40 869	9.96 922	5	41
20	9.56 085	33	9.59 168	37	10.40 832	9.96 917	5	**40**
21	9.56 118	32	9.59 205	38	10.40 795	9.96 912	5	39
22	9.56 150	32	9.59 243	37	10.40 757	9.96 907	4	38
23	9.56 182	33	9.59 280	37	10.40 720	9.96 903	5	37
24	9.56 215	32	9.59 317	37	10.40 683	9.96 898	5	36
25	9.56 247	32	9.59 354	37	10.40 646	9.96 893	5	35
26	9.56 279	32	9.59 391	38	10.40 609	9.96 888	5	34
27	9.56 311	32	9.59 429	37	10.40 571	9.96 883	5	33
28	9.56 343	32	9.59 466	37	10.40 534	9.96 878	5	32
29	9.56 375	33	9.59 503	37	10.40 497	9.96 873	5	31
30	9.56 408	32	9.59 540	37	10.40 460	9.96 868	5	**30**
31	9.56 440	32	9.59 577	37	10.40 423	9.96 863	5	29
32	9.56 472	32	9.59 614	37	10.40 386	9.96 858	5	28
33	9.56 504	32	9.59 651	37	10.40 349	9.96 853	5	27
34	9.56 536	32	9.59 688	37	10.40 312	9.96 848	5	26
35	9.56 568	31	9.59 725	37	10.40 275	9.96 843	5	25
36	9.56 599	32	9.59 762	37	10.40 238	9.96 838	5	24
37	9.56 631	32	9.59 799	36	10.40 201	9.96 833	5	23
38	9.56 663	32	9.59 835	37	10.40 165	9.96 828	5	22
39	9.56 695	32	9.59 872	37	10.40 128	9.96 823	5	21
40	9.56 727	32	9.59 909	37	10.40 091	9.96 818	5	**20**
41	9.56 759	31	9.59 946	37	10.40 054	9.96 813	5	19
42	9.56 790	32	9.59 983	36	10.40 017	9.96 808	5	18
43	9.56 822	32	9.60 019	37	10.39 981	9.96 803	5	17
44	9.56 854	32	9.60 056	37	10.39 944	9.96 798	5	16
45	9.56 886	31	9.60 093	37	10.39 907	9.96 793	5	15
46	9.56 917	32	9.60 130	36	10.39 870	9.96 788	5	14
47	9.56 949	31	9.60 166	37	10.39 834	9.96 783	5	13
48	9.56 980	32	9.60 203	37	10.39 797	9.96 778	6	12
49	9.57 012	32	9.60 240	36	10.39 760	9.96 772	5	11
50	9.57 044	31	9.60 276	37	10.39 724	9.96 767	5	**10**
51	9.57 075	32	9.60 313	36	10.39 687	9.96 762	5	9
52	9.57 107	31	9.60 349	37	10.39 651	9.96 757	5	8
53	9.57 138	31	9.60 386	36	10.39 614	9.96 752	5	7
54	9.57 169	32	9.60 422	37	10.39 578	9.96 747	5	6
55	9.57 201	31	9.60 459	36	10.39 541	9.96 742	5	5
56	9.57 232	32	9.60 495	37	10.39 505	9.96 737	5	4
57	9.57 264	31	9.60 532	36	10.39 468	9.96 732	5	3
58	9.57 295	31	9.60 568	37	10.39 432	9.96 727	5	2
59	9.57 326	32	9.60 605	36	10.39 395	9.96 722	5	1
60	9.57 358		9.60 641		10.39 359	9.96 717		**0**
	L Cos	d	L Cot	c d	L Tan	L Sin	d	′

Prop. Pts.

	38	37	36
1	3.8	3.7	3.6
2	7.6	7.4	7.2
3	11.4	11.1	10.8
4	15.2	14.8	14.4
5	19.0	18.5	18.0
6	22.8	22.2	21.6
7	26.6	25.9	25.2
8	30.4	29.6	28.8
9	34.2	33.3	32.4

	33	32	31
1	3.3	3.2	3.1
2	6.6	6.4	6.2
3	9.9	9.6	9.3
4	13.2	12.8	12.4
5	16.5	16.0	15.5
6	19.8	19.2	18.6
7	23.1	22.4	21.7
8	26.4	25.6	24.8
9	29.7	28.8	27.9

	6	5	4
1	0.6	0.5	0.4
2	1.2	1.0	0.8
3	1.8	1.5	1.2
4	2.4	2.0	1.6
5	3.0	2.5	2.0
6	3.6	3.0	2.4
7	4.2	3.5	2.8
8	4.8	4.0	3.2
9	5.4	4.5	3.6

Prop. Pts.

68°

Table D (Continued)

22°

'	L Sin	d	L Tan	c d	L Cot	L Cos	d	
0	9.57 358	31	9.60 641	36	10.39 359	9.96 717	6	**60**
1	9.57 389	31	9.60 677	37	10.39 323	9.96 711	5	59
2	9.57 420	31	9.60 714	36	10.39 286	9.96 706	5	58
3	9.57 451	31	9.60 750	36	10.39 250	9.96 701	5	57
4	9.57 482	32	9.60 786	37	10.39 214	9.96 696	5	56
5	9.57 514	31	9.60 823	36	10.39 177	9.96 691	5	55
6	9.57 545	31	9.60 859	36	10.39 141	9.96 686	5	54
7	9.57 576	31	9.60 895	36	10.39 105	9.96 681	5	53
8	9.57 607	31	9.60 931	36	10.39 069	9.96 676	6	52
9	9.57 638	31	9.60 967	37	10.39 033	9.96 670	5	51
10	9.57 669	31	9.61 004	36	10.38 996	9.96 665	5	**50**
11	9.57 700	31	9.61 040	36	10.38 960	9.96 660	5	49
12	9.57 731	31	9.61 076	36	10.38 924	9.96 655	5	48
13	9.57 762	31	9.61 112	36	10.38 888	9.96 650	5	47
14	9.57 793	31	9.61 148	36	10.38 852	9.96 645	5	46
15	9.57 824	31	9.61 184	36	10.38 816	9.96 640	6	45
16	9.57 855	30	9.61 220	36	10.38 780	9.96 634	5	44
17	9.57 885	31	9.61 256	36	10.38 744	9.96 629	5	43
18	9.57 916	31	9.61 292	36	10.38 708	9.96 624	5	42
19	9.57 947	31	9.61 328	36	10.38 672	9.96 619	5	41
20	9.57 978	30	9.61 364	36	10.38 636	9.96 614	6	**40**
21	9.58 008	31	9.61 400	36	10.38 600	9.96 608	5	39
22	9.58 039	31	9.61 436	36	10.38 564	9.96 603	5	38
23	9.58 070	31	9.61 472	36	10.38 528	9.96 598	5	37
24	9.58 101	30	9.61 508	36	10.38 492	9.96 593	5	36
25	9.58 131	31	9.61 544	35	10.38 456	9.96 588	6	35
26	9.58 162	30	9.61 579	36	10.38 421	9.96 582	5	34
27	9.58 192	31	9.61 615	36	10.38 385	9.96 577	5	33
28	9.58 223	30	9.61 651	36	10.38 349	9.96 572	5	32
29	9.58 253	31	9.61 687	35	10.38 313	9.96 567	5	31
30	9.58 284	30	9.61 722	36	10.38 278	9.96 562	6	**30**
31	9.58 314	31	9.61 758	36	10.38 242	9.96 556	5	29
32	9.58 345	30	9.61 794	36	10.38 206	9.96 551	5	28
33	9.58 375	31	9.61 830	35	10.38 170	9.96 546	5	27
34	9.58 406	30	9.61 865	36	10.38 135	9.96 541	6	26
35	9.58 436	31	9.61 901	35	10.38 099	9.96 535	5	25
36	9.58 467	30	9.61 936	36	10.38 064	9.96 530	5	24
37	9.58 497	30	9.61 972	36	10.38 028	9.96 525	5	23
38	9.58 527	30	9.62 008	35	10.37 992	9.96 520	6	22
39	9.58 557	31	9.62 043	36	10.37 957	9.96 514	5	21
40	9.58 588	30	9.62 079	35	10.37 921	9.96 509	5	**20**
41	9.58 618	30	9.62 114	36	10.37 886	9.96 504	6	19
42	9.58 648	30	9.62 150	35	10.37 850	9.96 498	5	18
43	9.58 678	31	9.62 185	36	10.37 815	9.96 493	5	17
44	9.58 709	30	9.62 221	35	10.37 779	9.96 488	5	16
45	9.58 739	30	9.62 256	36	10.37 744	9.96 483	6	15
46	9.58 769	30	9.62 292	35	10.37 708	9.96 477	5	14
47	9.58 799	30	9.62 327	35	10.37 673	9.96 472	5	13
48	9.58 829	30	9.62 362	36	10.37 638	9.96 467	6	12
49	9.58 859	30	9.62 398	35	10.37 602	9.96 461	5	11
50	9.58 889	30	9.62 433	35	10.37 567	9.96 456	5	**10**
51	9.58 919	30	9.62 468	36	10.37 532	9.96 451	6	9
52	9.58 949	30	9.62 504	35	10.37 496	9.96 445	5	8
53	9.58 979	30	9.62 539	35	10.37 461	9.96 440	5	7
54	9.59 009	30	9.62 574	35	10.37 426	9.96 435	6	6
55	9.59 039	30	9.62 609	36	10.37 391	9.96 429	5	5
56	9.59 069	29	9.62 645	35	10.37 355	9.96 424	5	4
57	9.59 098	30	9.62 680	35	10.37 320	9.96 419	6	3
58	9.59 128	30	9.62 715	35	10.37 285	9.96 413	5	2
59	9.59 158	30	9.62 750	35	10.37 250	9.96 408	5	1
60	9.59 188		9.62 785		10.37 215	9.96 403		**0**
	L Cos	d	L Cot	c d	L Tan	L Sin	d	'

67°

Prop. Pts.

	37	36	35
1	3.7	3.6	3.5
2	7.4	7.2	7.0
3	11.1	10.8	10.5
4	14.8	14.4	14.0
5	18.5	18.0	17.5
6	22.2	21.6	21.0
7	25.9	25.2	24.5
8	29.6	28.8	28.0
9	33.3	32.4	31.5

	32	31	30
1	3.2	3.1	3.0
2	6.4	6.2	6.0
3	9.6	9.3	9.0
4	12.8	12.4	12.0
5	16.0	15.5	15.0
6	19.2	18.6	18.0
7	22.4	21.7	21.0
8	25.6	24.8	24.0
9	28.8	27.9	27.0

	29	6	5
1	2.9	0.6	0.5
2	5.8	1.2	1.0
3	8.7	1.8	1.5
4	11.6	2.4	2.0
5	14.5	3.0	2.5
6	17.4	3.6	3.0
7	20.3	4.2	3.5
8	23.2	4.8	4.0
9	26.1	5.4	4.5

Table D (Continued)

23°

′	L Sin	d	L Tan	c d	L Cot	L Cos	d	
0	9.59 188	30	9.62 785	35	10.37 215	9.96 403	6	**60**
1	9.59 218	29	9.62 820	35	10.37 180	9.96 397	5	59
2	9.59 247	30	9.62 855	35	10.37 145	9.96 392	5	58
3	9.59 277	30	9.62 890	36	10.37 110	9.96 387	6	57
4	9.59 307	29	9.62 926	35	10.37 074	9.96 381	5	56
5	9.59 336	30	9.62 961	35	10.37 039	9.96 376	6	55
6	9.59 366	30	9.62 996	35	10.37 004	9.96 370	5	54
7	9.59 396	29	9.63 031	35	10.36 969	9.96 365	5	53
8	9.59 425	30	9.63 066	35	10.36 934	9.96 360	6	52
9	9.59 455	29	9.63 101	34	10.36 899	9.96 354	5	51
10	9.59 484	30	9.63 135	35	10.36 865	9.96 349	6	**50**
11	9.59 514	29	9.63 170	35	10.36 830	9.96 343	5	49
12	9.59 543	30	9.63 205	35	10.36 795	9.96 338	5	48
13	9.59 573	29	9.63 240	35	10.36 760	9.96 333	6	47
14	9.59 602	30	9.63 275	35	10.36 725	9.96 327	5	46
15	9.59 632	29	9.63 310	35	10.36 690	9.96 322	6	45
16	9.59 661	29	9.63 345	34	10.36 655	9.96 316	5	44
17	9.59 690	30	9.63 379	35	10.36 621	9.96 311	6	43
18	9.59 720	29	9.63 414	35	10.36 586	9.96 305	5	42
19	9.59 749	29	9.63 449	35	10.36 551	9.96 300	6	41
20	9.59 778	30	9.63 484	35	10.36 516	9.96 294	5	**40**
21	9.59 808	29	9.63 519	34	10.36 481	9.96 289	5	39
22	9.59 839	29	9.63 553	35	10.36 447	9.96 284	6	38
23	9.59 866	29	9.63 588	35	10.36 412	9.96 278	5	37
24	9.59 895	29	9.63 623	34	10.36 377	9.96 273	6	36
25	9.59 924	30	9.63 657	35	10.36 343	9.96 267	5	35
26	9.59 954	29	9.63 692	34	10.36 308	9.96 262	6	34
27	9.59 983	29	9.63 726	35	10.36 274	9.96 256	5	33
28	9.60 012	29	9.63 761	35	10.36 239	9.96 251	6	32
29	9.60 041	29	9.63 796	34	10.36 204	9.96 245	5	31
30	9.60 070	29	9.63 830	35	10.36 170	9.96 240	6	**30**
31	9.60 099	29	9.63 865	34	10.36 135	9.96 234	5	29
32	9.60 128	29	9.63 899	35	10.36 101	9.96 229	6	28
33	9.60 157	29	9.63 934	34	10.36 066	9.96 223	5	27
34	9.60 186	29	9.63 968	35	10.36 032	9.96 218	6	26
35	9.60 215	29	9.64 003	34	10.35 997	9.96 212	5	25
36	9.60 244	29	9.64 037	35	10.35 963	9.96 207	6	24
37	9.60 273	29	9.64 072	34	10.35 928	9.96 201	5	23
38	9.60 302	29	9.64 106	34	10.35 894	9.96 196	6	22
39	9.60 331	28	9.64 140	35	10.35 860	9.96 190	5	21
40	9.60 359	29	9.64 175	34	10.35 825	9.96 185	6	**20**
41	9.60 388	29	9.64 209	34	10.35 791	9.96 179	5	19
42	9.60 417	29	9.64 243	35	10.35 757	9.96 174	6	18
43	9.60 446	28	9.64 278	34	10.35 722	9.96 168	6	17
44	9.60 474	29	9.64 312	34	10.35 688	9.96 162	5	16
45	9.60 503	29	9.64 346	35	10.35 654	9.96 157	6	15
46	9.60 532	29	9.64 381	34	10.35 619	9.96 151	5	14
47	9.60 561	28	9.64 415	34	10.35 585	9.96 146	6	13
48	9.60 589	29	9.64 449	34	10.35 551	9.96 140	5	12
49	9.60 618	28	9.64 483	34	10.35 517	9.96 135	6	11
50	9.60 646	29	9.64 517	35	10.35 483	9.96 129	6	**10**
51	9.60 675	29	9.64 552	34	10.35 448	9.96 123	5	9
52	9.60 704	28	9.64 586	34	10.35 414	9.96 118	6	8
53	9.60 732	29	9.64 620	34	10.35 380	9.96 112	5	7
54	9.60 761	28	9.64 654	34	10.35 346	9.96 107	6	6
55	9.60 789	29	9.64 688	34	10.35 312	9.96 101	6	5
56	9.60 818	28	9.64 722	34	10.35 278	9.96 095	5	4
57	9.60 846	29	9.64 756	34	10.35 244	9.96 090	6	3
58	9.60 875	28	9.64 790	34	10.35 210	9.96 084	5	2
59	9.60 903	28	9.64 824	34	10.35 176	9.96 079	6	1
60	9.60 931		9.64 858		10.35 142	9.96 073		**0**
	L Cos	d	L Cot	c d	L Tan	L Sin	d	′

Prop. Pts.

	36	35	34
1	3.6	3.5	3.4
2	7.2	7.0	6.8
3	10.8	10.5	10.2
4	14.4	14.0	13.6
5	18.0	17.5	17.0
6	21.6	21.0	20.4
7	25.2	24.5	23.8
8	28.8	28.0	27.2
9	32.4	31.5	30.6

	30	29	28
1	3.0	2.9	2.8
2	6.0	5.8	5.6
3	9.0	8.7	8.4
4	12.0	11.6	11.2
5	15.0	14.5	14.0
6	18.0	17.4	16.8
7	21.0	20.3	19.6
8	24.0	23.2	22.4
9	27.0	26.1	25.2

	6	5
1	0.6	0.5
2	1.2	1.0
3	1.8	1.5
4	2.4	2.0
5	3.0	2.5
6	3.6	3.0
7	4.2	3.5
8	4.8	4.0
9	5.4	4.5

Prop. Pts.

66°

Table D (Continued)

24°

′	L Sin	d	L Tan	c d	L Cot	L Cos	d	
0	9.60 931	29	9.64 858	34	10.35 142	9.96 073	6	**60**
1	9.60 960	28	9.64 892	34	10.35 108	9.96 067	5	59
2	9.60 988	28	9.64 926	34	10.35 074	9.96 062	6	58
3	9.61 016	29	9.64 960	34	10.35 040	9.96 056	6	57
4	9.61 045	28	9.64 994	34	10.35 006	9.96 050	5	56
5	9.61 073	28	9.65 028	34	10.34 972	9.96 045	6	55
6	9.61 101	28	9.65 062	34	10.34 938	9.96 039	5	54
7	9.61 129	29	9.65 096	34	10.34 904	9.96 034	6	53
8	9.61 158	28	9.65 130	34	10.34 870	9.96 028	6	52
9	9.61 186	28	9.65 164	33	10.34 836	9.96 022	5	51
10	9.61 214	28	9.65 197	34	10.34 803	9.96 017	6	**50**
11	9.61 242	28	9.65 231	34	10.34 769	9.96 011	6	49
12	9.61 270	28	9.65 265	34	10.34 735	9.96 005	5	48
13	9.61 298	28	9.65 299	34	10.34 701	9.96 000	6	47
14	9.61 326	28	9.65 333	33	10.34 667	9.95 994	6	46
15	9.61 354	28	9.65 366	34	10.34 634	9.95 988	6	45
16	9.61 382	29	9.65 400	34	10.34 600	9.95 982	5	44
17	9.61 411	27	9.65 434	33	10.34 566	9.95 977	6	43
18	9.61 438	28	9.65 467	34	10.34 533	9.95 971	6	42
19	9.61 466	28	9.65 501	34	10.34 499	9.95 965	5	41
20	9.61 494	28	9.65 535	33	10.34 465	9.95 960	6	**40**
21	9.61 522	28	9.65 568	34	10.34 432	9.95 954	6	39
22	9.61 550	28	9.65 602	34	10.34 398	9.95 948	6	38
23	9.61 578	28	9.65 636	33	10.34 364	9.95 942	5	37
24	9.61 606	28	9.65 669	34	10.34 331	9.95 937	6	36
25	9.61 634	28	9.65 703	33	10.34 297	9.95 931	6	35
26	9.61 662	27	9.65 736	34	10.34 264	9.95 925	5	34
27	9.61 689	28	9.65 770	33	10.34 230	9.95 920	6	33
28	9.61 717	28	9.65 803	34	10.34 197	9.95 914	6	32
29	9.61 745	28	9.65 837	33	10.34 163	9.95 908	6	31
30	9.61 773	27	9.65 870	34	10.34 130	9.95 902	5	**30**
31	9.61 800	28	9.65 904	33	10.34 096	9.95 897	6	29
32	9.61 828	28	9.65 937	34	10.34 063	9.95 891	6	28
33	9.61 856	27	9.65 971	33	10.34 029	9.95 885	6	27
34	9.61 883	28	9.66 004	34	10.33 996	9.95 879	6	26
35	9.61 911	28	9.66 038	33	10.33 962	9.95 873	5	25
36	9.61 939	27	9.66 071	33	10.33 929	9.95 868	6	24
37	9.61 966	28	9.66 104	34	10.33 896	9.95 862	6	23
38	9.61 994	27	9.66 138	33	10.33 862	9.95 856	6	22
39	9.62 021	28	9.66 171	33	10.33 829	9.95 850	6	21
40	9.62 049	27	9.66 204	34	10.33 796	9.95 844	5	**20**
41	9.62 076	28	9.66 238	33	10.33 762	9.95 839	6	19
42	9.62 104	27	9.66 271	33	10.33 729	9.95 833	6	18
43	9.62 131	28	9.66 304	33	10.33 696	9.95 827	6	17
44	9.62 159	27	9.66 337	34	10.33 663	9.95 821	6	16
45	9.62 186	28	9.66 371	33	10.33 629	9.95 815	5	15
46	9.62 214	27	9.66 404	33	10.33 596	9.95 810	6	14
47	9.62 241	27	9.66 437	33	10.33 563	9.95 804	6	13
48	9.62 268	28	9.66 470	33	10.33 530	9.95 798	6	12
49	9.62 296	27	9.66 503	34	10.33 497	9.95 792	6	11
50	9.62 323	27	9.66 537	33	10.33 463	9.95 786	6	**10**
51	9.62 350	27	9.66 570	33	10.33 430	9.95 780	5	9
52	9.62 377	28	9.66 603	33	10.33 397	9.95 775	6	8
53	9.62 405	27	9.66 636	33	10.33 364	9.95 769	6	7
54	9.62 432	27	9.66 669	33	10.33 331	9.95 763	6	6
55	9.62 459	27	9.66 702	33	10.33 298	9.95 757	6	5
56	9.62 486	27	9.66 735	33	10.33 265	9.95 751	6	4
57	9.62 513	28	9.66 768	33	10.33 232	9.95 745	6	3
58	9.62 541	27	9.66 801	33	10.33 199	9.95 739	6	2
59	9.62 568	27	9.66 834	33	10.33 166	9.95 733	5	1
60	9.62 595		9.66 867		10.33 133	9.95 728		**0**
	L Cos	d	L Cot	c d	L Tan	L Sin	d	′

65°

Prop. Pts.

	34	33
1	3.4	3.3
2	6.8	6.6
3	10.2	9.9
4	13.6	13.2
5	17.0	16.5
6	20.4	19.8
7	23.8	23.1
8	27.2	26.4
9	30.6	29.7

	29	28	27
1	2.9	2.8	2.7
2	5.8	5.6	5.4
3	8.7	8.4	8.1
4	11.6	11.2	10.8
5	14.5	14.0	13.5
6	17.4	16.8	16.2
7	20.3	19.6	18.9
8	23.2	22.4	21.6
9	26.1	25.2	24.3

	6	5
1	0.6	0.5
2	1.2	1.0
3	1.8	1.5
4	2.4	2.0
5	3.0	2.5
6	3.6	3.0
7	4.2	3.5
8	4.8	4.0
9	5.4	4.5

Prop. Pts.

Table D (Continued)

25°

′	L Sin	d	L Tan	c d	L Cot	L Cos	d	
0	9.62 595	27	9.66 867	33	10.33 133	9.95 728	6	**60**
1	9.62 622	27	9.66 900	33	10.33 100	9.95 722	6	59
2	9.62 649	27	9.66 933	33	10.33 067	9.95 716	6	58
3	9.62 676	27	9.66 966	33	10.33 034	9.95 710	6	57
4	9.62 703	27	9.66 999	33	10.33 001	9.95 704	6	56
5	9.62 730	27	9.67 032	33	10.32 968	9.95 698	6	55
6	9.62 757	27	9.67 065	33	10.32 935	9.95 692	6	54
7	9.62 784	27	9.67 098	33	10.32 902	9.95 686	6	53
8	9.62 811	27	9.67 131	32	10.32 869	9.95 680	6	52
9	9.62 838	27	9.67 163	33	10.32 837	9.95 674	6	51
10	9.62 865	27	9.67 196	33	10.32 804	9.95 668	5	**50**
11	9.62 892	26	9.67 229	33	10.32 771	9.95 663	6	49
12	9.62 918	27	9.67 262	33	10.32 738	9.95 657	6	48
13	9.62 945	27	9.67 295	32	10.32 705	9.95 651	6	47
14	9.62 972	27	9.67 327	33	10.32 673	9.95 645	6	46
15	9.62 999	27	9.67 360	33	10.32 640	9.95 639	6	45
16	9.63 026	26	9.67 393	33	10.32 607	9.95 633	6	44
17	9.63 052	27	9.67 426	32	10.32 574	9.95 627	6	43
18	9.63 079	27	9.67 458	33	10.32 542	9.95 621	6	42
19	9.63 106	27	9.67 491	33	10.32 509	9.95 615	6	41
20	9.63 133	26	9.67 524	32	10.32 476	9.95 609	6	**40**
21	9.63 159	27	9.67 556	33	10.32 444	9.95 603	6	39
22	9.63 186	27	9.67 589	33	10.32 411	9.95 597	6	38
23	9.63 213	26	9.67 622	32	10.32 378	9.95 591	6	37
24	9.63 239	27	9.67 654	33	10.32 346	9.95 585	6	36
25	9.63 266	26	9.67 687	32	10.32 313	9.95 579	6	35
26	9.63 292	27	9.67 719	33	10.32 281	9.95 573	6	34
27	9.63 319	26	9.67 752	33	10.32 248	9.95 567	6	33
28	9.63 345	27	9.67 785	32	10.32 215	9.95 561	6	32
29	9.63 372	26	9.67 817	33	10.32 183	9.95 555	6	31
30	9.63 398	27	9.67 850	32	10.32 150	9.95 549	6	**30**
31	9.63 425	26	9.67 882	33	10.32 118	9.95 543	6	29
32	9.63 451	27	9.67 915	32	10.32 085	9.95 537	6	28
33	9.63 478	26	9.67 947	33	10.32 053	9.95 531	6	27
34	9.63 504	27	9.67 980	32	10.32 020	9.95 525	6	26
35	9.63 531	26	9.68 012	32	10.31 988	9.95 519	6	25
36	9.63 557	26	9.68 044	33	10.31 956	9.95 513	6	24
37	9.63 583	27	9.68 077	32	10.31 923	9.95 507	7	23
38	9.63 610	26	9.68 109	33	10.31 891	9.95 500	6	22
39	9.63 636	26	9.68 142	32	10.31 858	9.95 494	6	21
40	9.63 662	27	9.68 174	32	10.31 826	9.95 488	6	**20**
41	9.63 689	26	9.68 206	33	10.31 794	9.95 482	6	19
42	9.63 715	26	9.68 239	32	10.31 761	9.95 476	6	18
43	9.63 741	26	9.68 271	32	10.31 729	9.95 470	6	17
44	9.63 767	27	9.68 303	33	10.31 697	9.95 464	6	16
45	9.63 794	26	9.68 336	32	10.31 664	9.95 458	6	15
46	9.63 820	26	9.68 368	32	10.31 632	9.95 452	6	14
47	9.63 846	26	9.68 400	32	10.31 600	9.95 446	6	13
48	9.63 872	26	9.68 432	33	10.31 568	9.95 440	6	12
49	9.63 898	26	9.68 465	32	10.31 535	9.95 434	7	11
50	9.63 924	26	9.68 497	32	10.31 503	9.95 427	6	**10**
51	9.63 950	26	9.68 529	32	10.31 471	9.95 421	6	9
52	9.63 976	26	9.68 561	32	10.31 439	9.95 415	6	8
53	9.64 002	26	9.68 593	33	10.31 407	9.95 409	6	7
54	9.64 028	26	9.68 626	32	10.31 374	9.95 403	6	6
55	9.64 054	26	9.68 658	32	10.31 342	9.95 397	6	5
56	9.64 080	26	9.68 690	32	10.31 310	9.95 391	7	4
57	9.64 106	26	9.68 722	32	10.31 278	9.95 384	6	3
58	9.64 132	26	9.68 754	32	10.31 246	9.95 378	6	2
59	9.64 158	26	9.68 786	32	10.31 214	9.95 372	6	1
60	9.64 184		9.68 818		10.31 182	9.95 366		**0**
	L Cos	**d**	**L Cot**	**c d**	**L Tan**	**L Sin**	**d**	**′**

64°

Prop. Pts.

	33	32
1	3.3	3.2
2	6.6	6.4
3	9.9	9.6
4	13.2	12.8
5	16.5	16.0
6	19.8	19.2
7	23.1	22.4
8	26.4	25.6
9	29.7	28.8

	27	26
1	2.7	2.6
2	5.4	5.2
3	8.1	7.8
4	10.8	10.4
5	13.5	13.0
6	16.2	15.6
7	18.9	18.2
8	21.6	20.8
9	24.3	23.4

	7	6	5
1	0.7	0.6	0.5
2	1.4	1.2	1.0
3	2.1	1.8	1.5
4	2.8	2.4	2.0
5	3.5	3.0	2.5
6	4.2	3.6	3.0
7	4.9	4.2	3.5
8	5.6	4.8	4.0
9	6.3	5.4	4.5

Table D (Continued)

26°

′	L Sin	d	L Tan	c d	L Cot	L Cos	d	
0	9.64 184	26	9.68 818	32	10.31 182	9.95 366	6	**60**
1	9.64 210	26	9.68 850	32	10.31 150	9.95 360	6	59
2	9.64 236	26	9.68 882	32	10.31 118	9.95 354	6	58
3	9.64 262	26	9.68 914	32	10.31 086	9.95 348	7	57
4	9.64 288	25	9.68 946	32	10.31 054	9.95 341	6	56
5	9.64 313	26	9.68 978	32	10.31 022	9.95 335	6	55
6	9.64 339	26	9.69 010	32	10.30 990	9.95 329	6	54
7	9.64 365	26	9.69 042	32	10.30 958	9.95 323	6	53
8	9.64 391	26	9.69 074	32	10.30 926	9.95 317	7	52
9	9.64 417	25	9.69 106	32	10.30 894	9.95 310	6	51
10	9.64 442	26	9.69 138	32	10.30 862	9.95 304	6	**50**
11	9.64 468	26	9.69 170	32	10.30 830	9.95 298	6	49
12	9.64 494	25	9.69 202	32	10.30 798	9.95 292	6	48
13	9.64 519	26	9.69 234	32	10.30 766	9.95 286	7	47
14	9.64 545	26	9.69 266	32	10.30 734	9.95 279	6	46
15	9.64 571	25	9.69 298	31	10.30 702	9.95 273	6	45
16	9.64 596	26	9.69 329	32	10.30 671	9.95 267	6	44
17	9.64 622	25	9.69 361	32	10.30 639	9.95 261	7	43
18	9.64 647	26	9.69 393	32	10.30 607	9.95 254	6	42
19	9.64 673	25	9.69 425	32	10.30 575	9.95 248	6	41
20	9.64 698	26	9.69 457	31	10.30 543	9.95 242	6	**40**
21	9.64 724	25	9.69 488	32	10.30 512	9.95 236	7	39
22	9.64 749	26	9.69 520	32	10.30 480	9.95 229	6	38
23	9.64 775	25	9.69 552	32	10.30 448	9.95 223	6	37
24	9.64 800	26	9.69 584	31	10.30 416	9.95 217	6	36
25	9.64 826	25	9.69 615	32	10.30 385	9.95 211	7	35
26	9.64 851	26	9.69 647	32	10.30 353	9.95 204	6	34
27	9.64 877	25	9.69 679	31	10.30 321	9.95 198	6	33
28	9.64 902	25	9.69 710	32	10.30 290	9.95 192	7	32
29	9.64 927	26	9.69 742	32	10.30 258	9.95 185	6	31
30	9.64 953	25	9.69 774	31	10.30 226	9.95 179	6	**30**
31	9.64 978	25	9.69 805	32	10.30 195	9.95 173	6	29
32	9.65 003	26	9.69 837	31	10.30 163	9.95 167	7	28
33	9.65 029	25	9.69 868	32	10.30 132	9.95 160	6	27
34	9.65 054	25	9.69 900	32	10.30 100	9.95 154	6	26
35	9.65 079	25	9.69 932	31	10.30 068	9.95 148	7	25
36	9.65 104	26	9.69 963	32	10.30 037	9.95 141	6	24
37	9.65 130	25	9.69 995	31	10.30 005	9.95 135	6	23
38	9.65 155	25	9.70 026	32	10.29 974	9.95 129	7	22
39	9.65 180	25	9.70 058	31	10.29 942	9.95 122	6	21
40	9.65 205	25	9.70 089	32	10.29 911	9.95 116	6	**20**
41	9.65 230	25	9.70 121	31	10.29 879	9.95 110	7	19
42	9.65 255	26	9.70 152	32	10.29 848	9.95 103	6	18
43	9.65 281	25	9.70 184	31	10.29 816	9.95 097	7	17
44	9.65 306	25	9.70 215	32	10.29 785	9.95 090	6	16
45	9.65 331	25	9.70 247	31	10.29 753	9.95 084	6	15
46	9.65 356	25	9.70 278	31	10.29 722	9.95 078	7	14
47	9.65 381	25	9.70 309	32	10.29 691	9.95 071	6	13
48	9.65 406	25	9.70 341	31	10.29 659	9.95 065	6	12
49	9.65 431	25	9.70 372	32	10.29 628	9.95 059	7	11
50	9.65 456	25	9.70 404	31	10.29 596	9.95 052	6	**10**
51	9.65 481	25	9.70 435	31	10.29 565	9.95 046	7	9
52	9.65 506	25	9.70 466	32	10.29 534	9.95 039	6	8
53	9.65 531	25	9.70 498	31	10.29 502	9.95 033	6	7
54	9.65 556	24	9.70 529	31	10.29 471	9.95 027	7	6
55	9.65 580	25	9.70 560	32	10.29 440	9.95 020	6	5
56	9.65 605	25	9.70 592	31	10.29 408	9.95 014	7	4
57	9.65 630	25	9.70 623	31	10.29 377	9.95 007	6	3
58	9.65 655	25	9.70 654	31	10.29 346	9.95 001	6	2
59	9.65 680	25	9.70 685	32	10.29 315	9.94 995	7	1
60	9.65 705		9.70 717		10.29 283	9.94 988		**0**
	L Cos	d	L Cot	c d	L Tan	L Sin	d	′

Prop. Pts.

	32	**31**
1	3.2	3.1
2	6.4	6.2
3	9.6	9.3
4	12.8	12.4
5	16.0	15.5
6	19.2	18.6
7	22.4	21.7
8	25.6	24.8
9	28.8	27.9

	26	**25**	**24**
1	2.6	2.5	2.4
2	5.2	5.0	4.8
3	7.8	7.5	7.2
4	10.4	10.0	9.6
5	13.0	12.5	12.0
6	15.6	15.0	14.4
7	18.2	17.5	16.8
8	20.8	20.0	19.2
9	23.4	22.5	21.6

	7	**6**
1	0.7	0.6
2	1.4	1.2
3	2.1	1.8
4	2.8	2.4
5	3.5	3.0
6	4.2	3.6
7	4.9	4.2
8	5.6	4.8
9	6.3	5.4

Prop. Pts.

63°

Table D (Continued)

27°

′	L Sin	d	L Tan	c d	L Cot	L Cos	d	′
0	9.65 705	24	9.70 717	31	10.29 283	9.94 988	6	60
1	9.65 729	25	9.70 748	31	10.29 252	9.94 982	7	59
2	9.65 754	25	9.70 779	31	10.29 221	9.94 975	6	58
3	9.65 779	25	9.70 810	31	10.29 190	9.94 969	7	57
4	9.65 804	24	9.70 841	32	10.29 159	9.94 962	6	56
5	9.65 828	25	9.70 873	31	10.29 127	9.94 956	7	55
6	9.65 853	25	9.70 904	31	10.29 096	9.94 949	6	54
7	9.65 878	24	9.70 935	31	10.29 065	9.94 943	7	53
8	9.65 902	25	9.70 966	31	10.29 034	9.94 936	6	52
9	9.65 927	25	9.70 997	31	10.29 003	9.94 930	7	51
10	9.65 952	24	9.71 028	31	10.28 972	9.94 923	6	50
11	9.65 976	25	9.71 059	31	10.28 941	9.94 917	6	49
12	9.66 001	24	9.71 090	31	10.28 910	9.94 911	7	48
13	9.66 025	25	9.71 121	32	10.28 879	9.94 904	6	47
14	9.66 050	25	9.71 153	31	10.28 847	9.94 898	7	46
15	9.66 075	24	9.71 184	31	10.28 816	9.94 891	6	45
16	9.66 099	25	9.71 215	31	10.28 785	9.94 885	7	44
17	9.66 124	24	9.71 246	31	10.28 754	9.94 878	7	43
18	9.66 148	25	9.71 277	31	10.28 723	9.94 871	6	42
19	9.66 173	24	9.71 308	31	10.28 692	9.94 865	7	41
20	9.66 197	24	9.71 339	31	10.28 661	9.94 858	6	40
21	9.66 221	25	9.71 370	31	10.28 630	9.94 852	7	39
22	9.66 246	24	9.71 401	30	10.28 599	9.94 845	6	38
23	9.66 270	25	9.71 431	31	10.28 569	9.94 839	7	37
24	9.66 295	24	9.71 462	31	10.28 538	9.94 832	6	36
25	9.66 319	24	9.71 493	31	10.28 507	9.94 826	7	35
26	9.66 343	25	9.71 524	31	10.28 476	9.94 819	6	34
27	9.66 368	24	9.71 555	31	10.28 445	9.94 813	7	33
28	9.66 392	24	9.71 586	31	10.28 414	9.94 806	7	32
29	9.66 416	25	9.71 617	31	10.28 383	9.94 799	6	31
30	9.66 441	24	9.71 648	31	10.28 352	9.94 793	7	30
31	9.66 465	24	9.71 679	30	10.28 321	9.94 786	6	29
32	9.66 489	24	9.71 709	31	10.28 291	9.94 780	7	28
33	9.66 513	24	9.71 740	31	10.28 260	9.94 773	6	27
34	9.66 537	25	9.71 771	31	10.28 229	9.94 767	7	26
35	9.66 562	24	9.71 802	31	10.28 198	9.94 760	7	25
36	9.66 586	24	9.71 833	30	10.28 167	9.94 753	6	24
37	9.66 610	24	9.71 863	31	10.28 137	9.94 747	7	23
38	9.66 634	24	9.71 894	31	10.28 106	9.94 740	6	22
39	9.66 658	24	9.71 925	30	10.28 075	9.94 734	7	21
40	9.66 682	24	9.71 955	31	10.28 045	9.94 727	7	20
41	9.66 706	25	9.71 986	31	10.28 014	9.94 720	6	19
42	9.66 731	24	9.72 017	31	10.27 983	9.94 714	7	18
43	9.66 755	24	9.72 048	30	10.27 952	9.94 707	7	17
44	9.66 779	24	9.72 078	31	10.27 922	9.94 700	6	16
45	9.66 803	24	9.72 109	31	10.27 891	9.94 694	7	15
46	9.66 827	24	9.72 140	30	10.27 860	9.94 687	7	14
47	9.66 851	24	9.72 170	31	10.27 830	9.94 680	6	13
48	9.66 875	24	9.72 201	30	10.27 799	9.94 674	7	12
49	9.66 899	23	9.72 231	31	10.27 769	9.94 667	7	11
50	9.66 922	24	9.72 262	31	10.27 738	9.94 660	6	10
51	9.66 946	24	9.72 293	30	10.27 707	9.94 654	7	9
52	9.66 970	24	9.72 323	31	10.27 677	9.94 647	7	8
53	9.66 994	24	9.72 354	30	10.27 646	9.94 640	6	7
54	9.67 018	24	9.72 384	31	10.27 616	9.94 634	7	6
55	9.67 042	24	9.72 415	30	10.27 585	9.94 627	7	5
56	9.67 066	24	9.72 445	31	10.27 555	9.94 620	6	4
57	9.67 090	23	9.72 476	30	10.27 524	9.94 614	7	3
58	9.67 113	24	9.72 506	31	10.27 494	9.94 607	7	2
59	9.67 137	24	9.72 537	30	10.27 463	9.94 600	7	1
60	9.67 161		9.72 567		10.27 433	9.94 593		0
	L Cos	d	L Cot	c d	L Tan	L Sin	d	′

Prop. Pts.

	32	31	30
1	3.2	3.1	3.0
2	6.4	6.2	6.0
3	9.6	9.3	9.0
4	12.8	12.4	12.0
5	16.0	15.5	15.0
6	19.2	18.6	18.0
7	22.4	21.7	21.0
8	25.6	24.8	24.0
9	28.8	27.9	27.0

	25	24	23
1	2.5	2.4	2.3
2	5.0	4.8	4.6
3	7.5	7.2	6.9
4	10.0	9.6	9.2
5	12.5	12.0	11.5
6	15.0	14.4	13.8
7	17.5	16.8	16.1
8	20.0	19.2	18.4
9	22.5	21.6	20.7

	7	6
1	0.7	0.6
2	1.4	1.2
3	2.1	1.8
4	2.8	2.4
5	3.5	3.0
6	4.2	3.6
7	4.9	4.2
8	5.6	4.8
9	6.3	5.4

Prop. Pts.

62°

Table D (Continued)

28°

′	L Sin	d	L Tan	c d	L Cot	L Cos	d	
0	9.67 161	24	9.72 567	31	10.27 433	9.94 593	6	**60**
1	9.67 185	23	9.72 598	30	10.27 402	9.94 587	7	59
2	9.67 208	24	9.72 628	31	10.27 372	9.94 580	7	58
3	9.67 232	24	9.72 659	30	10.27 341	9.94 573	6	57
4	9.67 256	24	9.72 689	31	10.27 311	9.94 567	7	56
5	9.67 280	23	9.72 720	30	10.27 280	9.94 560	7	55
6	9.67 303	24	9.72 750	30	10.27 250	9.94 553	7	54
7	9.67 327	23	9.72 780	31	10.27 220	9.94 546	6	53
8	9.67 350	24	9.72 811	30	10.27 189	9.94 540	7	52
9	9.67 374	24	9.72 841	31	10.27 159	9.94 533	7	51
10	9.67 398	23	9.72 872	30	10.27 128	9.94 526	7	**50**
11	9.67 421	24	9.72 902	30	10.27 098	9.94 519	6	49
12	9.67 445	23	9.72 932	31	10.27 068	9.94 513	7	48
13	9.67 468	24	9.72 963	30	10.27 037	9.94 506	7	47
14	9.67 492	23	9.72 993	30	10.27 007	9.94 499	7	46
15	9.67 515	24	9.73 023	31	10.26 977	9.94 492	7	45
16	9.67 539	23	9.73 054	30	10.26 946	9.94 485	6	44
17	9.67 562	24	9.73 084	30	10.26 916	9.94 479	7	43
18	9.67 586	23	9.73 114	30	10.26 886	9.94 472	7	42
19	9.67 609	24	9.73 144	31	10.26 856	9.94 465	7	41
20	9.67 633	23	9.73 175	30	10.26 825	9.94 458	7	**40**
21	9.67 656	24	9.73 205	30	10.26 795	9.94 451	6	39
22	9.67 680	23	9.73 235	30	10.26 765	9.94 445	7	38
23	9.67 703	23	9.73 265	30	10.26 735	9.94 438	7	37
24	9.67 726	24	9.73 295	31	10.26 705	9.94 431	7	36
25	9.67 750	23	9.73 326	30	10.26 674	9.94 424	7	35
26	9.67 773	23	9.73 356	30	10.26 644	9.94 417	7	34
27	9.67 796	24	9.73 386	30	10.26 614	9.94 410	6	33
28	9.67 820	23	9.73 416	30	10.26 584	9.94 404	7	32
29	9.67 843	23	9.73 446	30	10.26 554	9.94 397	7	31
30	9.67 866	24	9.73 476	31	10.26 524	9.94 390	7	**30**
31	9.67 890	23	9.73 507	30	10.26 493	9.94 383	7	29
32	9.67 913	23	9.73 537	30	10.26 463	9.94 376	7	28
33	9.67 936	23	9.73 567	30	10.26 433	9.94 369	7	27
34	9.67 959	23	9.73 597	30	10.26 403	9.94 362	7	26
35	9.67 982	24	9.73 627	30	10.26 373	9.94 355	6	25
36	9.68 006	23	9.73 657	30	10.26 343	9.94 349	7	24
37	9.68 029	23	9.73 687	30	10.26 313	9.94 342	7	23
38	9.68 052	23	9.73 717	30	10.26 283	9.94 335	7	22
39	9.68 075	23	9.73 747	30	10.26 253	9.94 328	7	21
40	9.68 098	23	9.73 777	30	10.26 223	9.94 321	7	**20**
41	9.68 121	23	9.73 807	30	10.26 193	9.94 314	7	19
42	9.68 144	23	9.73 837	30	10.26 163	9.94 307	7	18
43	9.68 167	23	9.73 867	30	10.26 133	9.94 300	7	17
44	9.68 190	23	9.73 897	30	10.26 103	9.94 293	7	16
45	9.68 213	24	9.73 927	30	10.26 073	9.94 286	7	15
46	9.68 237	23	9.73 957	30	10.26 043	9.94 279	6	14
47	9.68 260	23	9.73 987	30	10.26 013	9.94 273	7	13
48	9.68 283	22	9.74 017	30	10.25 983	9.94 266	7	12
49	9.68 305	23	9.74 047	30	10.25 953	9.94 259	7	11
50	9.68 328	23	9.74 077	30	10.25 923	9.94 252	7	**10**
51	9.68 351	23	9.74 107	30	10.25 893	9.94 245	7	9
52	9.68 374	23	9.74 137	29	10.25 863	9.94 238	7	8
53	9.68 397	23	9.74 166	30	10.25 834	9.94 231	7	7
54	9.68 420	23	9.74 196	30	10.25 804	9.94 224	7	6
55	9.68 443	23	9.74 226	30	10.25 774	9.94 217	7	5
56	9.68 466	23	9.74 256	30	10.25 744	9.94 210	7	4
57	9.68 489	23	9.74 286	30	10.25 714	9.94 203	7	3
58	9.68 512	22	9.74 316	29	10.25 684	9.94 196	7	2
59	9.68 534	23	9.74 345	30	10.25 655	9.94 189	7	1
60	9.68 557		9.74 375		10.25 625	9.94 182		**0**
	L Cos	d	L Cot	c d	L Tan	L Sin	d	′

Prop. Pts.

	31	30	29
1	3.1	3.0	2.9
2	6.2	6.0	5.8
3	9.3	9.0	8.7
4	12.4	12.0	11.6
5	15.5	15.0	14.5
6	18.6	18.0	17.4
7	21.7	21.0	20.3
8	24.8	24.0	23.2
9	27.9	27.0	26.1

	24	23	22
1	2.4	2.3	2.2
2	4.8	4.6	4.4
3	7.2	6.9	6.6
4	9.6	9.2	8.8
5	12.0	11.5	11.0
6	14.4	13.8	13.2
7	16.8	16.1	15.4
8	19.2	18.4	17.6
9	21.6	20.7	19.8

	7	6
1	0.7	0.6
2	1.4	1.2
3	2.1	1.8
4	2.8	2.4
5	3.5	3.0
6	4.2	3.6
7	4.9	4.2
8	5.6	4.8
9	6.3	5.4

Prop. Pts.

61°

Table D (Continued)

29°

′	L Sin	d	L Tan	c d	L Cot	L Cos	d	
0	9.68 557	23	9.74 375	30	10.25 625	9.94 182	7	**60**
1	9.68 580	23	9.74 405	30	10.25 595	9.94 175	7	59
2	9.68 603	22	9.74 435	30	10.25 565	9.94 168	7	58
3	9.68 625	23	9.74 465	29	10.25 535	9.94 161	7	57
4	9.68 648	23	9.74 494	30	10.25 506	9.94 154	7	56
5	9.68 671	23	9.74 524	30	10.25 476	9.94 147	7	55
6	9.68 694	22	9.74 554	29	10.25 446	9.94 140	7	54
7	9.68 716	23	9.74 583	30	10.25 417	9.94 133	7	53
8	9.68 739	23	9.74 613	30	10.25 387	9.94 126	7	52
9	9.68 762	22	9.74 643	30	10.25 357	9.94 119	7	51
10	9.68 784	23	9.74 673	29	10.25 327	9.94 112	7	**50**
11	9.68 807	22	9.74 702	30	10.25 298	9.94 105	7	49
12	9.68 829	23	9.74 732	30	10.25 268	9.94 098	8	48
13	9.68 852	23	9.74 762	29	10.25 238	9.94 090	7	47
14	9.68 875	22	9.74 791	30	10.25 209	9.94 083	7	46
15	9.68 897	23	9.74 821	30	10.25 179	9.94 076	7	45
16	9.68 920	22	9.74 851	29	10.25 149	9.94 069	7	44
17	9.68 942	23	9.74 880	30	10.25 120	9.94 062	7	43
18	9.68 965	22	9.74 910	29	10.25 090	9.94 055	7	42
19	9.68 987	23	9.74 939	30	10.25 061	9.94 048	7	41
20	9.69 010	22	9.74 969	29	10.25 031	9.94 041	7	**40**
21	9.69 032	23	9.74 998	30	10.25 002	9.94 034	7	39
22	9.69 055	22	9.75 028	30	10.24 972	9.94 027	7	38
23	9.69 077	23	9.75 058	29	10.24 942	9.94 020	8	37
24	9.69 100	22	9.75 087	30	10.24 913	9.94 012	7	36
25	9.69 122	22	9.75 117	29	10.24 883	9.94 005	7	35
26	9.69 144	23	9.75 146	30	10.24 854	9.93 998	7	34
27	9.69 167	22	9.75 176	29	10.24 824	9.93 991	7	33
28	9.69 189	23	9.75 205	30	10.24 795	9.93 984	7	32
29	9.69 212	22	9.75 235	29	10.24 765	9.93 977	7	31
30	9.69 234	22	9.75 264	30	10.24 736	9.93 970	7	**30**
31	9.69 256	23	9.75 294	29	10.24 706	9.93 963	8	29
32	9.69 279	22	9.75 323	30	10.24 677	9.93 955	7	28
33	9.69 301	22	9.75 353	29	10.24 647	9.93 948	7	27
34	9.69 323	22	9.75 382	29	10.24 618	9.93 941	7	26
35	9.69 345	23	9.75 411	30	10.24 589	9.93 934	7	25
36	9.69 368	22	9.75 441	29	10.24 559	9.93 927	7	24
37	9.69 390	22	9.75 470	30	10.24 530	9.93 920	8	23
38	9.69 412	22	9.75 500	29	10.24 500	9.93 912	7	22
39	9.69 434	22	9.75 529	29	10.24 471	9.93 905	7	21
40	9.69 456	23	9.75 558	30	10.24 442	9.93 898	7	**20**
41	9.69 479	22	9.75 588	29	10.24 412	9.93 891	7	19
42	9.69 501	22	9.75 617	30	10.24 383	9.93 884	8	18
43	9.69 523	22	9.75 647	29	10.24 353	9.93 876	7	17
44	9.69 545	22	9.75 676	29	10.24 324	9.93 869	7	16
45	9.69 567	22	9.75 705	30	10.24 295	9.93 862	7	15
46	9.69 589	22	9.75 735	29	10.24 265	9.93 855	8	14
47	9.69 611	22	9.75 764	29	10.24 236	9.93 847	7	13
48	9.69 633	22	9.75 793	29	10.24 207	9.93 840	7	12
49	9.69 655	22	9.75 822	30	10.24 178	9.93 833	7	11
50	9.69 677	22	9.75 852	29	10.24 148	9.93 826	7	**10**
51	9.69 699	22	9.75 881	29	10.24 119	9.93 819	8	9
52	9.69 721	22	9.75 910	29	10.24 090	9.93 811	7	8
53	9.69 743	22	9.75 939	30	10.24 061	9.93 804	7	7
54	9.69 765	22	9.75 969	29	10.24 031	9.93 797	8	6
55	9.69 787	22	9.75 998	29	10.24 002	9.93 789	7	5
56	9.69 809	22	9.76 027	29	10.23 973	9.93 782	7	4
57	9.69 831	22	9.76 056	30	10.23 944	9.93 775	7	3
58	9.69 853	22	9.76 086	29	10.23 914	9.93 768	8	2
59	9.69 875	22	9.76 115	29	10.23 885	9.93 760	7	1
60	9.69 897		9.76 144		10.23 856	9.93 753		**0**
	L Cos	d	L Cot	c d	L Tan	L Sin	d	′

Prop. Pts.

	30	29
1	3.0	2.9
2	6.0	5.8
3	9.0	8.7
4	12.0	11.6
5	15.0	14.5
6	18.0	17.4
7	21.0	20.3
8	24.0	23.2
9	27.0	26.1

	23	22
1	2.3	2.2
2	4.6	4.4
3	6.9	6.6
4	9.2	8.8
5	11.5	11.0
6	13.8	13.2
7	16.1	15.4
8	18.4	17.6
9	20.7	19.8

	8	7
1	0.8	0.7
2	1.6	1.4
3	2.4	2.1
4	3.2	2.8
5	4.0	3.5
6	4.8	4.2
7	5.6	4.9
8	6.4	5.6
9	7.2	6.3

Prop. Pts.

60°

Table D (Continued)

30°

′	L Sin	d	L Tan	c d	L Cot	L Cos	d	
0	9.69 897		9.76 144		10.23 856	9.93 753		60
1	9.69 919	22	9.76 173	29	10.23 827	9.93 746	7	59
2	9.69 941	22	9.76 202	29	10.23 798	9.93 738	8	58
3	9.69 963	22	9.76 231	29	10.23 769	9.93 731	7	57
4	9.69 984	21	9.76 261	30	10.23 739	9.93 724	7	56
5	9.70 006	22	9.76 290	29	10.23 710	9.93 717	7	55
6	9.70 028	22	9.76 319	29	10.23 681	9.93 709	8	54
7	9.70 050	22	9.76 348	29	10.23 652	9.93 702	7	53
8	9.70 072	22	9.76 377	29	10.23 623	9.93 695	7	52
9	9.70 093	21	9.76 406	29	10.23 594	9.93 687	8	51
10	9.70 115	22	9.76 435	29	10.23 565	9.93 680	7	50
11	9.70 137	22	9.76 464	29	10.23 536	9.93 673	7	49
12	9.70 159	22	9.76 493	29	10.23 507	9.93 665	8	48
13	9.70 180	21	9.76 522	29	10.23 478	9.93 658	7	47
14	9.70 202	22	9.76 551	29	10.23 449	9.93 650	8	46
15	9.70 224	22	9.76 580	29	10.23 420	9.93 643	7	45
16	9.70 245	21	9.76 609	29	10.23 391	9.93 636	7	44
17	9.70 267	22	9.76 639	30	10.23 361	9.93 628	8	43
18	9.70 288	21	9.76 668	29	10.23 332	9.93 621	7	42
19	9.70 310	22	9.76 697	29	10.23 303	9.93 614	7	41
20	9.70 332	22	9.76 725	28	10.23 275	9.93 606	8	40
21	9.70 353	21	9.76 754	29	10.23 246	9.93 599	7	39
22	9.70 375	22	9.76 783	29	10.23 217	9.93 591	8	38
23	9.70 396	21	9.76 812	29	10.23 188	9.93 584	7	37
24	9.70 418	22	9.76 841	29	10.23 159	9.93 577	7	36
25	9.70 439	21	9.76 870	29	10.23 130	9.93 569	8	35
26	9.70 461	22	9.76 899	29	10.23 101	9.93 562	7	34
27	9.70 482	21	9.76 928	29	10.23 072	9.93 554	8	33
28	9.70 504	22	9.76 957	29	10.23 043	9.93 547	7	32
29	9.70 525	21	9.76 986	29	10.23 014	9.93 539	8	31
30	9.70 547	22	9.77 015	29	10.22 985	9.93 532	7	30
31	9.70 568	21	9.77 044	29	10.22 956	9.93 525	7	29
32	9.70 590	22	9.77 073	29	10.22 927	9.93 517	8	28
33	9.70 611	21	9.77 101	28	10.22 899	9.93 510	7	27
34	9.70 633	22	9.77 130	29	10.22 870	9.93 502	8	26
35	9.70 654	21	9.77 159	29	10.22 841	9.93 495	7	25
36	9.70 675	21	9.77 188	29	10.22 812	9.93 487	8	24
37	9.70 796	22	9.77 217	29	10.22 783	9.93 480	7	23
38	9.70 718	21	9.77 246	29	10.22 754	9.93 472	8	22
39	9.70 739	21	9.77 274	28	10.22 726	9.93 465	7	21
40	9.70 761	22	9.77 303	29	10.22 697	9.93 457	8	20
41	9.70 782	21	9.77 332	29	10.22 668	9.93 450	7	19
42	9.70 803	21	9.77 361	29	10.22 639	9.93 442	8	18
43	9.70 824	21	9.77 390	29	10.22 610	9.93 435	7	17
44	9.70 846	22	9.77 418	28	10.22 582	9.93 427	8	16
45	9.70 867	21	9.77 447	29	10.22 553	9.93 420	7	15
46	9.70 888	21	9.77 476	29	10.22 524	9.93 412	8	14
47	9.70 909	21	9.77 505	29	10.22 495	9.93 405	7	13
48	9.70 931	22	9.77 533	28	10.22 467	9.93 397	8	12
49	9.70 952	21	9.77 562	29	10.22 438	9.93 390	7	11
50	9.70 973	21	9.77 591	29	10.22 409	9.93 382	8	10
51	9.70 994	21	9.77 619	28	10.22 381	9.93 375	7	9
52	9.71 015	21	9.77 648	29	10.22 352	9.93 367	8	8
53	9.71 036	21	9.77 677	29	10.22 323	9.93 360	7	7
54	9.71 058	22	9.77 706	29	10.22 294	9.93 352	8	6
55	9.71 079	21	9.77 734	28	10.22 266	9.93 344	8	5
56	9.71 100	21	9.77 763	29	10.22 237	9.93 337	7	4
57	9.71 121	21	9.77 791	28	10.22 209	9.93 329	8	3
58	9.71 142	21	9.77 820	29	10.22 180	9.93 322	7	2
59	9.71 163	21	9.77 849	29	10.22 151	9.93 314	8	1
60	9.71 184	21	9.77 877	28	10.22 123	9.93 307	7	0
	L Cos	d	L Cot	c d	L Tan	L Sin	d	′

Prop. Pts.

	30	29	28
1	3.0	2.9	2.8
2	6.0	5.8	5.6
3	9.0	8.7	8.4
4	12.0	11.6	11.2
5	15.0	14.5	14.0
6	18.0	17.4	16.8
7	21.0	20.3	19.6
8	24.0	23.2	22.4
9	27.0	26.1	25.2

	22	21
1	2.2	2.1
2	4.4	4.2
3	6.6	6.3
4	8.8	8.4
5	11.0	10.5
6	13.2	12.6
7	15.4	14.7
8	17.6	16.8
9	19.8	18.9

	8	7
1	0.8	0.7
2	1.6	1.4
3	2.4	2.1
4	3.2	2.8
5	4.0	3.5
6	4.8	4.2
7	5.6	4.9
8	6.4	5.6
9	7.2	6.3

Prop. Pts.

59°

Table D (Continued)

31°

′	L Sin	d	L Tan	c d	L Cot	L Cos	d	
0	9.71 184	21	9.77 877	29	10.22 123	9.93 307	8	**60**
1	9.71 205	21	9.77 906	29	10.22 094	9.93 299	8	59
2	9.71 226	21	9.77 935	28	10.22 065	9.93 291	7	58
3	9.71 247	21	9.77 963	29	10.22 037	9.93 284	8	57
4	9.71 268	21	9.77 992	28	10.22 008	9.93 276	7	56
5	9.71 289	21	9.78 020	29	10.21 980	9.93 269	8	55
6	9.71 310	21	9.78 049	28	10.21 951	9.93 261	8	54
7	9.71 331	21	9.78 077	29	10.21 923	9.93 253	7	53
8	9.71 352	21	9.78 106	29	10.21 894	9.93 246	8	52
9	9.71 373	20	9.78 135	28	10.21 865	9.93 238	8	51
10	9.71 393	21	9.78 163	29	10.21 837	9.93 230	7	**50**
11	9.71 414	21	9.78 192	28	10.21 808	9.93 223	8	49
12	9.71 435	21	9.78 220	29	10.21 780	9.93 215	8	48
13	9.71 456	21	9.78 249	28	10.21 751	9.93 207	7	47
14	9.71 477	21	9.78 277	29	10.21 723	9.93 200	8	46
15	9.71 498	21	9.78 306	28	10.21 694	9.93 192	8	45
16	9.71 519	20	9.78 334	29	10.21 666	9.93 184	7	44
17	9.71 539	21	9.78 363	28	10.21 637	9.93 177	8	43
18	9.71 560	21	9.78 391	28	10.21 609	9.93 169	8	42
19	9.71 581	21	9.78 419	29	10.21 581	9.93 161	7	41
20	9.71 602	20	9.78 448	28	10.21 552	9.93 154	8	**40**
21	9.71 622	21	9.78 476	29	10.21 524	9.93 146	8	39
22	9.71 643	21	9.78 505	28	10.21 495	9.93 138	7	38
23	9.71 664	21	9.78 533	29	10.21 467	9.93 131	8	37
24	9.71 685	20	9.78 562	28	10.21 438	9.93 123	8	36
25	9.71 705	21	9.78 590	28	10.21 410	9.93 115	7	35
26	9.71 726	21	9.78 618	29	10.21 382	9.93 108	8	34
27	9.71 747	20	9.78 647	28	10.21 353	9.93 100	8	33
28	9.71 767	21	9.78 675	29	10.21 325	9.93 092	8	32
29	9.71 788	21	9.78 704	28	10.21 296	9.93 084	7	31
30	9.71 809	20	9.78 732	28	10.21 268	9.93 077	8	**30**
31	9.71 829	21	9.78 760	29	10.21 240	9.93 069	8	29
32	9.71 850	20	9.78 789	28	10.21 211	9.93 061	8	28
33	9.71 870	21	9.78 817	28	10.21 183	9.93 053	7	27
34	9.71 891	20	9.78 845	29	10.21 155	9.93 046	8	26
35	9.71 911	21	9.78 874	28	10.21 126	9.93 038	8	25
36	9.71 932	20	9.78 902	28	10.21 098	9.93 030	8	24
37	9.71 952	21	9.78 930	29	10.21 070	9.93 022	8	23
38	9.71 973	21	9.78 959	28	10.21 041	9.93 014	7	22
39	9.71 994	20	9.78 987	28	10.21 013	9.93 007	8	21
40	9.72 014	20	9.79 015	28	10.20 985	9.92 999	8	**20**
41	9.72 034	21	9.79 043	29	10.20 957	9.92 991	8	19
42	9.72 055	20	9.79 072	28	10.20 928	9.92 983	7	18
43	9.72 075	21	9.79 100	28	10.20 900	9.92 976	8	17
44	9.72 096	20	9.79 128	28	10.20 872	9.92 968	8	16
45	9.72 116	21	9.79 156	29	10.20 844	9.92 960	8	15
46	9.72 137	20	9.79 185	28	10.20 815	9.92 952	8	14
47	9.72 157	20	9.79 213	28	10.20 787	9.92 944	8	13
48	9.72 177	21	9.79 241	28	10.20 759	9.92 936	7	12
49	9.72 198	20	9.79 269	28	10.20 731	9.92 929	8	11
50	9.72 218	20	9.79 297	29	10.20 703	9.92 921	8	**10**
51	9.72 238	21	9.79 326	28	10.20 674	9.92 913	8	9
52	9.72 259	20	9.79 354	28	10.20 646	9.92 905	8	8
53	9.72 279	20	9.79 382	28	10.20 618	9.92 897	8	7
54	9.72 299	21	9.79 410	28	10.20 590	9.92 889	8	6
55	9.72 320	20	9.79 438	28	10.20 562	9.92 881	7	5
56	9.72 340	20	9.79 466	29	10.20 534	9.92 874	8	4
57	9.72 360	21	9.79 495	28	10.20 505	9.92 866	8	3
58	9.72 381	20	9.79 523	28	10.20 477	9.92 858	8	2
59	9.72 401	20	9.79 551	28	10.20 449	9.92 850	8	1
60	9.72 421		9.79 579		10.20 421	9.92 842		**0**
	L Cos	d	L Cot	c d	L Tan	L Sin	d	′

Prop. Pts.

	29	28
1	2.9	2.8
2	5.8	5.6
3	8.7	8.4
4	11.6	11.2
5	14.5	14.0
6	17.4	16.8
7	20.3	19.6
8	23.2	22.4
9	26.1	25.2

	21	20
1	2.1	2.0
2	4.2	4.0
3	6.3	6.0
4	8.4	8.0
5	10.5	10.0
6	12.6	12.0
7	14.7	14.0
8	16.8	16.0
9	18.9	18.0

	8	7
1	0.8	0.7
2	1.6	1.4
3	2.4	2.1
4	3.2	2.8
5	4.0	3.5
6	4.8	4.2
7	5.6	4.9
8	6.4	5.6
9	7.2	6.3

Prop Pts.

58°

Table D (Continued)

32°

′	L Sin	d	L Tan	c d	L Cot	L Cos	d	
0	9.72 421	20	9.79 579	28	10.20 421	9.92 842	8	**60**
1	9.72 441	20	9.79 607	28	10.20 393	9.92 834	8	59
2	9.72 461	21	9.79 635	28	10.20 365	9.92 826	8	58
3	9.72 482	20	9.79 663	28	10.20 337	9.92 818	8	57
4	9.72 502	20	9.79 691	28	10.20 309	9.92 810	7	56
5	9.72 522	20	9.79 719	28	10.20 281	9.92 803	8	55
6	9.72 542	20	9.79 747	29	10.20 253	9.92 795	8	54
7	9.72 562	20	9.79 776	28	10.20 224	9.92 787	8	53
8	9.72 582	20	9.79 804	28	10.20 196	9.92 779	8	52
9	9.72 602	20	9.79 832	28	10.20 168	9.92 771	8	51
10	9.72 622	21	9.79 860	28	10.20 140	9.92 763	8	**50**
11	9.72 643	20	9.79 888	28	10.20 112	9.92 755	8	49
12	9.72 663	20	9.79 916	28	10.20 084	9.92 747	8	48
13	9.72 683	20	9.79 944	28	10.20 056	9.92 739	8	47
14	9.72 703	20	9.79 972	28	10.20 028	9.92 731	8	46
15	9.72 723	20	9.80 000	28	10.20 000	9.92 723	8	45
16	9.72 743	20	9.80 028	28	10.19 972	9.92 715	8	44
17	9.72 763	20	9.80 056	28	10.19 944	9.92 707	8	43
18	9.72 783	20	9.80 084	28	10.19 916	9.92 699	8	42
19	9.72 803	20	9.80 112	28	10.19 888	9.92 691	8	41
20	9.72 823	20	9.80 140	28	10.19 860	9.92 683	8	**40**
21	9.72 843	20	9.80 168	27	10.19 832	9.92 675	8	39
22	9.72 863	20	9.80 195	28	10.19 805	9.92 667	8	38
23	9.72 883	19	9.80 223	28	10.19 777	9.92 659	8	37
24	9.72 902	20	9.80 251	28	10.19 749	9.92 651	8	36
25	9.72 922	20	9.80 279	28	10.19 721	9.92 643	8	35
26	9.72 942	20	9.80 307	28	10.19 693	9.92 635	8	34
27	9.72 962	20	9.80 335	28	10.19 665	9.92 627	8	33
28	9.72 982	20	9.80 363	28	10.19 637	9.92 619	8	32
29	9.73 002	20	9.80 391	28	10.19 609	9.92 611	8	31
30	9.73 022	19	9.80 419	28	10.19 581	9.92 603	8	**30**
31	9.73 041	20	9.80 447	27	10.19 553	9.92 595	8	29
32	9.73 061	20	9.80 474	28	10.19 526	9.92 587	8	28
33	9.73 081	20	9.80 502	28	10.19 498	9.92 579	8	27
34	9.73 101	20	9.80 530	28	10.19 470	9.92 571	8	26
35	9.73 121	19	9.80 558	28	10.19 442	9.92 563	8	25
36	9.73 140	20	9.80 586	28	10.19 414	9.92 555	9	24
37	9.73 160	20	9.80 614	28	10.19 386	9.92 546	8	23
38	9.73 180	20	9.80 642	27	10.19 358	9.92 538	8	22
39	9.73 200	19	9.80 669	28	10.19 331	9.92 530	8	21
40	9.73 219	20	9.80 697	28	10.19 303	9.92 522	8	**20**
41	9.73 239	20	9.80 725	28	10.19 275	9.92 514	8	19
42	9.73 259	19	9.80 753	28	10.19 247	9.92 506	8	18
43	9.73 278	20	9.80 781	27	10.19 219	9.92 498	8	17
44	9.73 298	20	9.80 808	28	10.19 192	9.92 490	8	16
45	9.73 318	19	9.80 836	28	10.19 164	9.92 482	9	15
46	9.73 337	20	9.80 864	28	10.19 136	9.92 473	8	14
47	9.73 357	20	9.80 892	27	10.19 108	9.92 465	8	13
48	9.73 377	19	9.80 919	28	10.19 081	9.92 457	8	12
49	9.73 396	20	9.80 947	28	10.19 053	9.92 449	8	11
50	9.73 416	19	9.80 975	28	10.19 025	9.92 441	8	**10**
51	9.73 435	20	9.81 003	27	10.18 997	9.92 433	8	9
52	9.73 455	19	9.81 030	28	10.18 970	9.92 425	9	8
53	9.73 474	20	9.81 058	28	10.18 942	9.92 416	8	7
54	9.73 494	19	9.81 086	27	10.18 914	9.92 408	8	6
55	9.73 513	20	9.81 113	28	10.18 887	9.92 400	8	5
56	9.73 533	19	9.81 141	28	10.18 859	9.92 392	8	4
57	9.73 552	20	9.81 169	27	10.18 831	9.92 384	8	3
58	9.73 572	19	9.81 196	28	10.18 804	9.92 376	9	2
59	9.73 591	20	9.81 224	28	10.18 776	9.92 367	8	1
60	9.73 611		9.81 252		10.18 748	9.92 359		**0**
	L Cos	d	L Cot	c d	L Tan	L Sin	d	′

Prop. Pts.

	29	28	27
1	2.9	2.8	2.7
2	5.8	5.6	5.4
3	8.7	8.4	8.1
4	11.6	11.2	10.8
5	14.5	14.0	13.5
6	17.4	16.8	16.2
7	20.3	19.6	18.9
8	23.2	22.4	21.6
9	26.1	25.2	24.3

	21	20	19
1	2.1	2.0	1.9
2	4.2	4.0	3.8
3	6.3	6.0	5.7
4	8.4	8.0	7.6
5	10.5	10.0	9.5
6	12.6	12.0	11.4
7	14.7	14.0	13.3
8	16.8	16.0	15.2
9	18.9	18.0	17.1

	9	8	7
1	0.9	0.8	0.7
2	1.8	1.6	1.4
3	2.7	2.4	2.1
4	3.6	3.2	2.8
5	4.5	4.0	3.5
6	5.4	4.8	4.2
7	6.3	5.6	4.9
8	7.2	6.4	5.6
9	8.1	7.2	6.3

Prop. Pts.

57°

Table D (Continued)

33°

′	L Sin	d	L Tan	c d	L Cot	L Cos	d	
0	9.73 611	19	9.81 252	27	10.18 748	9.92 359	8	**60**
1	9.73 630	20	9.81 279	28	10.18 721	9.92 351	8	59
2	9.73 650	19	9.81 307	28	10.18 693	9.92 343	8	58
3	9.73 669	20	9.81 335	27	10.18 665	9.92 335	9	57
4	9.73 689	19	9.81 362	28	10.18 638	9.92 326	8	56
5	9.73 708	19	9.81 390	28	10.18 610	9.92 318	8	55
6	9.73 727	20	9.81 418	27	10.18 582	9.92 310	8	54
7	9.73 747	19	9.81 445	28	10.18 555	9.92 302	9	53
8	9.73 766	19	9.81 473	27	10.18 527	9.92 293	8	52
9	9.73 785	20	9.81 500	28	10.18 500	9.92 285	8	51
10	9.73 805	19	9.81 528	28	10.18 472	9.92 277	8	**50**
11	9.73 824	19	9.81 556	27	10.18 444	9.92 269	9	49
12	9.73 843	20	9.81 583	28	10.18 417	9.92 260	8	48
13	9.73 863	19	9.81 611	27	10.18 389	9.92 252	8	47
14	9.73 882	19	9.81 638	28	10.18 362	9.92 244	9	46
15	9.73 901	20	9.81 666	27	10.18 334	9.92 235	8	45
16	9.73 921	19	9.81 693	28	10.18 307	9.92 227	8	44
17	9.73 940	19	9.81 721	27	10.18 279	9.92 219	8	43
18	9.73 959	19	9.81 748	28	10.18 252	9.92 211	9	42
19	9.73 978	19	9.81 776	27	10.18 224	9.92 202	8	41
20	9.73 997	20	9.81 803	28	10.18 197	9.92 194	8	**40**
21	9.74 017	19	9.81 831	27	10.18 169	9.92 186	9	39
22	9.74 036	19	9.81 858	28	10.18 142	9.92 177	8	38
23	9.74 055	19	9.81 886	27	10.18 114	9.92 169	8	37
24	9.74 074	19	9.81 913	28	10.18 087	9.92 161	9	36
25	9.74 093	20	9.81 941	27	10.18 059	9.92 152	8	35
26	9.74 113	19	9.81 968	28	10.18 032	9.92 144	8	34
27	9.74 132	19	9.81 996	27	10.18 004	9.92 136	9	33
28	9.74 151	19	9.82 023	28	10.17 977	9.92 127	8	32
29	9.74 170	19	9.82 051	27	10.17 949	9.92 119	8	31
30	9.74 189	19	9.82 078	28	10.17 922	9.92 111	9	**30**
31	9.74 208	19	9.82 106	27	10.17 894	9.92 102	8	29
32	9.74 227	19	9.82 133	28	10.17 867	9.92 094	8	28
33	9.74 246	19	9.82 161	27	10.17 839	9.92 086	9	27
34	9.74 265	19	9.82 188	27	10.17 812	9.92 077	8	26
35	9.74 284	19	9.82 215	28	10.17 785	9.92 069	9	25
36	9.74 303	19	9.82 243	27	10.17 757	9.92 060	8	24
37	9.74 322	19	9.82 270	28	10.17 730	9.92 052	8	23
38	9.74 341	19	9.82 298	27	10.17 702	9.92 044	9	22
39	9.74 360	19	9.82 325	27	10.17 675	9.92 035	8	21
40	9.74 379	19	9.82 352	28	10.17 648	9.92 027	9	**20**
41	9.74 398	19	9.82 380	27	10.17 620	9.92 018	8	19
42	9.74 417	19	9.82 407	28	10.17 593	9.92 010	8	18
43	9.74 436	19	9.82 435	27	10.17 565	9.92 002	9	17
44	9.74 455	19	9.82 462	27	10.17 538	9.91 993	8	16
45	9.74 474	19	9.82 489	28	10.17 511	9.91 985	9	15
46	9.74 493	19	9.82 517	27	10.17 483	9.91 976	8	14
47	9.74 512	19	9.82 544	27	10.17 456	9.91 968	9	13
48	9.74 531	18	9.82 571	28	10.17 429	9.91 959	8	12
49	9.74 549	19	9.82 599	27	10.17 401	9.91 951	9	11
50	9.74 568	19	9.82 626	27	10.17 374	9.91 942	8	**10**
51	9.74 587	19	9.82 653	28	10.17 347	9.91 934	9	9
52	9.74 606	19	9.82 681	27	10.17 319	9.91 925	8	8
53	9.74 625	19	9.82 708	27	10.17 292	9.91 917	9	7
54	9.74 644	18	9.82 735	27	10.17 265	9.91 908	8	6
55	9.74 662	19	9.82 762	28	10.17 238	9.91 900	9	5
56	9.74 681	19	9.82 790	27	10.17 210	9.91 891	8	4
57	9.74 700	19	9.82 817	27	10.17 183	9.91 883	9	3
58	9.74 719	18	9.82 844	27	10.17 156	9.91 874	8	2
59	9.74 737	19	9.82 871	28	10.17 129	9.91 866	9	1
60	9.74 756		9.82 899		10.17 101	9.91 857		**0**
	L Cos	d	L Cot	c d	L Tan	L Sin	d	′

Prop. Pts.

	28	**27**
1	2.8	2.7
2	5.6	5.4
3	8.4	8.1
4	11.2	10.8
5	14.0	13.5
6	16.8	16.2
7	19.6	18.9
8	22.4	21.6
9	25.2	24.3

	20	**19**	**18**
1	2.0	1.9	1.8
2	4.0	3.8	3.6
3	6.0	5.7	5.4
4	8.0	7.6	7.2
5	10.0	9.5	9.0
6	12.0	11.4	10.8
7	14.0	13.3	12.6
8	16.0	15.2	14.4
9	18.0	17.1	16.2

	9	**8**
1	0.9	0.8
2	1.8	1.6
3	2.7	2.4
4	3.6	3.2
5	4.5	4.0
6	5.4	4.8
7	6.3	5.6
8	7.2	6.4
9	8.1	7.2

Prop. Pts.

56°

Table D (Continued)

34°

′	L Sin	d	L Tan	c d	L Cot	L Cos	d	
0	9.74 756		9.82 899		10.17 101	9.91 857		**60**
1	9.74 775	19	9.82 926	27	10.17 074	9.91 849	8	59
2	9.74 794	19	9.82 953	27	10.17 047	9.91 840	9	58
3	9.74 812	18	9.82 980	27	10.17 020	9.91 832	8	57
4	9.74 831	19	9.83 008	28	10.16 992	9.91 823	9	56
5	9.74 850	19	9.83 035	27	10.16 965	9.91 815	8	55
6	9.74 868	18	9.83 062	27	10.16 938	9.91 806	9	54
7	9.74 887	19	9.83 089	27	10.16 911	9.91 798	8	53
8	9.74 906	19	9.83 117	28	10.16 883	9.91 789	9	52
9	9.74 924	18	9.83 144	27	10.16 856	9.91 781	8	51
10	9.74 943	19	9.83 171	27	10.16 829	9.91 772	9	**50**
11	9.74 961	18	9.83 198	27	10.16 802	9.91 763	9	49
12	9.74 980	19	9.83 225	27	10.16 775	9.91 755	8	48
13	9.74 999	19	9.83 252	27	10.16 748	9.91 746	9	47
14	9.75 017	18	9.83 280	28	10.16 720	9.91 738	8	46
15	9.75 036	19	9.83 307	27	10.16 693	9.91 729	9	45
16	9.75 054	18	9.83 334	27	10.16 666	9.91 720	9	44
17	9.75 073	19	9.83 361	27	10.16 639	9.91 712	8	43
18	9.75 091	18	9.83 388	27	10.16 612	9.91 703	9	42
19	9.75 110	19	9.83 415	27	10.16 585	9.91 695	8	41
20	9.75 128	18	9.83 442	27	10.16 558	9.91 686	9	**40**
21	9.75 147	19	9.83 470	28	10.16 530	9.91 677	9	39
22	9.75 165	18	9.83 497	27	10.16 503	9.91 669	8	38
23	9.75 184	19	9.83 524	27	10.16 476	9.91 660	9	37
24	9.75 202	18	9.83 551	27	10.16 449	9.91 651	9	36
25	9.75 221	19	9.83 578	27	10.16 422	9.91 643	8	35
26	9.75 239	18	9.83 605	27	10.16 395	9.91 634	9	34
27	9.75 258	19	9.83 632	27	10.16 368	9.91 625	9	33
28	9.75 276	18	9.83 659	27	10.16 341	9.91 617	8	32
29	9.75 294	18	9.83 686	27	10.16 314	9.91 608	9	31
30	9.75 313	19	9.83 713	27	10.16 287	9.91 599	9	**30**
31	9.75 331	18	9.83 740	27	10.16 260	9.91 591	8	29
32	9.75 350	19	9.83 768	28	10.16 232	9.91 582	9	28
33	9.75 368	18	9.83 795	27	10.16 205	9.91 573	9	27
34	9.75 386	18	9.83 822	27	10.16 178	9.91 565	8	26
35	9.75 405	19	9.83 849	27	10.16 151	9.91 556	9	25
36	9.75 423	18	9.83 876	27	10.16 124	9.91 547	9	24
37	9.75 441	18	9.83 903	27	10.16 097	9.91 538	9	23
38	9.75 459	18	9.83 930	27	10.16 070	9.91 530	8	22
39	9.75 478	19	9.83 957	27	10.16 043	9.91 521	9	21
40	9.75 496	18	9.83 984	27	10.16 016	9.91 512	9	**20**
41	9.75 514	18	9.84 011	27	10.15 989	9.91 504	8	19
42	9.75 533	19	9.84 038	27	10.15 962	9.91 495	9	18
43	9.75 551	18	9.84 065	27	10.15 935	9.91 486	9	17
44	9.75 569	18	9.84 092	27	10.15 908	9.91 477	9	16
45	9.75 587	18	9.84 119	27	10.15 881	9.91 469	8	15
46	9.75 605	18	9.84 146	27	10.15 854	9.91 460	9	14
47	9.75 624	19	9.84 173	27	10.15 827	9.91 451	9	13
48	9.75 642	18	9.84 200	27	10.15 800	9.91 442	9	12
49	9.75 660	18	9.84 227	27	10.15 773	9.91 433	9	11
50	9.75 678	18	9.84 254	27	10.15 746	9.91 425	8	**10**
51	9.75 696	18	9.84 280	26	10.15 720	9.91 416	9	9
52	9.75 714	18	9.84 307	27	10.15 693	9.91 407	9	8
53	9.75 733	19	9.84 334	27	10.15 666	9.91 398	9	7
54	9.75 751	18	9.84 361	27	10.15 639	9.91 389	9	6
55	9.75 769	18	9.84 388	27	10.15 612	9.91 381	8	5
56	9.75 787	18	9.84 415	27	10.15 585	9.91 372	9	4
57	9.75 805	18	9.84 442	27	10.15 558	9.91 363	9	3
58	9.75 823	18	9.84 469	27	10.15 531	9.91 354	9	2
59	9.75 841	18	9.84 496	27	10.15 504	9.91 345	9	1
60	9.75 859	18	9.84 523	27	10.15 477	9.91 336	9	**0**
	L Cos	d	L Cot	c d	L Tan	L Sin	d	′

Prop. Pts.

	28	27	26
1	2.8	2.7	2.6
2	5.6	5.4	5.2
3	8.4	8.1	7.8
4	11.2	10.8	10.4
5	14.0	13.5	13.0
6	16.8	16.2	15.6
7	19.6	18.9	18.2
8	22.4	21.6	20.8
9	25.2	24.3	23.4

	19	18
1	1.9	1.8
2	3.8	3.6
3	5.7	5.4
4	7.6	7.2
5	9.5	9.0
6	11.4	10.8
7	13.3	12.6
8	15.2	14.4
9	17.1	16.2

	9	8
1	0.9	0.8
2	1.8	1.6
3	2.7	2.4
4	3.6	3.2
5	4.5	4.0
6	5.4	4.8
7	6.3	5.6
8	7.2	6.4
9	8.1	7.2

Prop. Pts.

55°

Table D (Continued)

35°

′	L Sin	d	L Tan	c d	L Cot	L Cos	d	
0	9.75 859	18	9.84 523	27	10.15 477	9.91 336	8	**60**
1	9.75 877	18	9.84 550	26	10.15 450	9.91 328	9	59
2	9.75 895	18	9.84 576	27	10.15 424	9.91 319	9	58
3	9.75 913	18	9.84 603	27	10.15 397	9.91 310	9	57
4	9.75 931	18	9.84 630	27	10.15 370	9.91 301	9	56
5	9.75 949	18	9.84 657	27	10.15 343	9.91 292	9	55
6	9.75 967	18	9.84 684	27	10.15 316	9.91 283	9	54
7	9.75 985	18	9.84 711	27	10.15 289	9.91 274	8	53
8	9.76 003	18	9.84 738	26	10.15 262	9.91 266	9	52
9	9.76 021	18	9.84 764	27	10.15 236	9.91 257	9	51
10	9.76 039	18	9.84 791	27	10.15 209	9.91 248	9	**50**
11	9.76 057	18	9.84 818	27	10.15 182	9.91 239	9	49
12	9.76 075	18	9.84 845	27	10.15 155	9.91 230	9	48
13	9.76 093	18	9.84 872	27	10.15 128	9.91 221	9	47
14	9.76 111	18	9.84 899	26	10.15 101	9.91 212	9	46
15	9.76 129	17	9.84 925	27	10.15 075	9.91 203	9	45
16	9.76 146	18	9.84 952	27	10.15 048	9.91 194	9	44
17	9.76 164	18	9.84 979	27	10.15 021	9.91 185	9	43
18	9.76 182	18	9.85 006	27	10.14 994	9.91 176	9	42
19	9.76 200	18	9.85 033	26	10.14 967	9.91 167	9	41
20	9.76 218	18	9.85 059	27	10.14 941	9.91 158	9	**40**
21	9.76 236	17	9.85 086	27	10.14 914	9.91 149	8	39
22	9.76 253	18	9.85 113	27	19.14 887	9.91 141	9	38
23	9.76 271	18	9.85 140	26	10.14 860	9.91 132	9	37
24	9.76 289	18	9.85 166	27	10.14 834	9.91 123	9	36
25	9.76 307	17	9.85 193	27	10.14 807	9.91 114	9	35
26	9.76 324	18	9.85 220	27	10.14 780	9.91 105	9	34
27	9.76 342	18	9.85 247	26	10.14 753	9.91 096	9	33
28	9.76 360	18	9.85 273	27	10.14 727	9.91 087	9	32
29	9.76 378	17	9.85 300	27	10.14 700	9.91 078	9	31
30	9.76 395	18	9.85 327	27	10.14 673	9.91 069	9	**30**
31	9.76 413	18	9.85 354	26	10.14 646	9.91 060	9	29
32	9.76 431	17	9.85 380	27	10.14 620	9.91 051	9	28
33	9.76 448	18	9.85 407	27	10.14 593	9.91 042	9	27
34	9.76 466	18	9.85 434	26	10.14 566	9.91 033	10	26
35	9.76 484	17	9.85 460	27	10.14 540	9.91 023	9	25
36	9.76 501	18	9.85 487	27	10.14 513	9.91 014	9	24
37	9.76 519	18	9.85 514	26	10.14 486	9.91 005	9	23
38	9.76 537	17	9.85 540	27	10.14 460	9.90 996	9	22
39	9.76 554	18	9.85 567	27	10.14 433	9.90 987	9	21
40	9.76 572	18	9.85 594	26	10.14 406	9.90 978	9	**20**
41	9.76 590	17	9.85 620	27	10.14 380	9.90 969	9	19
42	9.76 607	18	9.85 647	27	10.14 353	9.90 960	9	18
43	9.76 625	17	9.85 674	26	10.14 326	9.90 951	9	17
44	9.76 642	18	9.85 700	27	10.14 300	9.90 942	9	16
45	9.76 660	17	9.85 727	27	10.14 273	9.90 933	9	15
46	9.76 677	18	9.85 754	26	10.14 246	9.90 924	9	14
47	9.76 695	17	9.85 780	27	10.14 220	9.90 915	9	13
48	9.76 712	18	9.85 807	27	10.14 193	9.90 906	10	12
49	9.76 730	17	9.85 834	26	10.14 166	9.90 896	9	11
50	9.76 747	18	9.85 860	27	10.14 140	9.90 887	9	**10**
51	9.76 765	17	9.85 887	26	10.14 113	9.90 878	9	9
52	9.76 782	18	9.85 913	27	10.14 087	9.90 869	9	8
53	9.76 800	17	9.85 940	27	10.14 060	9.90 860	9	7
54	9.76 817	18	9.85 967	26	10.14 033	9.90 851	9	6
55	9.76 835	17	9.85 993	27	10.14 007	9.90 842	10	5
56	9.76 852	18	9.86 020	26	10.13 980	9.90 832	9	4
57	9.76 870	17	9.86 046	27	10.13 954	9.90 823	9	3
58	9.76 887	17	9.86 073	27	10.13 927	9.90 814	9	2
59	9.76 904	18	9.86 100	26	10.13 900	9.90 805	9	1
60	9.76 922		9.86 126		10.13 874	9.90 796		**0**
	L Cos	d	L Cot	c d	L Tan	L Sin	d	′

Prop. Pts.

	27	26
1	2.7	2.6
2	5.4	5.2
3	8.1	7.8
4	10.8	10.4
5	13.5	13.0
6	16.2	15.6
7	18.9	18.2
8	21.6	20.8
9	24.3	23.4

	18	17
1	1.8	1.7
2	3.6	3.4
3	5.4	5.1
4	7.2	6.8
5	9.0	8.5
6	10.8	10.2
7	12.6	11.9
8	14.4	13.6
9	16.2	15.3

	10	9	8
1	1.0	0.9	0.8
2	2.0	1.8	1.6
3	3.0	2.7	2.4
4	4.0	3.6	3.2
5	5.0	4.5	4.0
6	6.0	5.4	4.8
7	7.0	6.3	5.6
8	8.0	7.2	6.4
9	9.0	8.1	7.2

54°

Table D (Continued)

36°

′	L Sin	d	L Tan	c d	L Cot	L Cos	d	′
0	9.76 922	17	9.86 126	27	10.13 874	9.90 796	9	**60**
1	9.76 939	18	9.86 153	26	10.13 847	9.90 787	10	59
2	9.76 957	17	9.86 179	27	10.13 821	9.90 777	9	58
3	9.76 974	17	9.86 206	26	10.13 794	9.90 768	9	57
4	9.76 991	18	9.86 232	27	10.13 768	9.90 759	9	56
5	9.77 009	17	9.86 259	26	10.13 741	9.90 750	9	55
6	9.77 026	17	9.86 285	27	10.13 715	9.90 741	10	54
7	9.77 043	18	9.86 312	26	10.13 688	9.90 731	9	53
8	9.77 061	17	9.86 338	27	10.13 662	9.90 722	9	52
9	9.77 078	17	9.86 365	27	10.13 635	9.90 713	9	51
10	9.77 095	17	9.86 392	26	10.13 608	9.90 704	10	**50**
11	9.77 112	18	9.86 418	27	10.13 582	9.90 694	9	49
12	9.77 130	17	9.86 445	26	10.13 555	9.90 685	9	48
13	9.77 147	17	9.86 471	27	10.13 529	9.90 676	9	47
14	9.77 164	17	9.86 498	26	10.13 502	9.90 667	10	46
15	9.77 181	18	9.86 524	27	10.13 476	9.90 657	9	45
16	9.77 199	17	9.86 551	26	10.13 449	9.90 648	9	44
17	9.77 216	17	9.86 577	26	10.13 423	9.90 639	9	43
18	9.77 233	17	9.86 603	27	10.13 397	9.90 630	10	42
19	9.77 250	18	9.86 630	26	10.13 370	9.90 620	9	41
20	9.77 268	17	9.86 656	27	10.13 344	9.90 611	9	**40**
21	9.77 285	17	9.86 683	26	10.13 317	9.90 602	10	39
22	9.77 302	17	9.86 709	27	10.13 291	9.90 592	9	38
23	9.77 319	17	9.86 736	26	10.13 264	9.90 583	9	37
24	9.77 336	17	9.86 762	27	10.13 238	9.90 574	9	36
25	9.77 353	17	9.86 789	26	10.13 211	9.90 565	10	35
26	9.77 370	17	9.86 815	27	10.13 185	9.90 555	9	34
27	9.77 387	18	9.86 842	26	10.13 158	9.90 546	9	33
28	9.77 405	17	9.86 868	26	10.13 132	9.90 537	10	32
29	9.77 422	17	9.86 894	27	10.13 106	9.90 527	9	31
30	9.77 439	17	9.86 921	26	10.13 079	9.90 518	9	**30**
31	9.77 456	17	9.86 947	27	10.13 053	9.90 509	10	29
32	9.77 473	17	9.86 974	26	10.13 026	9.90 499	9	28
33	9.77 490	17	9.87 000	27	10.13 000	9.90 490	10	27
34	9.77 507	17	9.87 027	26	10.12 973	9.90 480	9	26
35	9.77 524	17	9.87 053	26	10.12 947	9.90 471	9	25
36	9.77 541	17	9.87 079	27	10.12 921	9.90 462	10	24
37	9.77 558	17	9.87 106	26	10.12 894	9.90 452	9	23
38	9.77 575	17	9.87 132	26	10.12 868	9.90 443	9	22
39	9.77 592	17	9.87 158	27	10.12 842	9.90 434	10	21
40	9.77 609	17	9.87 185	26	10.12 815	9.90 424	9	**20**
41	9.77 626	17	9.87 211	27	10.12 789	9.90 415	10	19
42	9.77 643	17	9.87 238	26	10.12 762	9.90 405	9	18
43	9.77 660	17	9.87 264	26	10.12 736	9.90 396	10	17
44	9.77 677	17	9.87 290	27	10.12 710	9.90 386	9	16
45	9.77 694	17	9.87 317	26	10.12 683	9.90 377	9	15
46	9.77 711	17	9.87 343	26	10.12 657	9.90 368	10	14
47	9.77 728	16	9.87 369	27	10.12 631	9.90 358	9	13
48	9.77 744	17	9.87 396	26	10.12 604	9.90 349	10	12
49	9.77 761	17	9.87 422	26	10.12 578	9.90 339	9	11
50	9.77 778	17	9.87 448	27	10.12 552	9.90 330	10	**10**
51	9.77 795	17	9.87 475	26	10.12 525	9.90 320	9	9
52	9.77 812	17	9.87 501	26	10.12 499	9.90 311	10	8
53	9.77 829	17	9.87 527	27	10.12 473	9.90 301	9	7
54	9.77 846	16	9.87 554	26	10.12 446	9.90 292	10	6
55	9.77 862	17	9.87 580	26	10.12 420	9.90 282	9	5
56	9.77 879	17	9.87 606	27	10.12 394	9.90 273	10	4
57	9.77 896	17	9.87 633	26	10.12 367	9.90 263	9	3
58	9.77 913	17	9.87 659	26	10.12 341	9.90 254	10	2
59	9.77 930	16	9.87 685	26	10.12 315	9.90 244	9	1
60	9.77 946		9.87 711		10.12 289	9.90 235		**0**
	L Cos	d	L Cot	c d	L Tan	L Sin	d	′

Prop. Pts.

	27	26
1	2.7	2.6
2	5.4	5.2
3	8.1	7.8
4	10.8	10.4
5	13.5	13.0
6	16.2	15.6
7	18.9	18.2
8	21.6	20.8
9	24.3	23.4

	18	17	16
1	1.8	1.7	1.6
2	3.6	3.4	3.2
3	5.4	5.1	4.8
4	7.2	6.8	6.4
5	9.0	8.5	8.0
6	10.8	10.2	9.6
7	12.6	11.9	11.2
8	14.4	13.6	12.8
9	16.2	15.3	14.4

	10	9
1	1.0	0.9
2	2.0	1.8
3	3.0	2.7
4	4.0	3.6
5	5.0	4.5
6	6.0	5.4
7	7.0	6.3
8	8.0	7.2
9	9.0	8.1

53°

Table D (Continued)

37°

′	L Sin	d	L Tan	c d	L Cot	L Cos	d	
0	9.77 946		9.87 711		10.12 289	9.90 235		**60**
1	9.77 963	17	9.87 738	27	10.12 262	9.90 225	10	59
2	9.77 980	17	9.87 764	26	10.12 236	9.90 216	9	58
3	9.77 997	17	9.87 790	26	10.12 210	9.90 206	10	57
4	9.78 013	16	9.87 817	27	10.12 183	9.90 197	9	56
5	9.78 030	17	9.87 843	26	10.12 157	9.90 187	10	55
6	9.78 047	17	9.87 869	26	10.12 131	9.90 178	9	54
7	9.78 063	16	9.87 895	26	10.12 105	9.90 168	10	53
8	9.78 080	17	9.87 922	27	10.12 078	9.90 159	9	52
9	9.78 097	17	9.87 948	26	10.12 052	9.90 149	10	51
10	9.78 113	16	9.87 974	26	10.12 026	9.90 139	10	**50**
11	9.78 130	17	9.88 000	26	10.12 000	9.90 130	9	49
12	9.78 147	17	9.88 027	27	10.11 973	9.90 120	10	48
13	9.78 163	16	9.88 053	26	10.11 947	9.90 111	9	47
14	9.78 180	17	9.88 079	26	10.11 921	9.90 101	10	46
15	9.78 197	17	9.88 105	26	10.11 895	9.90 091	10	45
16	9.78 213	16	9.88 131	26	10.11 869	9.90 082	9	44
17	9.78 230	17	9.88 158	27	10.11 842	9.90 072	10	43
18	9.78 246	16	9.88 184	26	10.11 816	9.90 063	9	42
19	9.78 263	17	9.88 210	26	10.11 790	9.90 053	10	41
20	9.78 280	17	9.88 236	26	10.11 764	9.90 043	10	**40**
21	9.78 296	16	9.88 262	26	10.11 738	9.90 034	9	39
22	9.78 313	17	9.88 289	27	10.11 711	9.90 024	10	38
23	9.78 329	16	9.88 315	26	10.11 685	9.90 014	10	37
24	9.78 346	17	9.88 341	26	10.11 659	9.90 005	9	36
25	9.78 362	16	9.88 367	26	10.11 633	9.89 995	10	35
26	9.78 379	17	9.88 393	26	10.11 607	9.89 985	10	34
27	9.78 395	16	9.88 420	27	10.11 580	9.89 976	9	33
28	9.78 412	17	9.88 446	26	10.11 554	9.89 966	10	32
29	9.78 428	16	9.88 472	26	10.11 528	9.89 956	10	31
30	9.78 445	17	9.88 498	26	10.11 502	9.89 947	9	**30**
31	9.78 461	16	9.88 524	26	10.11 476	9.89 937	10	29
32	9.78 478	17	9.88 550	26	10.11 450	9.89 927	10	28
33	9.78 494	16	9.88 577	27	10.11 423	9.89 918	9	27
34	9.78 510	16	9.88 603	26	10.11 397	9.89 908	10	26
35	9.78 527	17	9.88 629	26	10.11 371	9.89 898	10	25
36	9.78 543	16	9.88 655	26	10.11 345	9.89 888	10	24
37	9.78 560	17	9.88 681	26	10.11 319	9.89 879	9	23
38	9.78 576	16	9.88 707	26	10.11 293	9.89 869	10	22
39	9.78 592	16	9.88 733	26	10.11 267	9.89 859	10	21
40	9.78 609	17	9.88 759	26	10.11 241	9.89 849	10	**20**
41	9.78 625	16	9.88 786	27	10.11 214	9.89 840	9	19
42	9.78 642	17	9.88 812	26	10.11 188	9.89 830	10	18
43	9.78 658	16	9.88 838	26	10.11 162	9.89 820	10	17
44	9.78 674	16	9.88 864	26	10.11 136	9.89 810	10	16
45	9.78 691	17	9.88 890	26	10.11 110	9.89 801	9	15
46	9.78 707	16	9.88 916	26	10.11 084	9.89 791	10	14
47	9.78 723	16	9.88 942	26	10.11 058	9.89 781	10	13
48	9.78 739	16	9.88 968	26	10.11 032	9.89 771	10	12
49	9.78 756	17	9.88 994	26	10.11 006	9.89 761	10	11
50	9.78 772	16	9.89 020	26	10.10 980	9.89 752	9	**10**
51	9.78 788	16	9.89 046	26	10.10 954	9.89 742	10	9
52	9.78 805	17	9.89 073	27	10.10 927	9.89 732	10	8
53	9.78 821	16	9.89 099	26	10.10 901	9.89 722	10	7
54	9.78 837	16	9.89 125	26	10.10 875	9.89 712	10	6
55	9.78 853	16	9.89 151	26	10.10 849	9.89 702	10	5
56	9.78 869	16	9.89 177	26	10.10 823	9.89 693	9	4
57	9.78 886	17	9.89 203	26	10.10 797	9.89 683	10	3
58	9.78 902	16	9.89 229	26	10.10 771	9.89 673	10	2
59	9.78 918	16	9.89 255	26	10.10 745	9.89 663	10	1
60	9.78 934	16	9.89 281	26	10.10 719	9.89 653	10	**0**
	L Cos	d	L Cot	c d	L Tan	L Sin	d	′

Prop. Pts.

	27	26
1	2.7	2.6
2	5.4	5.2
3	8.1	7.8
4	10.8	10.4
5	13.5	13.0
6	16.2	15.6
7	18.9	18.2
8	21.6	20.8
9	24.3	23.4

	17	16
1	1.7	1.6
2	3.4	3.2
3	5.1	4.8
4	6.8	6.4
5	8.5	8.0
6	10.2	9.6
7	11.9	11.2
8	13.6	12.8
9	15.3	14.4

	10	9
1	1.0	0.9
2	2.0	1.8
3	3.0	2.7
4	4.0	3.6
5	5.0	4.5
6	6.0	5.4
7	7.0	6.3
8	8.0	7.2
9	9.0	8.1

Prop. Pts.

52°

Table D (Continued)

38°

′	L Sin	d	L Tan	c d	L Cot	L Cos	d	
0	9.78 934	16	9.89 281	26	10.10 719	9.89 653	10	**60**
1	9.78 950	17	9.89 307	26	10.10 693	9.89 643	10	59
2	9.78 967	16	9.89 333	26	10.10 667	9.89 633	9	58
3	9.78 983	16	9.89 359	26	10.10 641	9.89 624	10	57
4	9.78 999	16	9.89 385	26	10.10 615	9.89 614	10	56
5	9.79 015	16	9.89 411	26	10.10 589	9.89 604	10	55
6	9.79 031	16	9.89 437	26	10.10 563	9.89 594	10	54
7	9.79 047	16	9.89 463	26	10.10 537	9.89 584	10	53
8	9.79 063	16	9.89 489	26	10.10 511	9.89 574	10	52
9	9.79 079	16	9.89 515	26	10.10 485	9.89 564	10	51
10	9.79 095	16	9.89 541	26	10.10 459	9.89 554	10	**50**
11	9.79 111	17	9.89 567	26	10.10 433	9.89 544	10	49
12	9.79 128	16	9.89 593	26	10.10 407	9.89 534	10	48
13	9.79 144	16	9.89 619	26	10.10 381	9.89 524	10	47
14	9.79 160	16	9.89 645	26	10.10 355	9.89 514	10	46
15	9.79 176	16	9.89 671	26	10.10 329	9.89 504	9	45
16	9.79 192	16	9.89 697	26	10.10 303	9.89 495	10	44
17	9.79 208	16	9.89 723	26	10.10 277	9.89 485	10	43
18	9.79 224	16	9.89 749	26	10.10 251	9.89 475	10	42
19	9.79 240	16	9.89 775	26	10.10 225	9.89 465	10	41
20	9.79 256	16	9.89 801	26	10.10 199	9.89 455	10	**40**
21	9.79 272	16	9.89 827	26	10.10 173	9.89 445	10	39
22	9.79 288	16	9.89 853	26	10.10 147	9.89 435	10	38
23	9.79 304	15	9.89 879	26	10.10 121	9.89 425	10	37
24	9.79 319	16	9.89 905	26	10.10 095	9.89 415	10	36
25	9.79 335	16	9.89 931	26	10.10 069	9.89 405	10	35
26	9.79 351	16	9.89 957	26	10.10 043	9.89 395	10	34
27	9.79 367	16	9.89 983	26	10.10 017	9.89 385	10	33
28	9.79 383	16	9.90 009	26	10.09 991	9.89 375	11	32
29	9.79 399	16	9.90 035	26	10.09 965	9.89 364	10	31
30	9.79 415	16	9.90 061	25	10.09 939	9.89 354	10	**30**
31	9.79 431	16	9.90 086	26	10.09 914	9.89 344	10	29
32	9.79 447	16	9.90 112	26	10.09 888	9.89 334	10	28
33	9.79 463	15	9.90 138	26	10.09 862	9.89 324	10	27
34	9.79 478	16	9.90 164	26	10.09 836	9.89 314	10	26
35	9.79 494	16	9.90 190	26	10.09 810	9.89 304	10	25
36	9.79 510	16	9.90 216	26	10.09 784	9.89 294	10	24
37	9.79 526	16	9.90 242	26	10.09 758	9.89 284	10	23
38	9.79 542	16	9.90 268	26	10.09 732	9.89 274	10	22
39	9.79 558	15	9.90 294	26	10.09 706	9.89 264	10	21
40	9.79 573	16	9.90 320	26	10.09 680	9.89 254	10	**20**
41	9.79 589	16	9.90 346	25	10.09 654	9.89 244	11	19
42	9.79 605	16	9.90 371	26	10.09 629	9.89 233	10	18
43	9.79 621	15	9.90 397	26	10.09 603	9.89 223	10	17
44	9.79 636	16	9.90 423	26	10.09 577	9.89 213	10	16
45	9.79 652	16	9.90 449	26	10.09 551	9.89 203	10	15
46	9.79 668	16	9.90 475	26	10.09 525	9.89 193	10	14
47	9.79 684	15	9.90 501	26	10.09 499	9.89 183	10	13
48	9.79 699	16	9.90 527	26	10.09 473	9.89 173	11	12
49	9.79 715	16	9.90 553	25	10.09 447	9.89 162	10	11
50	9.79 731	15	9.90 578	26	10.09 422	9.89 152	10	**10**
51	9.79 746	16	9.90 604	26	10.09 396	9.89 142	10	9
52	9.79 762	16	9.90 630	26	10.09 370	9.89 132	10	8
53	9.79 778	15	9.90 656	26	10.09 344	9.89 122	10	7
54	9.79 793	16	9.90 682	26	10.09 318	9.89 112	11	6
55	9.79 809	16	9.90 708	26	10.09 292	9.89 101	10	5
56	9.79 825	15	9.90 734	25	10.09 266	9.89 091	10	4
57	9.79 840	16	9.90 759	26	10.09 241	9.89 081	10	3
58	9.79 856	16	9.90 785	26	10.09 215	9.89 071	11	2
59	9.79 872	15	9.90 811	26	10.09 189	9.89 060	10	1
60	9.79 887		9.90 837		10.09 163	9.89 050		**0**
	L Cos	d	L Cot	c d	L Tan	L Sin	d	′

Prop. Pts.

	26	25
1	2.6	2.5
2	5.2	5.0
3	7.8	7.5
4	10.4	10.0
5	13.0	12.5
6	15.6	15.0
7	18.2	17.5
8	20.8	20.0
9	23.4	22.5

	17	16	15
1	1.7	1.6	1.5
2	3.4	3.2	3.0
3	5.1	4.8	4.5
4	6.8	6.4	6.0
5	8.5	8.0	7.5
6	10.2	9.6	9.0
7	11.9	11.2	10.5
8	13.6	12.8	12.0
9	15.3	14.4	13.5

	11	10	9
1	1.1	1.0	0.9
2	2.2	2.0	1.8
3	3.3	3.0	2.7
4	4.4	4.0	3.6
5	5.5	5.0	4.5
6	6.6	6.0	5.4
7	7.7	7.0	6.3
8	8.8	8.0	7.2
9	9.9	9.0	8.1

Prop. Pts.

51°

Table D (Continued)

39°

′	L Sin	d	L Tan	c d	L Cot	L Cos	d	′
0	9.79 887	16	9.90 837	26	10.09 163	9.89 050	10	**60**
1	9.79 903	15	9.90 863	26	10.09 137	9.89 040	10	59
2	9.79 918	16	9.90 889	25	10.09 111	9.89 030	10	58
3	9.79 934	16	9.90 914	26	10.09 086	9.89 020	11	57
4	9.79 950	15	9.90 940	26	10.09 060	9.89 009	10	56
5	9.79 965	16	9.90 966	26	10.09 034	9.88 999	10	55
6	9.79 981	15	9.90 992	26	10.09 008	9.88 989	11	54
7	9.79 996	16	9.91 018	25	10.08 982	9.88 978	10	53
8	9.80 012	15	9.91 043	26	10.08 957	9.88 968	10	52
9	9.80 027	16	9.91 069	26	10.08 931	9.88 958	10	51
10	9.80 043	15	9.91 095	26	10.08 905	9.88 948	11	**50**
11	9.80 058	16	9.91 121	26	10.08 879	9.88 937	10	49
12	9.80 074	15	9.91 147	25	10.08 853	9.88 927	10	48
13	9.80 089	16	9.91 172	26	10.08 828	9.88 917	11	47
14	9.80 105	15	9.91 198	26	10.08 802	9.88 906	10	46
15	9.80 120	16	9.91 224	26	10.08 776	9.88 896	10	45
16	9.80 136	15	9.91 250	26	10.08 750	9.88 886	11	44
17	9.80 151	15	9.91 276	25	10.08 724	9.88 875	10	43
18	9.80 166	16	9.91 301	26	10.08 699	9.88 865	10	42
19	9.80 182	15	9.91 327	26	10.08 673	9.88 855	11	41
20	9.80 197	16	9.91 353	26	10.08 647	9.88 844	10	**40**
21	9.80 213	15	9.91 379	25	10.08 621	9.88 834	10	39
22	9.80 228	16	9.91 404	26	10.08 596	9.88 824	11	38
23	9.80 244	15	9.91 430	26	10.08 570	9.88 813	10	37
24	9.80 259	15	9.91 456	26	10.08 544	9.88 803	10	36
25	9.80 274	16	9.91 482	25	10.08 518	9.88 793	11	35
26	9.80 290	15	9.91 507	26	10.08 493	9.88 782	10	34
27	9.80 305	15	9.91 533	26	10.08 467	9.88 772	11	33
28	9.80 320	16	9.91 559	26	10.08 441	9.88 761	10	32
29	9.80 336	15	9.91 585	25	10.08 415	9.88 751	10	31
30	9.80 351	15	9.91 610	26	10.08 390	9.88 741	11	**30**
31	9.80 366	16	9.91 636	26	10.08 364	9.88 730	10	29
32	9.80 382	15	9.91 662	26	10.08 338	9.88 720	11	28
33	9.80 397	15	9.91 688	25	10.08 312	9.88 709	10	27
34	9.80 412	16	9.91 713	26	10.08 287	9.88 699	11	26
35	9.80 428	15	9.91 739	26	10.08 261	9.88 688	10	25
36	9.80 443	15	9.91 765	26	10.08 235	9.88 678	10	24
37	9.80 458	15	9.91 791	25	10.08 209	9.88 668	11	23
38	9.80 473	16	9.91 816	26	10.08 184	9.88 657	10	22
39	9.80 489	15	9.91 842	26	10.08 158	9.88 647	11	21
40	9.80 504	15	9.91 868	25	10.08 132	9.88 636	10	**20**
41	9.80 519	15	9.91 893	26	10.08 107	9.88 626	11	19
42	9.80 534	16	9.91 919	26	10.08 081	9.88 615	10	18
43	9.80 550	15	9.91 945	26	10.08 055	9.88 605	11	17
44	9.80 565	15	9.91 971	25	10.08 029	9.88 594	10	16
45	9.80 580	15	9.91 996	26	10.08 004	9.88 584	11	15
46	9.80 595	15	9.92 022	26	10.07 978	9.88 573	10	14
47	9.80 610	15	9.92 048	25	10.07 952	9.88 563	11	13
48	9.80 625	16	9.92 073	26	10.07 927	9.88 552	10	12
49	9.80 641	15	9.92 099	26	10.07 901	9.88 542	11	11
50	9.80 656	15	9.92 125	25	10.07 875	9.88 531	10	**10**
51	9.80 671	15	9.92 150	26	10.07 850	9.88 521	11	9
52	9.80 686	15	9.92 176	26	10.07 824	9.88 510	11	8
53	9.80 701	15	9.92 202	25	10.07 798	9.88 499	10	7
54	9.80 716	15	9.92 227	26	10.07 773	9.88 489	11	6
55	9.80 731	15	9.92 253	26	10.07 747	9.88 478	10	5
56	9.80 746	16	9.92 279	25	10.07 721	9.88 468	11	4
57	9.80 762	15	9.92 304	26	10.07 696	9.88 457	10	3
58	9.80 777	15	9.92 330	26	10.07 670	9.88 447	11	2
59	9.80 792	15	9.92 356	25	10.07 644	9.88 436	11	1
60	9.80 807		9.92 381		10.07 619	9.88 425		**0**
	L Cos	d	L Cot	c d	L Tan	L Sin	d	′

Prop. Pts.

	26	25
1	2.6	2.5
2	5.2	5.0
3	7.8	7.5
4	10.4	10.0
5	13.0	12.5
6	15.6	15.0
7	18.2	17.5
8	20.8	20.0
9	23.4	22.5

	16	15
1	1.6	1.5
2	3.2	3.0
3	4.8	4.5
4	6.4	6.0
5	8.0	7.5
6	9.6	9.0
7	11.2	10.5
8	12.8	12.0
9	14.4	13.5

	11	10
1	1.1	1.0
2	2.2	2.0
3	3.3	3.0
4	4.4	4.0
5	5.5	5.0
6	6.6	6.0
7	7.7	7.0
8	8.8	8.0
9	9.9	9.0

Prop. Pts.

50°

Table D (Continued)

40°

′	L Sin	d	L Tan	c d	L Cot	L Cos	d	′
0	9.80 807	15	9.92 381	26	10.07 619	9.88 425	10	**60**
1	9.80 822	15	9.92 407	26	10.07 593	9.88 415	11	59
2	9.80 837	15	9.92 433	25	10.07 567	9.88 404	10	58
3	9.80 852	15	9.92 458	26	10.07 542	9.88 394	11	57
4	9.80 867	15	9.92 484	26	10.07 516	9.88 383	11	56
5	9.80 882	15	9.92 510	25	10.07 490	9.88 372	10	55
6	9.80 897	15	9.92 535	26	10.07 465	9.88 362	11	54
7	9.80 912	15	9.92 561	26	10.07 439	9.88 351	11	53
8	9.80 927	15	9.92 587	25	10.07 413	9.88 340	10	52
9	9.80 942	15	9.92 612	26	10.07 388	9.88 330	11	51
10	9.80 957	15	9.92 638	25	10.07 362	9.88 319	11	**50**
11	9.80 972	15	9.92 663	26	10.07 337	9.88 308	10	49
12	9.80 987	15	9.92 689	26	10.07 311	9.88 298	11	48
13	9.81 002	15	9.92 715	25	10.07 285	9.88 287	11	47
14	9.81 017	15	9.92 740	26	10.07 260	9.88 276	10	46
15	9.81 032	15	9.92 766	26	10.07 234	9.88 266	11	45
16	9.81 047	14	9.92 792	25	10.07 208	9.88 255	11	44
17	9.81 061	15	9.92 817	26	10.07 183	9.88 244	10	43
18	9.81 076	15	9.92 843	25	10.07 157	9.88 234	11	42
19	9.81 091	15	9.92 868	26	10.07 132	9.88 223	11	41
20	9.81 106	15	9.92 894	26	10.07 106	9.88 212	11	**40**
21	9.81 121	15	9.92 920	25	10.07 080	9.88 201	10	39
22	9.81 136	15	9.92 945	26	10.07 055	9.88 191	11	38
23	9.81 151	15	9.92 971	25	10.07 029	9.88 180	11	37
24	9.81 166	14	9.92 996	26	10.07 004	9.88 169	11	36
25	9.81 180	15	9.93 022	26	10.06 978	9.88 158	10	35
26	9.81 195	15	9.93 048	25	10.06 952	9.88 148	11	34
27	9.81 210	15	9.93 073	26	10.06 927	9.88 137	11	33
28	9.81 225	15	9.93 099	25	10.06 901	9.88 126	11	32
29	9.81 240	14	9.93 124	26	10.06 876	9.88 115	10	31
30	9.81 254	15	9.93 150	25	10.06 850	9.88 105	11	**30**
31	9.81 269	15	9.93 175	26	10.06 825	9.88 094	11	29
32	9.81 284	15	9.93 201	26	10.06 799	9.88 083	11	28
33	9.81 299	15	9.93 227	25	10.06 773	9.88 072	11	27
34	9.81 314	14	9.93 252	26	10.06 748	9.88 061	10	26
35	9.81 328	15	9.93 278	25	10.06 722	9.88 051	11	25
36	9.81 343	15	9.93 303	26	10.06 697	9.88 040	11	24
37	9.81 358	14	9.93 329	25	10.06 671	9.88 029	11	23
38	9.81 372	15	9.93 354	26	10.06 646	9.88 018	11	22
39	9.81 387	15	9.93 380	26	10.06 620	9.88 007	11	21
40	9.81 402	15	9.93 406	25	10.06 594	9.87 996	11	**20**
41	9.81 417	14	9.93 431	26	10.06 569	9.87 985	10	19
42	9.81 431	15	9.93 457	25	10.06 543	9.87 975	11	18
43	9.81 446	15	9.93 482	26	10.06 518	9.87 964	11	17
44	9.81 461	14	9.93 508	25	10.06 492	9.87 953	11	16
45	9.81 475	15	9.93 533	26	10.06 467	9.87 942	11	15
46	9.81 490	15	9.93 559	25	10.06 441	9.87 931	11	14
47	9.81 505	14	9.93 584	26	10.06 416	9.87 920	11	13
48	9.81 519	15	9.93 610	26	10.06 390	9.87 909	11	12
49	9.81 534	15	9.93 636	25	10.06 364	9.87 898	11	11
50	9.81 549	14	9.93 661	26	10.06 339	9.87 887	10	**10**
51	9.81 563	15	9.93 687	25	10.06 313	9.87 877	11	9
52	9.81 578	14	9.93 712	26	10.06 288	9.87 866	11	8
53	9.81 592	15	9.93 738	25	10.06 262	9.87 855	11	7
54	9.81 607	15	9.93 763	26	10.06 237	9.87 844	11	6
55	9.81 622	14	9.93 789	25	10.06 211	9.87 833	11	5
56	9.81 636	15	9.93 814	26	10.06 186	9.87 822	11	4
57	9.81 651	14	9.93 840	25	10.06 160	9.87 811	11	3
58	9.81 665	15	9.93 865	26	10.06 135	9.87 800	11	2
59	9.81 680	14	9.93 891	25	10.06 109	9.87 789	11	1
60	9.81 694		9.93 916		10.06 084	9.87 778		**0**
	L Cos	d	L Cot	c d	L Tan	L Sin	d	′

Prop. Pts.

	26	25
1	2.6	2.5
2	5.2	5.0
3	7.8	7.5
4	10.4	10.0
5	13.0	12.5
6	15.6	15.0
7	18.2	17.5
8	20.8	20.0
9	23.4	22.5

	15	14
1	1.5	1.4
2	3.0	2.8
3	4.5	4.2
4	6.0	5.6
5	7.5	7.0
6	9.0	8.4
7	10.5	9.8
8	12.0	11.2
9	13.5	12.6

	11	10
1	1.1	1.0
2	2.2	2.0
3	3.3	3.0
4	4.4	4.0
5	5.5	5.0
6	6.6	6.0
7	7.7	7.0
8	8.8	8.0
9	9.9	9.0

49°

Table D (Continued)

41°

′	L Sin	d	L Tan	c d	L Cot	L Cos	d	′
0	9.81 694	15	9.93 916	26	10.06 084	9.87 778	11	**60**
1	9.81 709	14	9.93 942	25	10.06 058	9.87 767	11	59
2	9.81 723	15	9.93 967	26	10.06 033	9.87 756	11	58
3	9.81 738	14	9.93 993	25	10.06 007	9.87 745	11	57
4	9.81 752	15	9.94 018	26	10.05 982	9.87 734	11	56
5	9.81 767	14	9.94 044	25	10.05 956	9.87 723	11	55
6	9.81 781	15	9.94 069	26	10.05 931	9.87 712	11	54
7	9.81 796	14	9.94 095	25	10.05 905	9.87 701	11	53
8	9.81 810	15	9.94 120	26	10.05 880	9.87 690	11	52
9	9.81 825	14	9.94 146	25	10.05 854	9.87 679	11	51
10	9.81 839	15	9.94 171	26	10.05 829	9.87 668	11	**50**
11	9.81 854	14	9.94 197	25	10.05 803	9.87 657	11	49
12	9.81 868	14	9.94 222	26	10.05 778	9.87 646	11	48
13	9.81 882	15	9.94 248	25	10.05 752	9.87 635	11	47
14	9.81 897	14	9.94 273	26	10.05 727	9.87 624	11	46
15	9.81 911	15	9.94 299	25	10.05 701	9.87 613	12	45
16	9.81 926	14	9.94 324	26	10.05 676	9.87 601	11	44
17	9.81 940	15	9.94 350	25	10.05 650	9.87 590	11	43
18	9.81 955	14	9.94 375	26	10.05 625	9.87 579	11	42
19	9.81 969	14	9.94 401	25	10.05 599	9.87 568	11	41
20	9.81 983	15	9.94 426	26	10.05 574	9.87 557	11	**40**
21	9.81 998	14	9.94 452	25	10.05 548	9.87 546	11	39
22	9.82 012	14	9.94 477	26	10.05 523	9.87 535	11	38
23	9.82 026	15	9.94 503	25	10.05 497	9.87 524	11	37
24	9.82 041	14	9.94 528	26	10.05 472	9.87 513	12	36
25	9.82 055	14	9.94 554	25	10.05 446	9.87 501	11	35
26	9.82 069	15	9.94 579	25	10.05 421	9.87 490	11	34
27	9.82 084	14	9.94 604	26	10.05 396	9.87 479	11	33
28	9.82 098	14	9.94 630	25	10.05 370	9.87 468	11	32
29	9.82 112	14	9.94 655	26	10.05 345	9.87 457	11	31
30	9.82 126	15	9.94 681	25	10.05 319	9.87 446	12	**30**
31	9.82 141	14	9.94 706	26	10.05 294	9.87 434	11	29
32	9.82 155	14	9.94 732	25	10.05 268	9.87 423	11	28
33	9.82 169	15	9.94 757	26	10.05 243	9.87 412	11	27
34	9.82 184	14	9.94 783	25	10.05 217	9.87 401	11	26
35	9.82 198	14	9.94 808	26	10.05 192	9.87 390	12	25
36	9.82 212	14	9.94 834	25	10.05 166	9.87 378	11	24
37	9.82 226	14	9.94 859	25	10.05 141	9.87 367	11	23
38	9.82 240	15	9.94 884	26	10.05 116	9.87 356	11	22
39	9.82 255	14	9.94 910	25	10.05 090	9.87 345	11	21
40	9.82 269	14	9.94 935	26	10.05 065	9.87 334	12	**20**
41	9.82 283	14	9.94 961	25	10.05 039	9.87 322	11	19
42	9.82 297	14	9.94 986	26	10.05 014	9.87 311	11	18
43	9.82 311	15	9.95 012	25	10.04 988	9.87 300	12	17
44	9.82 326	14	9.95 037	25	10.04 963	9.87 288	11	16
45	9.82 340	14	9.95 062	26	10.04 938	9.87 277	11	15
46	9.82 354	14	9.95 088	25	10.04 912	9.87 266	11	14
47	9.82 368	14	9.95 113	26	10.04 887	9.87 255	12	13
48	9.82 382	14	9.95 139	25	10.04 861	9.87 243	11	12
49	9.82 396	14	9.95 164	26	10.04 836	9.87 232	11	11
50	9.82 410	14	9.95 190	25	10.04 810	9.87 221	12	**10**
51	9.82 424	15	9.95 215	25	10.04 785	9.87 209	11	9
52	9.82 439	14	9.95 240	26	10.04 760	9.87 198	11	8
53	9.82 453	14	9.95 266	25	10.04 734	9.87 187	12	7
54	9.82 467	14	9.95 291	26	10.04 709	9.87 175	11	6
55	9.82 481	14	9.95 317	25	10.04 683	9.87 164	11	5
56	9.82 495	14	9.95 342	26	10.04 658	9.87 153	12	4
57	9.82 509	14	9.95 368	25	10.04 632	9.87 141	11	3
58	9.82 523	14	9.95 393	25	10.04 607	9.87 130	11	2
59	9.82 537	14	9.95 418	26	10.04 582	9.87 119	12	1
60	9.82 551		9.95 444		10.04 556	9.87 107		**0**
	L Cos	d	L Cot	c d	L Tan	L Sin	d	′

Prop. Pts.

	26	25
1	2.6	2.5
2	5.2	5.0
3	7.8	7.5
4	10.4	10.0
5	13.0	12.5
6	15.6	15.0
7	18.2	17.5
8	20.8	20.0
9	23.4	22.5

	15	14
1	1.5	1.4
2	3.0	2.8
3	4.5	4.2
4	6.0	5.6
5	7.5	7.0
6	9.0	8.4
7	10.5	9.8
8	12.0	11.2
9	13.5	12.6

	12	11
1	1.2	1.1
2	2.4	2.2
3	3.6	3.3
4	4.8	4.4
5	6.0	5.5
6	7.2	6.6
7	8.4	7.7
8	9.6	8.8
9	10.8	9.9

Prop. Pts.

48°

42°

′	L Sin	d	L Tan	c d	L Cot	L Cos	d	
0	9.82 551	14	9.95 444	25	10.04 556	9.87 107	11	**60**
1	9.82 565	14	9.95 469	26	10.04 531	9.87 096	11	59
2	9.82 579	14	9.95 495	25	10.04 505	9.87 085	12	58
3	9.82 593	14	9.95 520	25	10.04 480	9.87 073	11	57
4	9.82 607	14	9.95 545	26	10.04 455	9.87 062	12	56
5	9.82 621	14	9.95 571	25	10.04 429	9.87 050	11	55
6	9.82 635	14	9.95 596	26	10.04 404	9.87 039	11	54
7	9.82 649	14	9.95 622	25	10.04 378	9.87 028	12	53
8	9.82 663	14	9.95 647	25	10.04 353	9.87 016	11	52
9	9.82 677	14	9.95 672	26	10.04 328	9.87 005	12	51
10	9.82 691	14	9.95 698	25	10.04 302	9.86 993	11	**50**
11	9.82 705	14	9.95 723	25	10.04 277	9.86 982	12	49
12	9.82 719	14	9.95 748	26	10.04 252	9.86 970	11	48
13	9.82 733	14	9.95 774	25	10.04 226	9.86 959	12	47
14	9.82 747	14	9.95 799	26	10.04 201	9.86 947	11	46
15	9.82 761	14	9.95 825	25	10.04 175	9.86 936	12	45
16	9.82 775	13	9.95 850	25	10.04 150	9.86 924	11	44
17	9.82 788	14	9.95 875	26	10.04 125	9.86 913	11	43
18	9.82 802	14	9.95 901	25	10.04 099	9.86 902	12	42
19	9.82 816	14	9.95 926	26	10.04 074	9.86 890	11	41
20	9.82 830	14	9.95 952	25	10.04 048	9.86 879	12	**40**
21	9.82 844	14	9.95 977	25	10.04 023	9.86 867	12	39
22	9.82 858	14	9.96 002	26	10.03 998	9.86 855	11	38
23	9.82 872	13	9.96 028	25	10.03 972	9.86 844	12	37
24	9.82 885	14	9.96 053	25	10.03 947	9.86 832	11	36
25	9.82 899	14	9.96 078	26	10.03 922	9.86 821	12	35
26	9.82 913	14	9.96 104	25	10.03 896	9.86 809	11	34
27	9.82 927	14	9.96 129	26	10.03 871	9.86 798	12	33
28	9.82 941	14	9.96 155	25	10.03 845	9.86 786	11	32
29	9.82 955	13	9.96 180	25	10.03 820	9.86 775	12	31
30	9.82 968	14	9.96 205	26	10.03 795	9.86 763	11	**30**
31	9.82 982	14	9.96 231	25	10.03 769	9.86 752	12	29
32	9.82 996	14	9.96 256	25	10.03 744	9.86 740	12	28
33	9.83 010	13	9.96 281	26	10.03 719	9.86 728	11	27
34	9.83 023	14	9.96 307	25	10.03 693	9.86 717	12	26
35	9.83 037	14	9.96 332	25	10.03 668	9.86 705	11	25
36	9.83 051	14	9.96 357	26	10.03 643	9.86 694	12	24
37	9.83 065	13	9.96 383	25	10.03 617	9.86 682	12	23
38	9.83 078	14	9.96 408	25	10.03 592	9.86 670	11	22
39	9.83 092	14	9.96 433	26	10.03 567	9.86 659	12	21
40	9.83 106	14	9.96 459	25	10.03 541	9.86 647	12	**20**
41	9.83 120	13	9.96 484	26	10.03 516	9.86 635	11	19
42	9.83 133	14	9.96 510	25	10.03 490	9.86 624	12	18
43	9.83 147	14	9.96 535	25	10.03 465	9.86 612	12	17
44	9.83 161	13	9.96 560	26	10.03 440	9.86 600	11	16
45	9.83 174	14	9.96 586	25	10.03 414	9.86 589	12	15
46	9.83 188	14	9.96 611	25	10.03 389	9.86 577	12	14
47	9.83 202	13	9.96 636	26	10.03 364	9.86 565	11	13
48	9.83 215	14	9.96 662	25	10.03 338	9.86 554	12	12
49	9.83 229	13	9.96 687	25	10.03 313	9.86 542	12	11
50	9.83 242	14	9.96 712	26	10.03 288	9.86 530	12	**10**
51	9.83 256	14	9.96 738	25	10.03 262	9.86 518	11	9
52	9.83 270	13	9.96 763	25	10.03 237	9.86 507	12	8
53	9.83 283	14	9.96 788	26	10.03 212	9.86 495	12	7
54	9.83 297	13	9.96 814	25	10.03 186	9.86 483	11	6
55	9.83 310	14	9.96 839	25	10.03 161	9.86 472	12	5
56	9.83 324	14	9.96 864	26	10.03 136	9.86 460	12	4
57	9.83 338	13	9.96 890	25	10.03 110	9.86 448	12	3
58	9.83 351	14	9.96 915	25	10.03 085	9.86 436	11	2
59	9.83 365	13	9.96 940	26	10.03 060	9.86 425	12	1
60	9.83 378		9.96 966		10.03 034	9.86 413		**0**
	L Cos	d	L Cot	c d	L Tan	L Sin	d	′

47°

Prop. Pts.

	26	25
1	2.6	2.5
2	5.2	5.0
3	7.8	7.5
4	10.4	10.0
5	13.0	12.5
6	15.6	15.0
7	18.2	17.5
8	20.8	20.0
9	23.4	22.5

	14	13
1	1.4	1.3
2	2.8	2.6
3	4.2	3.9
4	5.6	5.2
5	7.0	6.5
6	8.4	7.8
7	9.8	9.1
8	11.2	10.4
9	12.6	11.7

	12	11
1	1.2	1.1
2	2.4	2.2
3	3.6	3.3
4	4.8	4.4
5	6.0	5.5
6	7.2	6.6
7	8.4	7.7
8	9.6	8.8
9	10.8	9.9

Prop. Pts.

Table D (Continued)

43°

′	L Sin	d	L Tan	c d	L Cot	L Cos	d	
0	9.83 378	14	9.96 966	25	10.03 034	9.86 413	12	**60**
1	9.83 392	13	9.96 991	25	10.03 009	9.86 401	12	59
2	9.83 405	14	9.97 016	26	10.02 984	9.86 389	12	58
3	9.83 419	13	9.97 042	25	10.02 958	9.86 377	11	57
4	9.83 432	14	9.97 067	25	10.02 933	9.86 366	12	56
5	9.83 446	13	9.97 092	26	10.02 908	9.86 354	12	55
6	9.83 459	14	9.97 118	25	10.02 882	9.86 342	12	54
7	9.83 473	13	9.97 143	25	10.02 857	9.86 330	12	53
8	9.83 486	14	9.97 168	25	10.02 832	9.86 318	12	52
9	9.83 500	13	9.97 193	26	10.02 807	9.86 306	11	51
10	9.83 513	14	9.97 219	25	10.02 781	9.86 295	12	**50**
11	9.83 527	13	9.97 244	25	10.02 756	9.86 283	12	49
12	9.83 540	14	9.97 269	26	10.02 731	9.86 271	12	48
13	9.83 554	13	9.97 295	25	10.02 705	9.86 259	12	47
14	9.83 567	14	9.97 320	25	10.02 680	9.86 247	12	46
15	9.83 581	13	9.97 345	26	10.02 655	9.86 235	12	45
16	9.83 594	14	9.97 371	25	10.02 629	9.86 223	12	44
17	9.83 608	13	9.97 396	25	10.02 604	9.86 211	11	43
18	9.83 621	13	9.97 421	26	10.02 579	9.86 200	12	42
19	9.83 634	14	9.97 447	25	10.02 553	9.86 188	12	41
20	9.83 648	13	9.97 472	25	10.02 528	9.86 176	12	**40**
21	9.83 661	13	9.97 497	26	10.02 503	9.86 164	12	39
22	9.83 674	14	9.97 523	25	10.02 477	9.86 152	12	38
23	9.83 688	13	9.97 548	25	10.02 452	9.86 140	12	37
24	9.83 701	14	9.97 573	25	10.02 427	9.86 128	12	36
25	9.83 715	13	9.97 598	26	10.02 402	9.86 116	12	35
26	9.83 728	13	9.97 624	25	10.02 376	9.86 104	12	34
27	9.83 741	14	9.97 649	25	10.02 351	9.86 092	12	33
28	9.83 755	13	9.97 674	26	10.02 326	9.86 080	12	32
29	9.83 768	13	9.97 700	25	10.02 300	9.86 068	12	31
30	9.83 781	14	9.97 725	25	10.02 275	9.86 056	12	**30**
31	9.83 795	13	9.97 750	26	10.02 250	9.86 044	12	29
32	9.83 808	13	9.97 776	25	10.02 224	9.86 032	12	28
33	9.83 821	13	9.97 801	25	10.02 199	9.86 020	12	27
34	9.83 834	14	9.97 826	25	10.02 174	9.86 008	12	26
35	9.83 848	13	9.97 851	26	10.02 149	9.85 996	12	25
36	9.83 861	13	9.97 877	25	10.02 123	9.85 984	12	24
37	9.83 874	13	9.97 902	25	10.02 098	9.85 972	12	23
38	9.83 887	14	9.97 927	26	10.02 073	9.85 960	12	22
39	9.83 901	13	9.97 953	25	10.02 047	9.85 948	12	21
40	9.83 914	13	9.97 978	25	10.02 022	9.85 936	12	**20**
41	9.83 927	13	9.98 003	26	10.01 997	9.85 924	12	19
42	9.83 940	14	9.98 029	25	10.01 971	9.85 912	12	18
43	9.83 954	13	9.98 054	25	10.01 946	9.85 900	12	17
44	9.83 967	13	9.98 079	25	10.01 921	9.85 888	12	16
45	9.83 980	13	9.98 104	26	10.01 896	9.85 876	12	15
46	9.83 993	13	9.98 130	25	10.01 870	9.85 864	13	14
47	9.84 006	14	9.98 155	25	10.01 845	9.85 851	12	13
48	9.84 020	13	9.98 180	26	10.01 820	9.85 839	12	12
49	9.84 033	13	9.98 206	25	10.01 794	9.85 827	12	11
50	9.84 046	13	9.98 231	25	10.01 769	9.85 815	12	**10**
51	9.84 059	13	9.98 256	25	10.01 744	9.85 803	12	9
52	9.84 072	13	9.98 281	26	10.01 719	9.85 791	12	8
53	9.84 085	13	9.98 307	25	10.01 693	9.85 779	13	7
54	9.84 098	14	9.98 332	25	10.01 668	9.85 766	12	6
55	9.84 112	13	9.98 357	26	10.01 643	9.85 754	12	5
56	9.84 125	13	9.98 383	25	10.01 617	9.85 742	12	4
57	9.84 138	13	9.98 408	25	10.01 592	9.85 730	12	3
58	9.84 151	13	9.98 433	25	10.01 567	9.85 718	12	2
59	9.84 164	13	9.98 458	26	10.01 542	9.85 706	13	1
60	9.84 177		9.98 484		10.01 516	9.85 693		**0**
	L Cos	d	L Cot	c d	L Tan	L Sin	d	′

Prop. Pts.

	26	25
1	2.6	2.5
2	5.2	5.0
3	7.8	7.5
4	10.4	10.0
5	13.0	12.5
6	15.6	15.0
7	18.2	17.5
8	20.8	20.0
9	23.4	22.5

	14	13
1	1.4	1.3
2	2.8	2.6
3	4.2	3.9
4	5.6	5.2
5	7.0	6.5
6	8.4	7.8
7	9.8	9.1
8	11.2	10.4
9	12.6	11.7

	12	11
1	1.2	1.1
2	2.4	2.2
3	3.6	3.3
4	4.8	4.4
5	6.0	5.5
6	7.2	6.6
7	8.4	7.7
8	9.6	8.8
9	10.8	9.9

Prop. Pts.

46°

Table D (Continued)

44°

′	L Sin	d	L Tan	c d	L Cot	L Cos	d	
0	9.84 177		9.98 484		10.01 516	9.85 693		**60**
1	9.84 190	13	9.98 509	25	10.01 491	9.85 681	12	59
2	9.84 203	13	9.98 534	25	10.01 466	9.85 669	12	58
3	9.84 216	13	9.98 560	26	10.01 440	9.85 657	12	57
4	9.84 229	13	9.98 585	25	10.01 415	9.85 645	12	56
5	9.84 242	13	9.98 610	25	10.01 390	9.85 632	13	55
6	9.84 255	13	9.98 635	25	10.01 365	9.85 620	12	54
7	9.84 269	14	9.98 661	26	10.01 339	9.85 608	12	53
8	9.84 282	13	9.98 686	25	10.01 314	9.85 596	12	52
9	9.84 295	13	9.98 711	25	10.01 289	9.85 583	13	51
10	9.84 308	13	9.98 737	26	10.01 263	9.85 571	12	**50**
11	9.84 321	13	9.98 762	25	10.01 238	9.85 559	12	49
12	9.84 334	13	9.98 787	25	10.01 213	9.85 547	12	48
13	9.84 347	13	9.98 812	25	10.01 188	9.85 534	13	47
14	9.84 360	13	9.98 838	26	10.01 162	9.85 522	12	46
15	9.84 373	13	9.98 863	25	10.01 137	9.85 510	12	45
16	9.84 385	12	9.98 888	25	10.01 112	9.85 497	13	44
17	9.84 398	13	9.98 913	25	10.01 087	9.85 485	12	43
18	9.84 411	13	9.98 939	26	10.01 061	9.85 473	12	42
19	9.84 424	13	9.98 964	25	10.01 036	9.85 460	13	41
20	9.84 437	13	9.98 989	25	10.01 011	9.85 448	12	**40**
21	9.84 450	13	9.99 015	26	10.00 985	9.85 436	12	39
22	9.84 463	13	9.99 040	25	10.00 960	9.85 423	13	38
23	9.84 476	13	9.99 065	25	10.00 935	9.85 411	12	37
24	9.84 489	13	9.99 090	25	10.00 910	9.85 399	12	36
25	9.84 502	13	9.99 116	26	10.00 884	9.85 386	13	35
26	9.84 515	13	9.99 141	25	10.00 859	9.85 374	12	34
27	9.84 528	13	9.99 166	25	10.00 834	9.85 361	13	33
28	9.84 540	12	9.99 191	25	10.00 809	9.85 349	12	32
29	9.84 553	13	9.99 217	26	10.00 783	9.85 337	12	31
30	9.84 566	13	9.99 242	25	10.00 758	9.85 324	13	**30**
31	9.84 579	13	9.99 267	25	10.00 733	9.85 312	12	29
32	9.84 592	13	9.99 293	26	10.00 707	9.85 299	13	28
33	9.84 605	13	9.99 318	25	10.00 682	9.85 287	12	27
34	9.84 618	13	9.99 343	25	10.00 657	9.85 274	13	26
35	9.84 630	12	9.99 368	25	10.00 632	9.85 262	12	25
36	9.84 643	13	9.99 394	26	10.00 606	9.85 250	12	24
37	9.84 656	13	9.99 419	25	10.00 581	9.85 237	13	23
38	9.84 669	13	9.99 444	25	10.00 556	9.85 225	12	22
39	9.84 682	13	9.99 469	25	10.00 531	9.85 212	13	21
40	9.84 694	12	9.99 495	26	10.00 505	9.85 200	12	**20**
41	9.84 707	13	9.99 520	25	10.00 480	9.85 187	13	19
42	9.84 720	13	9.99 545	25	10.00 455	9.85 175	12	18
43	9.84 733	13	9.99 570	25	10.00 430	9.85 162	13	17
44	9.84 745	12	9.99 596	26	10.00 404	9.85 150	12	16
45	9.84 758	13	9.99 621	25	10.00 379	9.85 137	13	15
46	9.84 771	13	9.99 646	25	10.00 354	9.85 125	12	14
47	9.84 784	13	9.99 672	26	10.00 328	9.85 112	13	13
48	9.84 796	12	9.99 697	25	10.00 303	9.85 100	12	12
49	9.84 809	13	9.99 722	25	10.00 278	9.85 087	13	11
50	9.84 822	13	9.99 747	25	10.00 253	9.85 074	13	**10**
51	9.84 835	13	9.99 773	26	10.00 227	9.85 062	12	9
52	9.84 847	12	9.99 798	25	10.00 202	9.85 049	13	8
53	9.84 860	13	9.99 823	25	10.00 177	9.85 037	12	7
54	9.84 873	13	9.99 848	25	10.00 152	9.85 024	13	6
55	9.84 885	12	9.99 874	26	10.00 126	9.85 012	12	5
56	9.84 898	13	9.99 899	25	10.00 101	9.84 999	13	4
57	9.84 911	13	9.99 924	25	10.00 076	9.84 986	13	3
58	9.84 923	12	9.99 949	25	10.00 051	9.84 974	12	2
59	9.84 936	13	9.99 975	26	10.00 025	9.84 961	13	1
60	9.84 949	13	10.00 000	25	10.00 000	9.84 949	12	**0**
	L Cos	d	L Cot	c d	L Tan	L Sin	d	′

Prop. Pts.

	26	25
1	2.6	2.5
2	5.2	5.0
3	7.8	7.5
4	10.4	10.0
5	13.0	12.5
6	15.6	15.0
7	18.2	17.5
8	20.8	20.0
9	23.4	22.5

	14	13	12
1	1.4	1.3	1.2
2	2.8	2.6	2.4
3	4.2	3.9	3.6
4	5.6	5.2	4.8
5	7.0	6.5	6.0
6	8.4	7.8	7.2
7	9.8	9.1	8.4
8	11.2	10.4	9.6
9	12.6	11.7	10.8

Prop. Pts.

45°

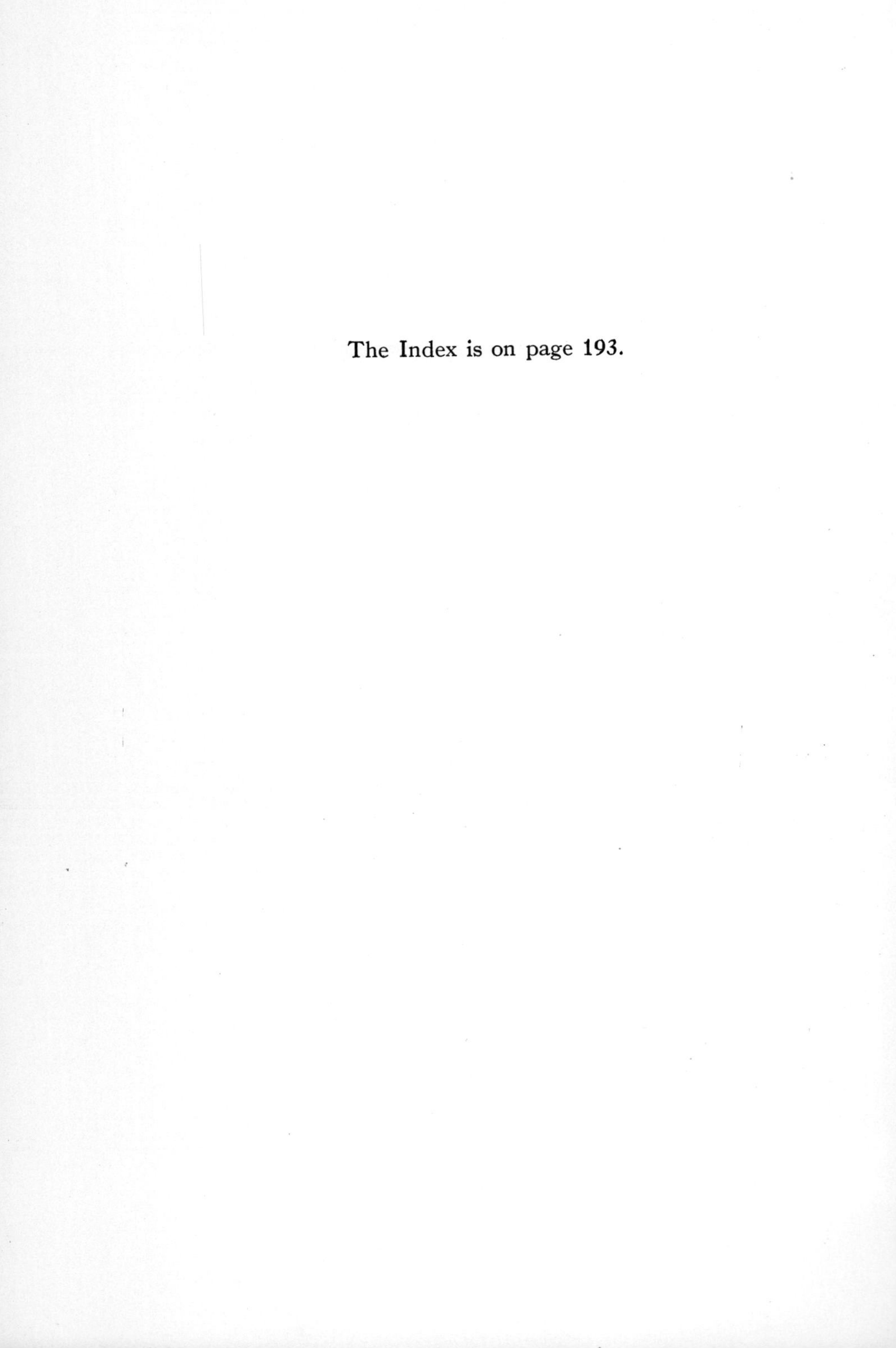

The Index is on page 193.